# Industry and Technology

## Keys to Oceanic Development

**Volume 2**

**Panel Reports
of the Commission
on Marine Science,
Engineering and Resources**

For sale by the Superintendent of Documents, U.S. Government Printing Office
Washington, D.C. 20402 - Sold in sets of 3 volumes only

Contents

# Part V

## Report of the Panel
## on Industry
## and Private Investment

Contents
_____

Early in its history, the Commission organized seven panels. Each dealt with a major area of interest pertinent to the responsibilities assigned to the Commission by the Marine Resources and Engineering Development Act of 1966, P.L. 89-454. Thus, a means was provided to focus on the basic problems and to recommend solutions in critical areas. This report is the work of the Panel on Industry and Private Investment.

The panel gathered information from many people,[1] including approximately 150 personal interviews with key figures. A series of conferences was sponsored by the Ocean Science and Technology Advisory Committee (OSTAC) of the National Security Industrial Association (NSIA) to assist the panel. The panel utilized detailed statements and reports provided by: OSTAC; the National Chamber of Commerce; the Oceanographic Committee of the National Association of Manufacturers; the National Academy of Engineering, Committee on Ocean Engineering; the National Oceanography Association; and various organizations under contract to the Commission and the National Council on Marine Resources and Engineering Development. Much information was derived from symposia sponsored by various technical societies and universities during the period in which this report was being prepared. In addition, the panel participated in formal hearings with representatives from Federal and State government agencies, industry, universities, and non-profit institutions. Finally, the help of Charles C. Convers and J. Stan Stephan was enlisted for particular portions of the text.

The report has been carefully reviewed by consultants and various experts throughout government and industry, to whom the panel is indebted.

Kenneth Drummond, of Texas Instruments, served as Panel Executive Secretary. Of major assistance to the panel in writing the report were the following staff members: Timothy J. Coleman, Union Carbide Corp.; James W. Drewry, University of Virginia; Amor L. Lane, American Machine & Foundry Co.; and R. Lawrence Snideman II, The Oceanic Foundation. The panel greatly appreciates the contributions of these individuals and the time made available by their organizations.

Respectfully submitted,

Richard A. Geyer, *Chairman*
Charles F. Baird
Taylor A. Pryor
George H. Sullivan

---

[1] Individuals making primary contributions are listed in Appendix A.

This chapter includes summaries of highlight recommendations which are applicable to the broad sector of ocean industries.

## I. NEED FOR ADVISORY COMMITTEE

The Government and industry long have worked together at all levels in marine-oriented activities. To aid in the design and implementation of a meaningful National program future Government planning should continue to encourage and anticipate information and advice from industry. The Government also should solicit information and guidance from the States and the academic community. This need will increase as ocean resource development accelerates with an accompanying increase in multiple use conflicts.

The present need for closer cooperation has intensified for several reasons:

—Development of ocean resources is accelerating.

—This rapid development, accompanied by increased awareness of the ocean's vast potential and concern with pollution and conservation, requires the most efficient mobilization of the Nation's capability. Much of this capability already exists both without and within the Government, including extensive facilities, trained manpower, and experience in the development and use of marine resources.

—The accelerated development of marine resources has revealed that it is imperative to achieve understanding between multiple users in order to define the present and anticipated scope of conflicts and to recommend suitable mechanisms for resolving them.

The Commission was charged by Congress to recommend an adequate National marine science program and a Governmental organizational plan to carry it out. In determining the nature of this organization, the panel finds that provision should be made to allow meaningful participation of industry, the States, and the academic community in planning, execution, and review of this program.

Recommendation:

**An advisory committee composed of representatives appointed by the President from private industry, States and regions, and the academic community should be statutorily created. This committee would participate in the establishment of National marine goals and objectives and provide continuing guidance to the Federal Government.**

## II. NEED FOR CONSOLIDATION OF FEDERAL FUNCTIONS

Many Federal agencies have responsibilities in the ocean, but to date no strong focus and in some instances no clear delineation of responsibility exist.

Federal programs and functions should be consolidated to:

—Enable improved planning and direction of marine programs.

—Provide more efficient and meaningful services through better utilization of Government manpower, funds, and facilities.

—Permit more efficient conduct of non-military research and development required for expanded marine activities.

—Provide a means for handling special problems related to small, ocean-oriented businesses of critical importance.

—Provide a focus for information and technology exchange.

—Aid in training and education of required manpower.

Recommendation:

**Many marine functions of existing agencies and bureaus should, wherever possible, be consolidated to improve the effectiveness of the Government's participation in a National marine program.**

## III. MULTIPURPOSE TECHNOLOGY

Technology in itself is not a severe limitation to industry's physical ability to perform an operation in the ocean. Cost, however, may often be prohibitive. Consequently, future technological innovations that reduce costs will accelerate the utilization of the oceans. Therefore, early development of lower cost technology is required. In addition, other innovations may create opportunities to develop entirely new industries.

Technology and services that benefit a broad sector of present and potential users and which are beyond the capability of a given industry traditionally have been sponsored by the Government. When such programs are necessary they should be oriented to scientific and basic engineering problems. To insure an industrial base capable of supporting accelerating National ocean exploitation, it is imperative that development projects, where practical, be performed by industry under appropriate contractual arrangements.

### Recommendation:

**The Federal Government should initiate in the near future a program to assure development of basic multipurpose technology that will enhance the capability of a broad spectrum of users to perform useful work on and in the oceans.**

## IV. AVAILABILITY OF CAPITAL

Some ocean industries are so new in areas of advanced technology that their potential is not fully understood by investors. Nevertheless, many concepts of profitably using the ocean are sound, and the investment community has been intrigued greatly by overall ocean endeavors. It is the feeling in this community that raising funds for projects with reasonable profit potential will not be a problem, and therefore direct Government pecuniary aid will be rarely necessary.

In view of the National interest in the oceans, and lack in most cases of a need for direct Government financial aid, the panel feels that indirect incentives directed toward establishment of a favorable business climate should be employed where pertinent.

### Recommendation:

**Government policy should be to develop and maintain a business climate encouraging ocean-related investments. Special indirect incentives, rather than direct financial aid, are advised when a well defined National interest exists and the private sector's response is inadequate.**

## V. SEASTEADING—A MEANS TO ATTRACT ENTREPRENEURIAL INVESTMENT

The ocean environment has received much promotional attention and many ideas have been conceived for ocean development. At present, however, numerous jurisdictional bodies have no procedures at all to convey rights to submerged land. Where procedures exist, they are often in the form of complicated and expensive leases which constitute a particular burden to individuals and small companies. Thus, to stimulate the imaginative development of selected underwater areas, the States should adopt a system of simple, attractive leasing, which one might refer to as "seasteading." The term of the "seastead" should be sufficiently long to justify large investments that may be necessary. Among the possible applications of seasteading would be aquaculture and such recreational uses as underwater parks and hotels, but not development of petroleum and other minerals.

### Recommendation:

**To encourage innovative uses of the ocean other than petroleum and hard mineral development, State governments should initiate experimental programs for leasing submarine areas ("seasteading") within U.S. territorial waters, contingent on useful employment of the property. Such programs should be a part of a plan for the orderly, rational development of offshore regions.**

## I. PANEL OBJECTIVES

Two objectives of the Marine Resources and Engineering Development Act are to accelerate development of marine environment resources and to encourage private investment enterprise in exploration, technological development, marine commerce, and economic utilization of such resources.

These statutory objectives have established the framework for the work of the Panel on Industry and Private Investment. Thus the panel has proceeded from the premise that an increase in commercial marine activity is in the National interest and should be supported by both the public and private sector. The panel's principal mission has been to determine what specific actions are both necessary and appropriate and what mutual roles are to be played by the public and private sectors.

The panel particularly wishes to emphasize the key importance of industry's participation in advancing the Nation's use of the seas. It is industry which under its own initiative has developed much of the technology now used in ocean operations. The know-how of industrial personnel will be crucial to technological extension. Certain sectors of private industry also command capital resources substantially exceeding those government is likely to be able to assign to civil ocean projects.

The larger companies, at least, are capable of assigning resources to a steady and programmed effort that can be sustained over the years with greater confidence than a project subject to the uncertainties of annual Congressional appropriations. Industry can often sponsor programs in the ocean without fear of political criticism. Moreover, private companies can operate in foreign areas and reach agreements with foreign governments (such as those of the oil industry in the Near East or of mining companies off South Africa, England, and Malaysia) that would be more difficult to achieve at a government-to-government level.

The panel's work has been directed to the following major subjects:

—What are the implications of the statutory intent that marine resource development be accelerated in terms of regulatory policies, incentives, and services to industry?

—What impact would a strengthened Government program in marine science and engineering have upon private and industrial activity in the oceans and upon the economy as a whole?

—What will be the private sector's requirements for capital in order to realize the potential for ocean development?

—How can industry collaborate effectively with government and the academic community in the planning and execution of a truly National marine program?

These questions identify major problems to which the panel's efforts have been directed. From several alternative means to stimulate investment in marine industry, the panel has selected the most promising, attempting to weigh their benefits against possible detrimental effects.

This report should be read in conjunction with the Commission report and the other panel reports. For instance, the Panel on Marine Resources has reviewed in detail the potential of marine resources; the Marine Engineering and Technology Panel has proposed a fundamental technology development program intended to advance the Nation's capability to utilize such resources.

## II. POTENTIAL FOR INDUSTRIAL GROWTH

The potential for greatly expanded industrial activity in the oceans clearly is present. Within the next 20 years, the world population is expected to increase by some 50 per cent.[1] About three-to-four times more gas and oil will be required annually.[2] It has been estimated that offshore sources will provide in a decade about one-third of the world's petroleum.[3] It also has been estimated

---

[1] United Nations, "World Population Prospects," Population Studies No. 41, 1966, Table A3.2.

[2] Weeks, L. G., "The Gas, Oil, and Sulfur Potentials of the Sea," *Ocean Industry*, June 1968, p. 43.

[3] *Ibid.*, p. 48.

that world-wide fish catches can be quadrupled,[4] and many feel there is a great potential in aquaculture for raising marine species of high economic value. Ocean mining activities could expand rapidly as technology for economic recovery and processing develops, and an interesting, although still very ill-defined, potential exists for deriving new drugs from marine life.

More immediate opportunities are present among the non-consumptive uses of the sea and coastal zone—in recreation, transportation, waste disposal, and scientific inquiry. The demand for the major aquatic activities of outdoor recreation in this country will have tripled by the year 2000.[5] The annual tonnage of international trade is expected to double in 20 years.[6]

Profit-motivated private enterprise traditionally has provided one of the most potent avenues for growth. Providing a political and economic climate that will allow U.S. ocean industry to meet these needs is a challenge to the Nation.

## III. NATIONAL INTEREST IN THE OCEAN

Several reasons for Government encouragement of industrial activities in the ocean are listed below:[7]

—Expanding population and a rising standard of living will consume natural resources at an accelerating rate. Government and industry must have comprehensive knowledge of both renewable and non-renewable resource inventories, both in the ocean and on land, to manage these resources effectively and help determine international trade policy.

—Maintenance of reasonably stable prices and marketing arrangements requires an adequate level of proven reserves to meet future needs and a diversity of sources to establish a potential for competition.

—Due to the forecasted demand for natural resources, it is becoming increasingly important for industry to make the best possible projections and concomitant decisions concerning the most economical sources of supply.

—Domestic production of minerals offshore yields some foreign exchange savings when contrasted to an import alternative. The resultant relatively modest saving at this point may be offset by repercussions in markets for U.S. exports, but until the Nation's overall payments problem has eased, the balance-of-payments aspects cannot be ignored.

—Encouragement of appropriate ocean industries by the Government will contribute to the National economy in the form of capital investment, increased employment, and productivity.

—Many benefits accrue to National security from industrial competence in the oceans. These include industrial marine technology, equipment, manpower skilled in ocean operations, an ability to obtain critical natural resources needed during a prolonged National emergency, and the capability to build and maintain an adequate merchant fleet.

## IV. GOVERNMENT AND INDUSTRY ROLES

The profit motive is and should continue to be a dominant factor guiding this Nation's marine industries. With profit a primary objective, industry will have to develop the basic data, skills, and industrial organization necessary to utilize the sea.

The purpose of the programs recommended by this panel is to advance the capabilities of private business to develop ocean resources to a degree allowing comparison with onshore techniques, products, and services. With this capability, more rational investment choices can be made between land and ocean resources. To that end government and industry must work closely together.

### A. Government Role

The rate of marine industrial development will be the result of many factors that influence profitability: demand, availability of technology,

[4] Bullis, H. R., Jr. and Dr. J. R. Thompson, "Harvesting the Ocean in the Decade Ahead," *Ocean Industry,* June 1968, p. 60.

[5] Bureau of Outdoor Recreation.

[6] National Council on Marine Resources and Engineering Development, "Marine Science Affairs—A Year of Plans and Progress," Government Printing Office, Washington, D.C., February 1968, p. 73.

[7] Other factors justifying the National interest in the ocean are reviewed in some detail in two other reports: "Effective Use of the Sea," report of the Panel on Oceanography, President's Science Advisory Committee, June 1966, pp. 1-3; Report of the Commission on Marine Science, Engineering and Resources.

capital, manpower, domestic and international competition, and availability of alternative sources of food and minerals ashore. Government policy is an additional and important factor in marine development but cannot be truly effective unless supported by other determinants. Government policy cannot create, for instance, a thriving ocean mining or fisheries industry in the absence of an economically sound market situation.

Public policy sets the tone for industrial progress. The Government, through its establishment and interpretation of the political environment, determines the ultimate climate for industrial growth within its jurisdiction. This climate can be promotional or restrictive depending on the priorities established. Many phases of Government action can be used to promote ocean progress. At a minimum, Government has a responsibility to:[8]

—Enunciate National policies and objectives concerning U.S. marine interests.

—Assist in planning for optimum use of limited public resources and adjudication of conflicting uses of the sea.

—Adopt regulatory policies which will not discourage private investment.

—Provide special incentives to certain marine industries in their embryonic phase when in the National interest.

—Undertake and improve the description and prediction of the marine environment and assess possibilities of modifying it for the ultimate mutual benefit of all users of the sea and coastal zones.

—Initiate, support and encourage education and training programs to provide competent manpower on all necessary levels for marine-related activities.

—Provide for protecting life and property at sea.

—Sponsor programs to obtain basic information for industry's delineation and development of marine resources as well as ensuring proper conservation practices.

—Aid in the advance of science and basic technology necessary to operate within the marine environment.

—Negotiate acceptable international arrangements to conduct marine industrial activity.

—Assure that National security is given proper consideration in ocean development policies.

## B. Industry Role

Based on the profit motive, industry is the instrument that gives economic value to ocean resources. Discovery of new resource potentials will be of no benefit without the capability to exploit them economically. Development of an efficient marine industry, on the other hand, not only can make the riches of the seas accessible to this Nation and to the world, but also can assist U.S. economic development and help strengthen this Nation's position in international trade.

The traditional and proper role of industry is to:

—Generate the ideas, methods, and risk capital required for continued industrial progress.

—Discover, delineate, develop, and market marine resources within the constraints of proper conservation practices and equitable solutions promulgated to solve multi-user problems.

—Provide capital equipment and services fundamental to ocean operations.

—Contribute to the support of scientific research and technological development.

—Participate in development of manpower for ocean operations through in-house training programs and aid to education and research within the universities.

---

[8] The Government role defined here is substantially in agreement with the role stated by the President's Science Advisory Committee, Panel on Oceanography, in "Effective Use of the Sea," p. VIII, June 1966.

## I. PROFILE OF PRESENT INDUSTRIAL ACTIVITIES

The ocean industries are a heterogeneous group with a multitude of interests. In size, the activities vary from a major petroleum company operating many large offshore oil and gas fields to an independent fisherman earning less than $2,000 per year.

Chapter 4 reviews in greater detail the status and peculiar problems of several industries engaged in ocean resource recovery or use of the sea.

The following table depicts the status of domestic ocean industries in two broad categories—existing and future. It lists only those that use the ocean directly, as contrasted with such support industries as diving or instrument manufacture. Table 1 also takes into account that some segments of an industry fall into different categories. Thus, mining offshore sand, gravel, and oyster shells represents a mature segment of an ocean industry. On the other hand, offshore placer mining is a near-term, promising industry and sub-bottom mining (mining of deposits within the bedrock) is not envisioned until much later.

There are tremendous differences in present and anticipated rates of growth of ocean industries. Although all categories of ocean enterprise share common problems, distinct differences exist in their operating requirements, investment, degree of competition, and relationship with Government. Moreover, the needs of some industries such as fishing, vary in nature and degree from segment to segment.

Government action to foster development of specific industries must be flexible enough to take this heterogeneity into account. Thus, certain existing Federal policies and programs may need no more than minor adjustments for industries that are mature and have a healthy growth rate; for example, little or no direct aid is needed to boost oil and gas production on the Continental Shelf. On the other hand, where a technology with great potential has just begun to advance, such as desalination, the Government's assistance in research and development and participation in prototype construction might be decisive in maintaining the industry's initial momentum. Occasionally,

**Table 1**

### PRESENT STATUS OF DOMESTIC OCEAN INDUSTRIES

| Type | Examples |
|---|---|
| *Existing Industries* | |
| Mature, healthy, and growing | Continental shelf oil and gas |
| | Chemical extraction from sea water |
| | Mining of sand, gravel, sulfur |
| | Shrimp and tuna fishing |
| | Surface marine recreation |
| Early stage of growth | Desalination |
| | Bulk and container transportation systems and associated terminals |
| | Aquaculture, fresh water and estuarine |
| | Underwater recreation |
| Mature, but static or declining | Most segments of fishing |
| | Merchant shipbuilding |
| | Merchant shipping (U.S.-flag vessels) |
| *Future Industries* | |
| Near-term promising (where near-term is up to 15 years) | Mining of placer minerals |
| | Oil and gas beyond the continental shelf |
| Long-range | Sub-bottom mining (excluding sulfur) |
| | Aquaculture, open ocean |
| | Deep water mining |
| | Power generation from waves, currents, tides, and thermal differences |

positive action of a fiscal, legal/regulatory, or technological character might be needed, as in the steadily deteriorating groundfish fishery in view of the National interest in rehabilitating domestic fisheries. Finally, there are U.S. Continental Shelf industries, such as hard mineral mining, that are still in their infancy but whose economic potential and importance to the Nation justifies removal of legal and regulatory obstacles and creation of special indirect incentives to attract initial exploration.

## II. VALUE OF OCEAN ACTIVITY

Many public and private studies have been made to assess the overall scale of ocean business, using a variety of techniques to describe the size of the investment and the market. A survey of these studies revealed that no estimate is satisfactory for all purposes. Many are defective because of redundancies, oversights, and inaccuracies of component figures; inconsistencies in methods of compilation; and disagreement of essential definitions. Further, results have sometimes been oriented to such conflicting objectives as showing the magnitude of market opportunity, supporting advertising expenditure, or showing the need for greater private investment or further Government expenditures.

While estimates have been as high as $50 billion, the panel believes that the true value of ocean activity in terms of contribution to Gross National Product is between $15 and $25 billion. This includes recovery and processing of all natural resources, the sea transportation industry, the marine recreation industry, Government expenditures, and net export of marine goods and services.

The panel commends the National Council on Marine Resources and Engineering Development for the progress in quantitatively describing many areas of ocean activity. An urgent need exists, however, for more comprehensive statistics that will further identify the areas of redundancy, improve comparability, and take into account the statistics reflecting such factors as investment, sales, and contribution to GNP. The Government, working with industry, should develop a method to compile the data necessary to the periodic publication of the required statistics.

## III. INDUSTRY ATTITUDES TOWARD OCEAN INVESTMENTS

Because the United States has a free enterprise system, capital and effort are directed toward ventures offering the likelihood of the greatest returns on investment, whether they be on shore or at sea, at home or abroad. However, industry's evaluation of the prospects of profit in the oceans is influenced substantially by regulatory restraints, legal uncertainties, and the possibility that the Government will sponsor a major ocean program. On the other hand, the element of excitement in participating in a new industry may stimulate investment interest beyond the prospect of immediate return.

Both the intensity of interest and related hazards of investment in this field are evidenced by the number of acquisitions and mergers occurring now in ocean-oriented industries. Small companies in the field with limited capital and a restricted product line or service frequently find it advantageous to merge with larger firms. In some instances they are forced to terminate operations, a pattern typical of young industries.

The offshore petroleum service industry is an excellent example of the diversification trend. In particular, the offshore drilling companies, originally characterized by wide-ranging cycles of business activity, are now large, established firms. They have stabilized successfully their level of business by diversifying into such areas as ocean engineering, exploration, diving, mining, construction, pipelaying, and even fish processing. As a result, the Nation's largest drilling companies have more than quadrupled their gross revenues during the last five years.

Ocean industry, in general, is not looking for subsidization, which in this report is defined as direct financial aid. Instead, industry is seeking various indirect means to minimize risk. Such means usually are peculiar to certain phases of each industry, and include definition of jurisdictional boundaries, environmental prediction, fiscal incentives such as accelerated depreciation, ocean surveys, and such Government contracting policies as cost plus fixed fee.

For example, the mining industry has identified the need for reconnaissance surveys to guide further delineation of deposits; a petroleum operator would like longer-range scheduling of offshore lease sales; and a fisherman would sometimes desire the opportunity to use foreign-built vessels. The fewer the uncertainties and the less restrictive the regulation, the sooner capital and technology will be available for new ocean opportunities.

## IV. CAPITAL SOURCES AND REQUIREMENTS

Many ocean industries in areas of advanced technology are so new that they are not fully understood. Investors are concerned with such factors as obsolescence in a technology developing at an accelerating rate. Nevertheless, many concepts of profitably using the ocean are sound, and the investment community has been intrigued greatly by ocean endeavors. This enthusiasm has been indicated by considerable publicity and advertising in the popular press and business journals, the creation of two ocean mutual funds in the last year, and numerous symposia and publications sponsored by brokerage houses.

In general, capital has not been lacking to finance current industrial ocean projects, despite high economic risks. Further, it is anticipated that capital will remain available for projects judged by the investment community as having profit potential.

Capital for ocean projects is derived from many sources. The petroleum industry has in general been able to generate and/or obtain funds readily to meet its very substantial capital requirements for bonus bids, new technology, exploration, and drilling. A substantial portion is raised from the public based on an individual firm's credit, a factor constituting one of the great strengths in offshore growth. To date, about $18 billion has been invested world-wide by the offshore petroleum industry, about $13 billion by U.S. firms.[1] It is expected that by 1980 the world-wide cumulative investment will reach $55 billion. A large portion of this will have to be raised through borrowing or public subscription.

Capital for expansion and modernization of the U.S. fishing fleet has been far less plentiful due in large part to high economic risks and legal restraints. In addition, many fishing vessels are owned by small entrepreneurs having only limited access to capital markets. A detailed analysis of this industry's situation and recommendations to help meet its special capital needs is provided in the fishing section of the ocean industry chapter of this report (Chapter 4).

During the past few years, several large aerospace firms (such as Lockheed, North American-Rockwell, General Dynamics, and Grumman) and other large companies, (such as Westinghouse, General Electric, Alcoa, Reynolds Metals, and Union Carbide) have invested millions in ocean ventures. They have tended to emphasize the heavy hardware and systems approach required for special ocean work. Several of the Nation's largest shipyards now are controlled by aerospace or conglomerate firms intent upon instituting new and more efficient shipyard parctices.

Risk capital in the hands of entrepreneurs finances a variety of ocean ventures. It is very difficult to estimate the actual investment from this source. However, the reservoir of venture capital potentially available for raw investment opportunities, both land and ocean oriented, has been estimated at $3 billion.[2] The availability of so much risk capital is a very important characteristic of the Nation's ability to enter new fields and develop new technology. In summary, the panel finds that capital usually has been and is expected to be available to finance industrial ocean projects with profit potential.

In view of the National interest in the ocean, and lack in most cases of a need for direct Government financial aid, the panel feels that indirect incentives through establishment of a favorable business climate are essential.

Recommendation:

**Government policy should be to develop and maintain a business climate encouraging ocean-related investments. Special indirect incentives, rather than direct financial aid, are advised when a well defined national interest exists and the private sector's response is inadequate.**

---

[1] Richard J. Howe, "Petroleum Operations in the Sea—1980 and Beyond," *Ocean Industry*, August 1968, p. 30.

[2] Panel on Invention and Innovation, "Technological Innovation: Its Environment and Management," U.S. Department of Commerce, 1967, p. 42.

## I. GOVERNMENT SPONSORED RESEARCH AND DEVELOPMENT

Optimum utilization of ocean resources will require a very substantial increase in knowledge of ocean characteristics and development of new technology. The propriety of Government assistance to scientific and technical advancement commensurate with the National interest and industrial needs is well established and widely accepted. Furthermore, this means of accelerating industry's marine effort is cost-effective, impartial, and can be terminated as objectives are attained.

### A. Survey Programs

Far more information and greater research efforts are necessary if potential ocean uses are to stimulate the effort they merit. For example, programs are needed to generate survey data on living resources, reconnaissance-scale geological features, and environmental characteristics. At the same time research activities must be undertaken to advance the ability to interpret these data; without this ability the survey programs could not be effective.

Experience has demonstrated that such research and survey activity can stimulate development of technical capabilities, make existing operations more efficient, and accelerate innovation.

The panel has found that industry today will readily use additional bathymetric and geophysical surveys and geological analysis of the Continental Shelf, slope, and rise. This is of particular importance to the mining industry, but also would be helpful to the petroleum industry, particularly in deeper waters and in remote areas where even general geological characteristics remain unknown. These surveys should be reconnaissance in nature; *detailed* exploratory surveys should be conducted by industry.

Recommendation:
**Bathymetric base maps overlaid with geophysical and geological information should be prepared to a scale of 1:250,000 for the continental shelves, slopes, and rises of the United States within 15 to 20 years. Selection of areas to be surveyed should be based on priorities that take into account user needs.**

This information will provide the foundation for more detailed exploratory work by industry. Detailed exploration will be expensive, and a firm engaging in the work will require extensive initial survey data to reduce costs and risks. Further, reconnaissance surveys are expected to uncover a host of new industrial opportunities.[1]

Precedent for this work has been set by onshore mapping. Survey programs must not become ends in themselves but should support many objectives, including those of industry.

### B. Programs in Multipurpose Technology

Technological innovations that reduce an ocean operation's cost will improve profit outlooks and accelerate marine resource development. Consequently, a basic technology program oriented toward reducing costs relevant to a wide variety of user interests will compress the timetable for utilization of the seas' resources.

The Panel on Marine Engineering and Technology states that a 10-year program of intensive undersea development is in the National interest and recommends that it begin immediately, emphasizing fundamental, multipurpose technology.

Government sponsorship of such a program is appropriate if the effort concentrates on such basic and widely applicable areas as development of data on materials performance, concepts for simple tools, and hyperbaric physiology. In most instances, large-scale projects that benefit only a specific industry more properly should be carried out by that industry. The process of selecting specific projects must take into account needs of the Government, scientific community, and industry, and must avoid competition with private industry.

Recommendation:

**The Federal Government should initiate in the near future a program to assure development of basic multipurpose technology that will enhance the capability of a broad spectrum of users to perform useful work on and in the oceans.**

---

[1] Additional discussion of survey needs is found in the Report of the Marine Resources Panel.

## C. Nature and Extent of Government Sponsorship

Selected objectives wherever possible should be undertaken by the private sector under contract. This will permit private industry as well as the Government to be familiar with the objectives, characteristics, problems, and opportunities that become apparent during planning and implementation. Under these circumstances, we can expect that industry will aggressively seek commercial application of new technology.

Experience over the last 20 years clearly demonstrates the very great advantages that follow from the participation of numerous organizations in the pursuit of technological objectives. The use of contractors in research and development projects demonstrates its advantages both for the Government and private organizations. For example, the success of civil aviation followed in very large measure from Government's reliance on private firms to develop military aircraft. The private firms were able to draw upon this experience to design civilian aircraft. A similar process is applying nuclear energy to civilian use.

Another example of sponsored research and development is the extensive investigation by the Office of Saline Water of methods to recover fresh water from the sea. The program is conducted largely through contracts with industry, causing wide diffusion of knowledge and experience and stimulating private efforts.

Business firms in oceanographic industries, as in others, differ enormously in their relationship to new technology. There are a few firms whose business is primarily that to perform research and development and hence to generate new technology. A larger but still small group of firms undertakes to develop new technology only in order to support their principal activities. These two groups constitute the Nation's R&D industry. Most firms are receptive to new technology emerging from outside of their own organizations though the receptivity differs widely. Many firms lack the competence, capital, or interest to react to new technology except in immediately usable form and are dependent upon others for whatever changes occur. The conceptual problems and the absence of data make exact analysis impossible.[2]

One function of Government in promoting new technology should be to enhance the ability of firms to react to new technology at an early stage. Aside from reducing public costs thereby, this ability increases the variety of efforts and ensures that economic considerations are introduced early in the appraisal and development of new technology.

Since circumstances will differ project by project, the Government's arrangements for industry participation should continue to be highly flexible, consistent with the premise that Government should seek maximum utilization of private capabilities. In some circumstances, joint participation in a development project, including sharing of costs, would be appropriate. When industry has acquired the capabilities to pursue an objective, the Government should withdraw.

Withdrawal of Government support and control at the earliest time that private firms can assume responsibility will greatly increase the probability that innovations will be carried into the market place. Industrial groups are usually eager to assume complete sponsorship of technical projects as soon as the probability of success outweighs remaining risk and a reasonable return on investment can be expected.

Recommendation:

**When Government research and development programs are required in the National interest, they should be planned and administered to permit private industry to assume responsibility for further technology development at the earliest possible stage.**

### D. Technology Transfer

A recent Congressional report defined technology transfer as follows:[3]

*Technology transfer is the process of matching solutions in the form of existing science and engineering knowledge to problems in commerce or public programs. . . . The Federal Government "controls" (sponsors, directs, is responsible for) a large reservoir of technology ranging from research results, to practical techniques and devices, to patents.*

---

[2] A more complete discussion of this subject is found in "Basic Research, Applied Research, and Development in Industry, 1965," The National Science Foundation, 1967.

[3] A report of the Subcommittee on Science and Technology to the Select Committee on Small Business, U.S. Senate, "Policy Planning for Technology Transfer," April 6, 1967, p. 1.

Accurate information available on a timely basis is essential to all users whether industry, Government, or university oriented. Despite marked progress by all concerned in the past few years, problems of adequate dissemination have grown faster than generally recognized.

Another report summarizing a detailed study of technology transfer conducted for the National Commission on Technology, Automation and Economic Progress stated:[4]

*Devising means of channeling new technologies in promising directions—and bringing about the utilization of new technology for significant purposes other than the immediate use for which it was developed—has become an activity ranking among the most intellectually challenging of our time. . . . The transfer and utilization of new technology offer immense opportunity to the Nation. There is widespread agreement among those who have studied the issue that the knowledge resulting from the public investment in R. & D. constitutes a major, rapidly increasing, and insufficiently exploited national resource. Its effective use can increase the rate of economic growth, create new employment opportunities, help offset imbalances between regions and industries, aid the international competitive position of U.S. industry, enhance our national prestige, improve the quality of life, and assist significantly in filling unmet human and community needs. It is recommended that more effective use of this technology resource become a national goal established at the highest levels.*

The panel endorses the findings and recommendation quoted above.

Recommendation:

**Budgets of marine-related Federal agencies should be augmented in order to ensure proper documentation as well as satisfactory dissemination of data and technology.**

While it is important that new technology be documented and disseminated, publication of the information is not always sufficient to effectively transfer the new knowledge to potential users. Person-to-person contact is an extremely effective method of transfer, although slow and expensive.

Considerable know-how gained in technology development lies in a grey area between scientific information and patentable inventions.[5] If this exists in industry because of Government contracts, transference already has been accomplished to at least one user, and the marketplace will provide further transfer more effectively than if the information were held within the Government.

As an example, the Atomic Energy Commission provided financial assistance to develop new technology directly related to civilian use of nuclear energy. But knowledge of nuclear energy acquired by private firms as contractual performers of Government projects made possible the rapid transfer of this technology to civilian applications.

Recommendation:

**Person-to-person contacts should be encouraged between groups working in related technological fields. Such contacts could be achieved through contract programs, special information exchange programs, and reciprocal arrangements between industry, government, and the academic community whereby their scientists and engineers would be exchanged.**

Patents constitute another important form of technology transfer. The panel notes that the patent policies of all agencies of the Federal Government have been under review, that the Presidential memorandum of Oct. 10, 1963, was intended as a general Government policy statement, and a major review of such policy was to be published in late 1968.[6] The panel further recognizes the subject's complexity and notes that many procedures of the various agencies constitute serious inhibitions to the effective participation of private enterprise in advancing new technology.

An intense controversy exists over the policy of some agencies of the Government regarding rights in patents evolving from work supported partially

---

[4] Richard Lesher and George Howick, "Assessing Technology Transfer," National Aeronautics and Space Administration, 1966, p. 5.

[5] Senate Select Committee on Small Business, April 6, 1967, *op. cit.*, p. 1.

[6] Harbridge House, Inc., "Government Patent Policy Study, Final Report," Volumes I-III, Federal Council for Science and Technology, Committee on Government Patent Policy, Government Printing Office, Washington, D.C., 1968.

or fully through Federal grants and contracts. The magnitude of the problem is such that it cannot be ignored. Federal R&D expenditures now exceed $16 billion a year. For the past decade, the Government has provided by grant or contract more than one-half the R&D money spent in industry, thus tending to stimulate invention.

However, the basic principle of some agencies of the Government is that titles to patents on innovations arising from use of public monies should be assigned to the Government and the information contained therein made available to the public without payment of royalty where consistent with National security. On the other hand, industry, university, and other private interests contend that this policy tends to impair technology transfer and reduce innovation, as it deprives the inventor of initiative and discourages investment capital.

The paradox is that the Government at one and the same time stimulates invention through its vast R&D expenditures, yet it apparently impedes its spread into commerce through certain of its patent policies. A new equitable patent policy is needed urgently to renew the stimulation of inventiveness while protecting the taxpayers' interests.

Withholding scientific and technical data from the public because of security classification, or because of restrictions under the Mutual Security and Export Control Acts, is another source of difficulty. The panel commends the work of the Senate Small Business Committee in calling attention to the practical difficulties encountered by industry in obtaining Government-generated scientific and technical information. The overall problem is serious, and applies to all Federal agencies, although the Navy is of prime importance with respect to marine technology since the largest percentage has been developed under Navy sponsorship.

The Oceanographer of the Navy has estimated that more than 90 per cent of the Navy-developed raw oceanographic scientific information is unclassified and therefore should be made available to the public. Nevertheless, as indicated earlier, there are insufficient funds to disseminate such information except for standard charts and publications intended for the maritime industry. A much greater percentage of oceanographic technological information is not available to the public. One

major reason for this is that it is frequently found in reports associated with classified subjects. In addition, it has been stated in Congressional testimony that an important barrier in information release arises from a diverse interpretation of military security regulations.[7] Classified reports frequently contain important contributions to marine technology and should be reviewed periodically to identify those portions that can be released for public use. The panel recognizes that the Department of Defense is making a concerted effort to make available results of military research and development.

An important function to be performed within the Commission's Governmental organizational plan is developing cooperative arrangements involving DOD and the civil marine agencies to assure that all Government data are made available to the private sector at the earliest possible time consistent with National security. Special attention should be given to the criteria with which DOD assigns classification to ocean-related data as well as to employment of the "need to know" requirement for certain classified and unclassified material. The Atomic Energy Commission Advisory Committee on Non-Nuclear Technology has performed an important service in this area. The panel believes that this service should be extended to the oceanographic field.

**Recommendation:**

**The Department of Defense and civil marine agencies should be directed to review and modify their procedures to ensure that the private sector has timely access to all classified and unclassified Government data as soon as possible consistent with security considerations. Particular attention should be devoted to the information exchange problems of small business.**

**An advisory committee should be charged with periodic review of the effectiveness with which all Government marine agencies are able to identify and disseminate information to potential users.**

## II. SUPPORTING SERVICES

The Federal Government provides many services directly and indirectly affecting ocean indus-

---

[7] Senate Select Committee on Small Business, April 6, 1967, *op. cit.*, p. 27.

tries. Other than the resource management services and scientific research provided by many Government agencies, several additional areas are extremely important to industrial ocean operations. These include weather forecasting and charting operations of ESSA, geological survey work of the Department of the Interior, maintenance of navigable waterways by the Corps of Engineers, and navigational aids and life and property protection services of the Coast Guard. The Navy also provides important services in salvage, environmental prediction, and mapping and charting. The National Oceanographic Data Center provides the function of soliciting and disseminating those marine data capable of being machine processed.

Although the many Government services are not discussed in detail in this report, they are considered important. Indeed, the panel finds Government support services assist a great variety of ocean operations and often are critical to the success of industry efforts.

Some specific recommendations affecting present and future needs for these services are found in other sections of this report. Supporting services are discussed in more detail in the report of the full Commission. In general, it is essential that support services provided by the Federal and State governments for a variety of ocean operations be continued and increased wherever growing activity warrants. The effectiveness of these services can be increased by improved coordination and in some cases consolidation of effort and facilities.

## III. JURISDICTION AND LEASING POLICIES

Government and industry interests are intimately involved in the terms under which public lands are assigned for private use.

Almost all ocean mineral resources are located on public lands. The seabed and its resources fall within the sovereignty of the States along the coast out a distance of three miles except in two States.[8] Most of these lands have been retained under State ownership but in some instances development rights have been ceded to counties, townships, and private individuals.

Beyond the zone of State jurisdiction and out to a depth of 200 meters or beyond to where the

depth of the superjacent waters allows exploitation, the seabed and its resources are under the jurisdiction of the Federal Government. Although submerged lands beyond 200 meters in depth have been leased to private industry by the Government, the United States has not officially claimed jurisdiction over natural resources in the seabed and subsoil beyond the 200 meter line. U.S. jurisdiction over fisheries extends out to 12 miles.

### A. Definition of State Boundaries and Baselines

The boundaries dividing seabed areas of Federal, State, and local jurisdiction; those dividing privately-owned areas from the public domain; and those dividing the area appertaining to the United States and the ocean beds falling beyond U.S. jurisdiction are beset with ambiguities. These uncertainties already are troublesome for business operations and appear certain to grow more severe.

The problems are complex and varied. In many locations the definition of the shoreline itself is unclear due to the character of the terrain; marshlands, floating islands, tidal effects, and migrating sand bars all complicate boundary problems. Many instances are recorded of private property washed away or submerged by storms, where resulting doubts about title must be resolved in court. In other cases, the uncertainty of shoreline location and the manner in which baselines should be drawn across bays and between islands creates an ambiguity in locating the boundary between State and Federal jurisdiction.

A second major source of uncertainty is the historical claim for States' rights beyond the three-mile limit. Jurisdiction of three leagues (more than nine miles) from shore has been recognized by the Federal Government for Texas and the Gulf of Mexico shoreline of Florida. In the case of Florida, the lack of a definitive boundary between the Atlantic and Gulf Coasts at the southern end of Florida further complicates the issue. Maine, citing a pre-Revolutionary War charter as justification, recently claimed jurisdiction as distant as 200 miles from its coast and has sold oil and natural gas exploration rights within this zone, an action which the Federal Government is expected to challenge.

A myriad of local arrangements to develop nearshore resources, particularly shellfish, has caused further confusion. Among the States there is a great variety of legal conventions regarding

---

[8] Off Texas and the Gulf Coast of Florida the distance is three leagues (about nine miles). It should be noted that the boundary is not always precise due to a lack of agreement as to the coastal base line.

ownership of shoreline properties and rights within the tidal zone. There is confusion regarding the seaward extensions of the boundaries between States. A clear agreement between Federal and State governments as to responsibility for managing and developing fisheries within the three-to-twelve mile zone also is lacking.

The unsatisfactory status of the Nation's marine boundaries and the Federal Government's responsibility to take the lead in its clarification has long been recognized. The problem can be deferred no longer. A waiting policy operates only to discourage private investment and to complicate resolution of claims in areas where investments have been staked.

The panel endorses the recommendation for solving marine boundary problems proposed in the Panel Report on the Coastal Zone. It recommends formation of a National Commission to create new criteria for fixing shore boundaries, establish these limits for each coastal State, and negotiate with Federal and State interests regarding the limits. The intent is to establish fixed boundaries for domestic purposes only, breaking from traditional reliance upon the principles of common law.

## Recommendation:

**A National commission should be established immediately to clarify the marine jurisdictional limits of the U.S. coastal States.**

### B. Definition of National Jurisdiction

The legal problems presently hindering orderly industrial ocean development arise primarily from State and Federal laws and regulations. However, this concern with laws affecting activities within National boundaries also includes clarification of the National boundaries and the international aspects of exploiting resources beyond them. This subject is discussed in greater detail in the Report of the Commission's International Panel.

As an example of the difficulties encountered, two companies have acquired from two different nations the oil rights of the same section of sea floor off the Grand Banks. Canada believes it has jurisdiction over the mineral wealth of the Banks, but France, which owns the islands of St. Pierre and Miquelon, also claims a portion.

Because the United States has not officially recognized the jurisdictional boundaries of some nations, many problems arise, other than area access, that affect U.S. companies. A company mining, for instance, off the coast of South America in an area of disputed jurisdiction will not only find that it must pay U.S. import duties, but that it may not be allowed an investment tax credit or credit for taxes paid to the nation claiming jurisdiction. International agreement on national jurisdictions will eliminate uncertainty and permit U.S. companies operating in such areas to take advantage of many fiscal incentives normally available to domestic companies.

Companies considering offshore oil and mining ventures will be reluctant, and in some cases restrained, from making sizeable investments unless the Continental Shelf's limits are precisely defined and a new international legal-political framework is agreed upon to govern exploration and exploitation beyond these limits. Until this is accomplished, the United States should encourage continued exploration and exploitation beyond the 200 meter isobath.

## Recommendation:

**The U.S. Government should take the initiative in proposing a new international framework for exploiting ocean mineral resources to:**

**—Define clearly the limits of National jurisdictions.**

**—Govern operations beyond these limits.**

### C. Exploration and Lease Terms

Oil, gas, and sulfur are the only mineral resources being recovered from the outer Continental Shelf under Federal jurisdiction. Phosphates, gravels, sand, shells, and certain placers are being taken from inshore waters under State jurisdiction. Petroleum exploration and drilling conducted in both Federal and State regimes clearly dominate these activities.

The terms under which mineral rights in outer Continental Shelf lands may be assigned to private developers are specified in the 1953 Outer Continental Shelf Lands Act.[9]

The Act requires that rights to minerals be subject to competitive bidding. This system has

---

[9]This subject has been under extensive review for some time by the Public Land Law Review Commission.

worked effectively for the oil industry. But the mining industry believes strongly that considering the risks and very high costs associated with exploration and proving hard mineral reserves, the potential profits are not now sufficiently attractive to support competitive bidding. The problem is presented in detail in the Ocean Mining section of Chapter 4 in this report and in the report of the Marine Resources Panel. At a minimum, development of outer Continental Shelf hard mineral resources will require amendment of the Outer Continental Shelf Lands Act to take into account differences between petroleum and mining operations.

**Recommendation:**

**The Outer Continental Shelf Lands Act should be amended to give the Secretary of the Interior additional flexibility in assigning rights for mineral development.**

There also are barriers to assigning rights in areas within State jurisdictions. For economic and technological reasons, sea bottom mining can generally be expected to begin in the shallower waters, which are usually in State rather than Federal jurisdictions. Because of little actual ocean mining, State laws generally do not provide for it, although several along the coast now have corrective laws under consideration. This situation makes it very difficult for a company to evaluate a potential mining venture, because the leasing procedures, rights, and total costs cannot be determined readily.

**Recommendation:**

**The States should enact procedures that will encourage hard mineral exploration and exploitation on their submerged lands.**

Several guidelines for such procedures are discussed in the Ocean Mining section of Chapter 4.

## D. SEASTEADING

The panel believes that entrepreneurs' acquisition of rights to submarine areas would stimulate many facets of ocean development. There are countless ways an imaginative entrepreneur could develop the seabed and water column. However, the present legal and regulatory framework does not encourage individuals and small companies with innovative ideas to develop such real estate. Where procedures exist, they generally are limited to oil, gas, and mineral rights and require payment of sizeable legal fees and bonuses.

The person or company having an innovative idea often is unable to devote the time and money to obtain exclusive ocean rights. Initially, projects usually are high risk, and uncertainty in obtaining favorable leases often compounds the economic risk, making the expected value of the return too low to justify the capital investment.

The State governments should seek to devise "seasteading" arrangements—simple, attractive leasing procedures specifically for the innovative use of the seafloor and water column. Great benefits are to be gained by encouraging entrepreneurial investment. For example, the States should ponder the increase in tourism likely to spring from such underwater attractions as parks, hotels, and restaurants. In addition, aquacultural projects for shellfish and fin fish could be quite profitable and a source of tax revenue.

The procedure most attractive to both government and the entrepreneur probably will be a long-term, renewable lease conditioned upon useful development. The lessee should be allotted sufficient time to make a profit on his investment.

The seasteading approach also is fully consistent with the need for the orderly, rational development of marine areas. Leases can be carefully drafted so that each seasteader's operations will mesh with the desired pattern for overall development. Moreover, if decided that a particular seastead subsequently is more suitable for another use, perhaps petroleum or hard mineral development, the specific termination date of a lease enables a change at a time anticipated by the seasteader.

The leases should be established so as not to conflict with the more complex procedures already used to allocate sectors of the ocean bottom for petroleum exploration and development. Indeed, petroleum and other mineral rights should be expressly excluded from the leases.

In addition to many difficulties not yet foreseen, interference with such uses as navigation and fishing would pose special problems for seasteading. An obvious way to avoid conflict with other uses would be to select locations where such activity is light. The same purpose could be achieved by limiting development projects to certain parts of the water column.

Recommendation:

**To encourage innovative uses of the ocean other than petroleum and hard mineral development, State governments should initiate experimental programs for leasing submarine areas ("seasteading") within U.S. territorial waters, contingent on useful development of the property. Such programs should be a part of a plan for the orderly, rational development of offshore regions.**

Although the panel recommends seasteading only within territorial waters, such a concept will have increasing merit in waters farther offshore as ocean activities expand in new uses of the sea. Just as in the territorial waters, seasteading will be a means of providing investment protection to innovative users from multiple use conflicts. Therefore, the Government should consider the advantages of special leasing arrangements beyond territorial waters.

## IV. JOINT VENTURES

Joint ventures probably will allow many ocean ventures not otherwise possible considering investment size and high risk involved. Companies must be alert to such opportunities as:

—Collaboration in research and development of ship design and shipbuilding methods, as practiced in competitive countries, may be fruitful.

—Consortia for ocean mineral exploration and development may prove necessary in certain cases to attract sufficient risk capital.

—Joint ventures in expensive deep ocean research may shorten the period necessary to collect essential data in many fields.

—Insurance pools covering offshore equipment and structures may allow improved coverage for marine operations.

## V. INSURANCE

From large petroleum companies to small supply and diving businesses, offshore operators have had difficulty obtaining adequate insurance coverage. Many aspects of the problem are being solved by underwriters, but several remain, impeding progress. Two unsolved areas are discussed below.

### A. Offshore Installations

At one time, U.S. insurance companies insured such offshore items as rigs, platforms, pipelines and small submersibles. However, business became so unprofitable to the few companies in the field that U.S. underwriters vacated the market and left Lloyds of London as the sole insurer. Now the gross annual premiums on offshore installations have climbed to an estimated $80 million and U.S. companies are showing signs of renewed interest. For instance, several participate in reinsurance through Lloyds, while at least one U.S. company recently has written a direct policy in this area.

In 1968, several underwriters attempted to form a syndicate to cover this phase of offshore industry but the proposal had not been effected at the time of writing this report due to considerations of profitability and possible anti-trust implications. The panel encourages the efforts of the insurance companies to pool their resources to undertake the high offshore risks. In time, various factors will improve the insurability of offshore installations, including:

—Improved actuarial statistics.

—A lower rate of damage and loss due to improved technology.

—A broader insurance base resulting from accelerating offshore investments.

Until the insurance companies find the business more profitable, it appears that the companies operating offshore will continue to pay high premiums or in some cases resort to local pooling or self insurance arrangements.

### B. Personal Injury to Workers Offshore

The panel finds the insurance cost for personal injury in the offshore areas extremely high and for some small companies prohibitive. A major reason for this is that by law many offshore workers may choose between compensation and litigation when seeking recovery for injury; thus the underwriters have no sound basis to evaluate premium ratings.

At present, insurance companies cannot predict whether litigation or compensation procedures will be followed in each case of accidental injury to an offshore worker. Litigation awards are determined by juries and are often extremely high; yet, the injured worker may receive a substantially reduced amount of recovery, perhaps nothing at all, if he is proved negligent. Recovery under compensation laws, on the other hand, is automatic, but the amounts fixed by compensation schedules for the various kinds and degrees of injuries are generally much lower than litigation awards.

The dilemma relates to the coverage of the Federal Longshoremen's and Harbor Workers' Act, which sets rates of compensation for injuries occurring upon navigable waters to maritime employees *other than seamen*. The Act provides an administrative procedure to eliminate the need for redress through litigation in this specific area. However, it has not been modernized to account for such equipment as manned submersibles and mobile drilling rigs. Thus, employees on mobile equipment at sea are able to seek recovery either through compensation under the Longshoremen's Act or by litigation on the theory that they are "seamen."

When a claimant has such a choice, he can elect the method that maximizes his recovery. Thus the probable claim liability is higher, resulting in larger premium costs to the offshore operator. If only one means of recovery were available, the claim liability would be reduced. Consequently, the panel recommends enactment of legislation to ensure that only one method can be used to determine claim liability. Since it is simpler, less time-consuming, and establishes greater certainty in predicting liability, the compensation procedure is preferable to litigation.

Recommendation:

**In order to reduce insurance costs, the Longshoremen's and Harbor Workers' Compensation Act should be amended so it will be the exclusive method to determine claim liability for injuries to offshore workers.**

## VI. COLLABORATION IN DEVELOPMENT PLANNING

In today's economy, industry finds its operations affected crucially by Government actions. In turn, the plans of industry have a critical effect on meeting National objectives. Clearly ocean development must be a total National enterprise in which government, industry and the academic community plan and work together on a continuing and effective basis.

The consequences of uncoordinated action are easy to foresee. For example, installations located in areas of doubtful sovereignty might be rendered worthless should international agreements change; expensive port developments might be circumvented by new modes of transportation; investment in recreation facilities might be jeopardized by changes in the environment.

Yet the difficulty of achieving effective collaboration in development planning should not be underestimated. Oceanic activities inherently involve great risk. No one can forecast accurately the rate of technological development nor the manner in which international law will develop. There are additional uncertainties which constrain participants from commitments necessary to an effective plan. The Government, for instance, inhibited by political circumstances from committing funds to multiyear projects, usually stipulates that its plans are contingent upon the availability of appropriations. Many industries, then, hedge their plans to protect themselves against changes in costs and markets.

### A. Consolidation of Federal Functions

The Panel finds there is no single focus within the Government for fostering industrial development of ocean resources. Many Federal agencies have responsibilities in the ocean, but to date no strong focus and in some instances no clear delineation of responsibility has occurred. Consolidating some existing functions would have many beneficial effects.

Planning and implementation functions have in the past been less than optimum due to the variety of interests and the fragmented responsibility for ocean endeavors. Improvement is needed in research planning, budgeting, and administration of funds. A means for better coordination and direction is imperative as ocean development accelerates and conflicts of use multiply. This could best be achieved if a number of Government functions were consolidated. Industry is not only perplexed with the number of agencies that must be satisfied in conducting marine-oriented operations, but is seriously impeded in its own planning process when, as often happens, uncertainty and conflict arise in the plans of various agencies. This is particularly true for service oriented Government agencies.

Many agencies that influence ocean operations do so by providing such services as weather forecasting, charting, and collection of a variety of oceanographic data. It is believed that unintentional duplication could be minimized and superior service could be provided for industry if some of these functions were consolidated. Not only could priorities be better determined, but greater efficiency could be achieved in the use of manpower and facilities, improving assistance to industry without increasing expenditures.

Numerous civilian agencies with ocean interests splinter non-military research and development. Failure to clearly assign responsibility for ocean work often results in program oversights in important areas or frequently contributes to unnecessary duplication. The fragmentation of effort and lack of effective coordination and planning often result in priority and funding assignments at the project level that are inappropriate to the total National program. A far better base for conducting research and developing multipurpose technology would result from consolidation of some functions of existing agencies.

Consolidation of some Government functions would provide greater visibility for ocean development, giving a great impetus to industrial development in the marine environment. A unified group can serve effectively as an information distribution center. Private organizations wishing to obtain or exchange data or information and to submit unsolicited proposals could make fewer contacts. A focus within the Government would provide one strong voice rather than many uncoordinated small voices. It would be extremely valuable to the President, the Congress, all the Federal agencies, and the entire Nation.

### Recommendation:

**Many marine functions of existing agencies and bureaus should, wherever possible, be consolidated to improve the effectiveness of the Government's participation in a National marine program.**

## B. Government-Industry Planning Mechanism

The Federal Government, industry, the States, and the academic community can make better decisions if fully aware of each other's plans and activities. Better communication between the public and private sectors would help ensure orderly development of a National marine program. With the diverse nature of private oceanic endeavors and the size of private spending, it is essential that effective liaison be established between Federal administrators and the private sector. The Government's need for information and advice from industry, States and regions, and the academic community is becoming increasingly essential as development of ocean resources accelerates with an accompanying increase in multiple use conflicts.

Marine operations are replete with examples where joint planning is needed or must be improved:

—The National Projects proposed in the Report of the Marine Engineering and Technology Panel will require especially close collaboration in planning, as much of the multipurpose technology developed will be of value to industry.

—Consultation is important in development and marketing of products and processes. Items being developed under Government sponsorship should not be competitive with those produced solely through the private sector.

—More effective Government and industry consultation is needed in projecting schedules for leasing offshore lands.

—The need to plan coastal zone use and resolve conflicts presents an especially important challenge to Government and industry. The Panel Report on Management and Development of the Coastal Zone has recommended the establishment of coastal zone authorities on the State and local government levels.[10]

The role of these authorities would include planning for multiple use of coastal and lakeshore waters and lands and resolving conflicts of mul-

---

[10] Panel Report on Management and Development of the Coastal Zone, Chapter 10.

tiple use. The Panel on Industry and Private Investment concurs in this recommendation. These authorities would solve routine cases of user conflict, leaving only problems of National scope to be resolved through Federal executive, legislative, or judicial procedures.

Recommendation:

**An advisory committee composed of representatives appointed by the President from private industry, States and regions, and the academic** community should be statutorily created. This committee would participate in the establishment of National marine goals and objectives and provide continuing guidance to the Federal Government.

Additional details concerning the nature and proposed functions of such an advisory committee are given in the Report of the Marine Engineering and Technology Panel and are endorsed by this panel.

## I. INTRODUCTION

The panel has placed major emphasis on resource industries (oil, natural gas, mining, fishing, and aquaculture), recognizing, however, that such other users of the ocean as the recreation and transportation industries also are immensely important. Sea transportation is discussed in this chapter in general terms. A detailed discussion of recreation is found in the Report of the Marine Resources Panel.

Since healthy and growing primary user and resource industries should foster sound supporting industries, each support and service industry has not been discussed individually. Instrument production, petroleum drilling, pipeline laying, diving, salvage, and weather prediction are among the many support and service activities. To illustrate the problems faced by one such industry, the panel has included a section on instruments since the need for instruments pervades all other industries.

Several resource activities—chemicals from sea water, seaweeds, and marine pharmaceuticals—are mentioned only in this introduction.

### A. Chemical Extraction from Sea Water

Chemical extraction from sea water constitutes a successful industry with no major problems requiring Government action.[1] Salt, bromine, magnesium metal, and magnesium compounds are the only major inorganic chemicals presently extracted. These industries, well-established in the United States, compete favorably with land-based operations. For example, magnesium metal extracted from sea water accounts for over 90 per cent of total U.S. production, while bromine represents approximately half. These large shares of the market are produced in a single facility in Freeport, Texas. Salt production from sea water is centered in California. In addition, eight domestic plants rely on the ocean as a source of raw material to produce magnesium compounds. The approximate value of chemicals extracted from the water column adjacent to the United States is estimated at $127 million.[2]

### B. Seaweeds

Domestic harvesting of various seaweeds and extraction of many derivatives has evolved into a business with annual activity estimated by the panel in excess of $25 million. Algin, carrageenin, and agar are the most important commercial derivatives, but there are many others. They are utilized in many chemical processes, often in conjunction with the manufacture of food and cosmetic products including gelatin desserts, jams, baby foods, and toothpaste. In addition, kelp and other seaweeds have been used as fertilizer in an unprocessed form. Most seaweed harvested is brown kelp from California.

In addition to harvesting natural seaweed, it is anticipated that aquaculture techniques will supplement the supply by growing some types of marine algae. There is, for example, a potential for raising and processing seaweed in ponds and rivers for ultimate use as animal feed.

### C. Pharmaceuticals

The properties of marine bioactive substances have attracted widespread interest and appear to pose considerable promise regarding the prevention, treatment and cure of human ills.[3] Although the pharmaceuticals industry has sponsored some research there is little expressed interest in the marine pharmaceutical segment. Industry spokesmen have stated that most drug companies have many more research opportunities than they could possibly undertake, and the most promising of

---

[1] Such extraction is discussed in greater detail in the Report of the Panel on Marine Engineering and Technology.

[2] This represents the combined annual value of sea water production of salt ($8 million), magnesium metal ($57 million), bromine ($30 million), and magnesium compounds ($32 million). In addition, desalination of sea water in this country yields $8 million of potable water. W. F. McIlhenny, "Chemicals from Sea Water," *Proceedings of the Inter-American Conference on Materials Technology,* May 1968, p. 119.

[3] Report of the Panel on Oceanography, President's Science Advisory Committee, "Effective Use of the Sea," June 1966, pp. 52-54.

these are not associated with marine bioactive substances.

To discover a new compound may cost tens of thousands of dollars, either by synthesis or refinement from nature. However, once a drug is found, it usually costs millions of dollars to produce it commercially. Only one of every two to three thousand compounds investigated becomes marketable. Because of considerable development costs, a drug company must have some assurance of exclusive rights (patent or license) before it will spend the money, and it is often more difficult to obtain exclusive rights to naturally occurring products.

Nevertheless, drug companies continue to look to new sources of supply, including the ocean. If a marine specimen is found to contain a new substance with drug potential, the pharmaceutical companies may find it more economical either to synthesize the active ingredient, or culture the creature in the laboratory. In many cases, therefore, the sea may be an initial source for a given drug, but not a continuing one.

## II. PETROLEUM

### A. Present Status and Outlook

Demand for oil is expected to increase rapidly in the next 20 years. Much of the new domestic supply to meet this demand will be from offshore areas because a high percentage of the large, easily located accumulations on land already have been developed, while comparatively few have been found offshore.

The Marine Resources Panel's report includes recent projections of free world energy demand. It indicates that during the next 20 years the cumulative demand will be about three times the total produced throughout the free world during the last 100 years. Moreover, it is estimated that, between now and the year 2000, three-fourths of domestic energy needs will be met by oil and gas, despite increasing reliance on nuclear power and other new sources of energy.

Although U.S. production of oil and gas has increased rapidly, domestic consumption has grown even more dramatically, contributing to a steady decline in the ratio of proven domestic reserves to annual production from about 13 in 1950 to 10 in 1967. In addition, North America consumes about 45 per cent of free world petroleum production but has only about 13 per cent of the proven reserves.[4]

Hence a major problem facing the petroleum industry is to prove additional reserves. Those who forecast that the world soon would be running out of oil and gas supplies have seen advancing technology employed to find new reserves, and have had to revise their original prognostications. Today the oil industry is developing new technology that will enable companies to evaluate and hopefully develop not only offshore oil deposits, but tar sands, oil shale, coal conversion processes and other sources on land that are not now economically recoverable.

Petroleum producers are turning to the sea in the hope of finding and developing large quantities of new reserves more economically than they presently can on land. Thus, even though operating and capital costs are high offshore, the companies are hoping that fields not yet discovered in the comparatively virgin marine areas will be sufficiently large and productive to be highly competitive with land sources.

### B. Investment and Sales

The petroleum industry produced about $1.0 billion of crude oil in 1967 from the U.S.

#### Table 1
#### DOMESTIC OFFSHORE EXPENDITURES
#### (Billions of Dollars)

|  | 1968 (Est.) | Cumulative (Through 1968) |
|---|---|---|
| Lease Bonus and Rental Payments . . . . | $1.25 | $ 4.00 |
| Royalty Payments . . . . | 0.25 | 1.85 |
| Seismic, Gravity, and Magnetic Surveys . . . . | 0.10 | 1.10 |
| Drilling and Completing Wells . . . . | 0.35 | 3.10 |
| Platforms, Production Facilities, and Pipelines . . | 0.25 | 1.85 |
| Operating Costs . . . . . | 0.15 | 0.85 |
| TOTAL . . . . . | $2.35 | $12.75 |

Source: Richard J. Howe (Esso Production Research Co.), "Petroleum Operations in the Sea—1980 and Beyond," *Ocean Industry*, August 1968, p. 29.

[4] *Oil and Gas Journal*, Dec. 25, 1967, p. 119.

# Table 2

## EXTENT OF OFFSHORE CONTINENTAL SHELF ACTIVITY IN THE FREE WORLD[1]

| Category | Year | United States | Canada | Latin America | Europe | Africa | Mideast | Far East | Free World |
|---|---|---|---|---|---|---|---|---|---|
| Countries with Offshore Activity[2] | 1960 | 1 | 1 | 5 | 2 | 6 | 5 | 4 | 24 |
| | 1964 | 1 | 1 | 15 | 8 | 21 | 12 | 8 | 66 |
| | 1967 | 1 | 1 | 18 | 9 | 26 | 14 | 11 | 80 |
| Offshore Concession Acreage (Millions of acres) | 1960 | — | — | — | — | — | — | — | 300[3] |
| | 1964 | 7 | 154 | 87 | 48 | 56 | 34 | 422 | 807 |
| | 1966 | 9 | 202 | 125 | 69 | 127 | 53 | 760 | 1,345[4] |
| Geophysical Crew Months (Marine seismograph) | 1960 | 93 | 5 | 6 | — | 31 | — | — | 135 |
| | 1964 | 273 | 22 | 12 | 133 | 45 | 26 | 35 | 546 |
| | 1966 | 461 | 26 | 18 | 103 | 33 | 47 | 140 | 828[5] |
| Crude-Oil Production (Thousand b/d) | 1960 | 190 | — | 25 | — | — | 181 | — | 396 |
| | 1964 | 449 | — | 59 | 8 | 65 | 684 | 7 | 1,272 |
| | 1967 | 870 | — | 77 | 10 | 165 | 1,184 | 50 | 2,356 |
| Proved Crude Reserves (Million bbl) | 1960 | 1,700 | — | 220 | 100 | — | 14,750 | — | 16,770 |
| | 1964 | 2,200 | — | 260 | 100 | 1,050 | 32,300 | 100 | 35,910 |
| | 1967 | 4,100 | — | 330 | 220 | 3,150 | 43,350 | 1,400 | 52,550 |

[1] Does not take into account the activity in such protected waters as Venezuela's rich Lake Maracaibo.
[2] Excludes countries where onshore concessions extend into offshore areas and where there is no offshore activity.
[3] Breakdown not available.
[4] Data as of Jan. 1, 1967 not yet available.
[5] Data for 1967 not yet available.

Source: *Oil and Gas Journal*, May 6, 1968, p. 77.

Continental Shelf,[5] representing approximately 12 per cent of the total annual value of crude oil extracted in the United States.

Offshore production accounts for 16 per cent of total world production.[6] Comparing U.S. production of $1.0 billion with the estimated 1968 investment of $2.35 billion shown in Table 1, the offshore yield has yet to match the very large ocean expenditures by oil companies. Of the $4.0 billion of bonus and rental payments for offshore sites paid to date, $3.3 billion were paid to the U.S. Government and $0.7 billion to the States. The $1.85 billion of royalties paid to date, however, was divided equally between the States and U.S. Government.[7] Table 2 indicates the relative position of the United States in offshore oil activity throughout the free world and also reveals the industry's rapid growth since 1960.

## C. Nature of the Industry

The number and character of the companies in the industry defy concise description. At least 30 to 35 U.S. oil companies are involved in offshore production, supported by hundreds of contractors who provide services for a large portion of the work done at sea. A small percentage of these contractors is controlled by the oil companies through majority stockholdings. Because of high operating risks and the large capital outlays required, most companies producing oil offshore are large corporations. However, several small companies have formed groups to operate jointly offshore. Unlike offshore gas, the transmission of oil through pipelines is usually performed by the production companies.

## D. Problems and Recommendations

Oil economics is a complex subject—not only from the standpoint of domestic production but also in regard to world production and import restrictions. The price of oil has been at a relatively stable level in the United States in the past. In the future, however, as demand approaches conventional supply capability, the price will be affected by costs of offshore production, alternative domestic sources, and U.S. import restrictions. This Panel has not attempted to analyze the oil industry in detail but has concentrated on problems of the U.S. offshore oil industry and desirable adjustments to the present regulatory framework in light of higher offshore risks.

Much capital is involved in recovering oil from the ocean bottom. Existing platforms in the Gulf of Mexico cost between $1 and $6 million depending on water depths and location, whereas site preparation costs on land are minimal. In addition, costs of operating over water are two to four times those on land, and offshore pipelines generally cost two to four times those onshore.

One recent analysis of the costs of producing in a model field under actual conditions off Louisiana indicated that present-value net profit (using a nine per cent discount rate) dropped to only nine cents per barrel at ocean depths of 400 feet compared to 33 cents at 100 feet and 50 cents onshore.[8] No finding or bonus costs were included in this example because of variations from field to field. Moreover, a field of better-than-average size was assumed. It should be noted that the profits generated in deep water (nine cents) are not generally sufficient even to pay for either exploration or bonus costs. This example suggests that additional attention may be required for the problems related to the greater offshore depths in order to insure a continuing and healthy rate of activity in exploration and production.

### 1. Timing of Federal Lease Sales

The system of offshore lease sales is a complex subject now under intensive study by the Public Land Law Review Commission and the Department of the Interior. The competition in recent oil lease sales indicates the system is working reasonably well, but some aspects of the present policy should be altered.

The timing of Federal lease sales has been erratic. Notice of sales well ahead of time would greatly aid industry budgeting, would enable the industry to improve its utilization of capital,

[5] U.S. Bureau of Mines.

[6] Richard J. Howe (Esso Production Research Co.), "Petroleum Operations in the Sea—1980 and Beyond," *Ocean Industry,* August 1968, p. 29.

[7] *Ibid.*

[8] J. E. Wilson (Shell Oil Co.), "Economics of Offshore Louisiana," presented before the Louisiana-Arkansas Division of the Mid-Continent Oil and Gas Assn., Sept. 12, 1967.

manpower, and equipment, particularly with respect to exploration and development activity, and would permit the gathering of more data to evaluate the property to be leased.

### Recommendation:

**Federal lease sales for oil and gas development rights on the outer Continental Shelf should be announced further in advance than is current practice.**

### 2. Federal Lease Sales for Deep Water

In 1968, there was a $600 million lease sale in the Santa Barbara channel. Thus, several oil companies ventured into very deep water—over 60 per cent of the acreage is below 600 feet and the corner of one lease is in water more than 1,800 feet deep. The Santa Barbara sale involved special circumstances that compensated somewhat for the disadvantages inherent in greater depths. The tracts are very near the shore; the oceanographic and meteorological conditions are mild when compared to the Gulf of Mexico; oil is in short supply along the densely populated coast of Southern California; and there are no restrictions on rates of production. The degree to which the deeper Santa Barbara leases will allow economical production will depend greatly on technology yet to be developed or perfected and on finding large petroleum accumulations.

The OCS Lands Act now limits the primary term for exploration and development to a maximum of five years. Continuing the trend toward exploration and development in deep water, as well as hostile areas such as Cook Inlet, Alaska, may make it desirable to lengthen the primary lease term.

### 3. Production Rate Restrictions

The Gulf region produces most of the domestic offshore oil and has the most proven U.S. offshore reserves. Texas and Louisiana have set limits on the production rate of each well in accordance with a *percentage allowable*. In order to offset costs of operations over water, both States use the *equity allowable ratio* to permit companies to produce oil from nearshore and offshore areas at a more rapid rate than on land. State ratios traditionally have been followed closely by the U.S.

Government for application to offshore areas in the Gulf beyond State jurisdiction.

Removal of restrictions on production from Federal leases might well make Federal tracts, deeper and further offshore, more attractive to oil companies. However, this would result in loss of severance tax revenue to Texas and Louisiana because of reduced onshore output and might cause the States to respond in kind, thus upsetting the existing economic and political stability. Past arguments in support of restrictions have included:

—Restrictions are useful to balance supply and demand and to improve conservation.

—Fields with marginal economics would be unable to compete with large efficient fields if the supply were not prorated. Thus, it has been reasoned that restrictions help maintain a standby production capability that could be mobilized quickly in times of need such as the Middle East crisis.

The subject of prorationing involves political and economic ramifications related to the varying interests of large companies, small companies, and consumers. These extremely complex issues presently are being reviewed by the Public Land Law Review Commission.

The percentage allowable is continuing to rise due to ever increasing demand for petroleum. This increase will probably continue until the capacity of all wells is attained. Many expect this point to be reached in the next 5 to 10 years.

### 4. Environmental Prediction

The offshore oil industry operates in a hostile environment, particularly in hurricane areas. For operations under normal climatic conditions, the oil companies and their offshore contractors receive adequate environmental forecasts from the U.S. Weather Bureau and many private meteorological companies. Nevertheless, improved data and forecasting techniques would provide immediate cost savings. In view of substantial added costs during the hurricane season in the Gulf of Mexico, better hurricane data and prediction would be beneficial.

The cost of shutting down during a hurricane threat in the Gulf of Mexico can be considerable. Offshore operations are shut down to varying degrees depending on the type of operation, degree of control and automation, and strength and proximity of the hurricane. It has been estimated that Hurricane Inez in 1966 cost Louisiana operators $1.5 million in expenses and lost production even though the hurricane did not come near enough to cause any property damage.

Property losses, as differentiated from shut downs, have been even greater. Hurricanes Hilda (1964) and Betsy (1965) each caused offshore property losses exceeding $100 million.

Improved hurricane path prediction will reduce the degree and length of shutdowns. Greater knowledge of the wind, wave, and subsurface forces associated with hurricanes will allow improved design and construction techniques resulting in savings in construction cost, property losses, and insurance premiums.

Modification of intensity or path of hurricanes would have obvious advantages not only to the petroleum industry but all other marine and coastal interests. However, progress in hurricane research has been disappointingly slow; accurate prediction, modification, and perhaps control remain hopes for the future. To help in this problem, the Environmental Science Services Administration recently has intensified research at its National Hurricane Center.

Very little is known about the size, shape, speed, and destructive power of hurricane waves. The more than 1,000 existing offshore platforms represent potential instrument sites to measure environmental conditions and their effects. Several offshore operators have indicated willingness to make their platforms available for data gathering. In addition, the use of laser or radar altimeters by aircraft may have potential for studying hurricane waves, and the study of their feasibility deserves a high priority.

Recommendation:
**The U.S. Government, together with industry and the academic community, should intensify current efforts to improve understanding of hurricanes and their destructive effects.**

### 5. Technology Transfer[9]

A disappointingly small amount of the oceanographic and ocean engineering data and technology

---

[9]Oil and gas technology is discussed in the Report of the Panel on Marine Engineering and Technology.

acquired by various Government agencies has reached offshore operators. Such information and technology could benefit all offshore operations, especially the petroleum industry. Exploration, drilling, and production in deeper waters where technology must be more advanced make increased oceanographic knowledge more needed than ever.

The responsibility for information exchange should not fall exclusively on Government agencies. The petroleum companies, by virtue of their many research efforts and ocean operating experience, have accumulated considerable knowledge on their own. Much of this is not genuinely proprietary and could be of great value to the Nation if disseminated among other private interests and Government agencies.

Unfortunately, greater exchange of information will not be easy. The knowledge, customarily in the sole possession of a few experts, is rarely well documented or advertised. Consequently, because person-to-person transfer generally has been inefficient, enormous effort will be necessary to achieve greater interchange.

There already have been some cooperative efforts by Government, universities, and the petroleum industry to improve technology transfer in such subjects as environmental prediction, platform design, underwater completion, materials studies, and welding techniques. For example, one company with considerable expertise in underwater oil well completion gave a course on the subject. Seven petroleum companies signed up at $100,000 each, while the U.S. Geological Survey was invited to participate at no cost. On another occasion, a joint Navy-industry research project for measuring hurricane waves was established on a cost-sharing, information-sharing basis.

### 6. Multiple Use Conflicts

Conflicting uses of coastal and offshore marine areas is becoming an increasing burden to oil companies. Delays in offshore operations resulting from uncertainties brought about by such conflicts have cost the petroleum industry substantial sums. There is urgent need to bring private interests together with representatives from U.S., State, and local governments to develop a mechanism for rationally resolving the conflicts. The advisory committee recommended in Chapter 3 of this report could be helpful in developing such a mechanism. Further discussion on multiple use conflicts is also found in Chapter 3 with a more detailed discussion in the report on the Coastal Zone.

### 7. Major Oil Spills

The Nation is well aware of the deleterious effects of the grounding of the *Torrey Canyon* and other tankers. The subject of prevention and control of major oil spills is presently receiving a great deal of attention such as the joint pollution study conducted by the Departments of Interior and Transportation. A major part of the research is being done by petroleum companies. Nevertheless, the problem is far from solved and Government and industry attention is encouraged to develop technology to prevent, detect, and nullify the effects of oil spills from offshore production and transportation operations.

Government regulations and enforcement are necessary to define responsibility and liability, and to ensure equitable distribution of costs of prevention and cure. Because the problem is complex, and great knowledge of the subject is held by industry, such technology development and legislative action must be worked out by a combination of Federal, State, and industry experts. Emergency plans should be established to permit rapid action to contain and clean up major oil spills.

### 8. Other Problem Areas

Because of detailed treatment in other sections of this report and in other panel reports, surveys,[10] technology programs,[11] jurisdictional clarification,[12] and insurance problems[13] will not be discussed here. However, all these areas are of interest and importance to the petroleum industry.

## III. NATURAL GAS

### A. Present Status

The sequence of operation in bringing natural gas to the consumer involves three functions:

---

[10] See Chapter 3 of this report and the Report of the Panel on Marine Resources.

[11] See Chapter 3 of this report and the Report of the Panel on Marine Engineering and Technology.

[12] See Chapter 3 of this report and the Report of the International Panel.

[13] See Chapter 3 of this report.

---

production, transmission, and distribution. Petroleum companies normally explore for and produce the gas. Transportation is handled by the transmission companies regulated by the Federal Power Commission (FPC) in all matters of interstate commerce. Distribution to consumers usually involves a separate group of independent companies regulated at the State level. Although the three functions commonly are carried on by independent companies, a combination may be performed by one company through subsidiaries. Both the transmission and distribution industries are among the 10 largest U.S. industries in terms of capital investment.

Sales of natural gas are expected to increase at an annual rate of about four per cent in the next decade. In fact, the percentage of total energy consumption represented by natural gas is expected to increase slightly, in spite of the growth of new competitive primary sources of energy, particularly nuclear. As with oil, the offshore areas offer great potential for new reserves, and gas producers as well as transmission companies are making heavy commitments here. In 1967, over $300 million was paid to petroleum companies for natural gas produced offshore.

Occurring in the same environment, offshore oil and natural gas operations share many technical and regulatory problems. But beyond that the gas industry faces a special set of constraints associated with FPC regulatory policy. The growth of gas supply is closely tied to such policy not only through FPC regulation of gas transmission companies, but also regulation of the production companies to the extent of controlling the maximum price at which natural gas can be sold to the transmission companies.

### B. Problems and Recommendations

### 1. Reserves

The National reserve-to-production ratio (R/P) of natural gas has been declining steadily since 1950, falling from nearly 27 years to slightly less than 16 years in 1968.[14] The optimum level of reserves cannot be authoritatively stated. Some companies believe that the national R/P ratio can

---

[14] The R/P ratio is the proven reserves divided by the current rate of annual production, a level of reserves stated in years.

---

continue to decline for an additional period without causing undue concern, resulting in a lower level of idle development capital for producers. However, individual companies already have felt the pressure of declining reserves, and it is doubtful that it would be in the National interest to allow much further reduction. Although the R/P ratio for oil is about 10 years, valid reasons exist for maintaining natural gas reserves at a level above 10 years.

At some point the R/P must stop declining or the question of future ability to meet demand will cause concern to natural gas users and the financial community that provides funds for growth. When this point is reached, and certain companies feel that it has been, the National R/P ratio must be stabilized; with growing demand this implies a much greater rate of exploration and development than presently exists. Although conventional and perhaps completely new types of land sources will provide some supplies, it appears that the offshore areas will be of vital importance for several decades.

Before the reserve ratio can be stabilized, incentives to production companies will have to increase. Two areas of FPC regulatory policy could be modified to provide part of this incentive.

The maximum price a transmission company can pay for gas at the wellhead is FPC regulated. The FPC recognized the importance of incentives for discovery of new supplies by adopting a two-price system in the Permian area rate case and a multi-price system in South Louisiana, a location with great potential for offshore reserves. Although differences between offshore and onshore operations were mentioned in the South Louisiana rate opinion,[15] the rates do not appear to reflect adequately the increased costs associated with offshore operations. As a result, the petroleum companies believe there is little financial incentive for them to search for offshore gas except in unusual circumstances.

Recommendation:
**The Federal Power Commission should re-examine its differential price concept for natural gas production and make whatever adjustments are advisable to reflect adequately the increased cost of offshore production.**

[15] Federal Power Commission Opinion No. 546, Docket A.R. 61-2, Sept. 25, 1968.

Under current procedures a gas transmission company will receive permission to construct a new pipeline to a production area if it can prove to the FPC, that, among other things, sufficient reserves are in the area. A circular problem is therefore created. Transmission companies are unwilling to firmly commit themselves to the purchase of gas from undeveloped reserves, and producers are reluctant to make the considerable expenditures necessary to develop the reserves without prior assurance of buyers. Furthermore, producers are unwilling to have their proven reserves revealed to the FPC when such public disclosure would seriously hurt the companies in competition for offshore lease bids.

This problem does not lend itself to a simple solution. The panel recommends that the FPC study every possible solution, including the acceptance of sound business judgment as represented by suitable contractual commitments in substitution for geological evidence of reserves. The FPC also should examine its policies to determine the extent to which efforts to establish proven reserves results in disclosure adverse to a company and methods by which such impact, if any, can be legitimately minimized.

## 2. Technology

The natural gas industry is faced with increasing competitive pressure in the energy market from new, high-technology energy sources. This, combined with increasing cost of gas supply, should provide a strong incentive to the transmission companies to reduce pipeline costs through improved technology to prevent increasing costs to the ultimate consumer. Despite this incentive the gas transmission industry has an extremely low level of expenditures for research and development.

The industry lacks confidence in the present accounting procedures approved by the FPC for R&D. It is believed that lack of clear-cut definition places expenditures for some R&D activities in a very high risk category and therefore these are held to a minimum. When research is successful and results in improvement to a specific pipeline project, it is clear that the transmission company can capitalize the cost.

If research is not successful, or if of a general nature, the accounting treatment of the cost is not as clearly defined. In many cases it can be capitalized or allowed as an operating expense, but some projects may not be so treated. In the latter event, failure of a major R&D project would be a financial risk incurred by the company's owners. This increased business risk would not be offset automatically by a compensating potential for increased profit since the mechanism of regulated return assures that the economic benefits of successful R&D now are largely passed on to the customer or in some cases the producer. The net result is an extremely low R&D expenditure in the industry and a reluctance to undertake the large, uncertain R&D expenditures necessary for technological breakthrough.

To account for an R&D expenditure after the fact in terms of "success" or "failure" appears to be an accounting practice inconsistent with the basic premise of research itself. Even if initial hoped-for results are not achieved, the research has closed out one option and provided a great deal of useful information in the process. Consideration of this principle could resolve the lack of agreement between the gas transmission industry and the FPC concerning accounting treatment for research expenditures.

## Recommendation:

**The Federal Power Commission should review its accounting regulations for research and development activities to determine whether such regulations are consistent with the legitimate need of the gas transmission industry for clear and realistic guidelines.**

With appropriate encouragement, the gas transmission industry could foster new technology that would increase the economic feasibility of gas production and transmission further offshore and in deeper water and also be important to the National oceanographic effort. For example, improved techniques for laying large diameter pipelines in deeper waters may well depart from the concept of the traditional lay barge and involve new seafloor construction techniques using new tools, habitats, submersibles, etc.

## C. Planning

In recognition of the vital role of the offshore areas as a source of gas for the industry, the FPC recently assumed the responsibility to assure that adequate planning exists for natural gas transportation. Although a major proposal submitted by a consortium for sharing larger and more efficient pipeline systems was denied by the FPC in 1967, every indication, including policy statements issued in 1968, is that future offshore pipeline developments will require a joint industry planning approach to receive FPC approval. It is hoped that cooperation of producers, pipeline companies, and the FPC will lead to expediting the planning and processing of joint-use proposals; contribute to the more orderly development of offshore areas; encourage exploration efforts; and provide economies of scale of benefit to both the industry and its customers.

## IV. Ocean Mining

### A. Present Status

No hard mineral mining of practical significance is being conducted on the U.S. continental shelves except sulfur, sand, gravel, and oyster shells. There is no mineral mining in the deep ocean. Discussion of offshore mining, therefore, becomes largely a discussion of its potential, of ways to assure that the potential will be realized as soon as economics and technology allow, and of its importance to the Nation. Successful ocean mining is being undertaken in other parts of the world where favorable business climates in combination with adequate geological deposits make such ventures economically attractive. Most such operations are in comparatively shallow water.

A thorough discussion of marine mineral resources is found in the report of the Marine Resources Panel. That report notes that with some exceptions (gold, silver, and uranium) the supply of land-based hard minerals appears sufficient to meet projected demands to the year 2000.

This finding, however, must be qualified. The process of projecting demand for minerals and of estimating reserves is extremely complex and subject to many interpretations. Such a finding does not reflect the cost of alternative resources and is based only on known uses and metallurgical processes. The effect of new uses and the substitution of new materials is difficult to predict and can cause considerable error in forecasting mineral demands. World-wide population growth and accelerating industrialization, however, point to an ever increasing demand. Indeed, total demand for metals between 1965 and the year 2000 is expected to exceed the total of all metals consumed prior to 1965,[16] and for some specific metals the increase will be manyfold. A similar estimate applies to many non-metallic minerals.

Predicting sources of supply is perhaps even more difficult than predicting demand, due to many geological and economic unknowns. This problem is magnified in the case of ocean mineral resources because so little is known about the geology and the technology of recovery and processing that valid comparisons with present production from land sources are almost impossible.

Both accelerating demand and depletion of known mineral resources indicate that if the Nation is to enjoy a rising standard of living, particularly in the light of an ever increasing population, great attention must be paid to future supplies; and all indications are that over the long-term the ocean will become an important source of supply.

With the possible exception of certain strategic minerals, the ocean resources will be recovered by private industry only when economically attractive. For such minerals as sulfur, this point already has been reached. For others, timing is uncertain. It is not necessary to develop most hard mineral ocean resources immediately; thus no crash program is required. It is imperative, however, that the Nation begin now an orderly program to gain a better understanding of resources available and of basic ocean technology required to exploit them. Even with such basic knowledge, the time required on land to advance from early exploration to actual production is often 10 years or more, and due to the environment it probably will be even greater for most ocean minerals.

Because of growing demand for minerals, the inadequate knowledge of the oceans as a source, and the lead time required to gain an adequate understanding, the panel concludes that the Federal and State governments should take appropriate action now to stimulate ocean mining activity. This should include reconnaissance surveys and removal of some of the uncertainties and inappro-

priate regulations presently hindering industrial participation.

## B. Investment and Sales

No authoritative overall statistics on ocean mining are available but the order of magnitude of existing operations can be sensed from the following estimates:

Excluding sand, gravel, and oyster shell dredging, the world-wide investment in ocean mining is about $60 million, mostly in operations in southeast Asia and off England and South West Africa. The annual rate of investment is estimated in the order of $10 million and is rising.

About $200 million of minerals was taken world-wide from the ocean floor in 1967,[17] excluding coal and iron presently mined from onshore openings and chemicals extracted from sea water. Common sand and gravel accounted for more than half the total; sands bearing tin, iron, and other heavy minerals about 20 per cent; shells 15 per cent; sulfur 8 per cent; and diamonds 5 per cent. World-wide production of ocean minerals is growing rapidly.

At least a handful of U.S. companies now are involved to some extent in foreign offshore mining operations. Dozens more have collectively invested several million dollars in studies and exploration, indicating the degree of interest and the potential for rapid growth from today's relatively modest base.

## C. Industry Structure

Offshore mining in the United States is pursued in shallow water by relatively small companies dredging sand, gravel, and oyster shells in response to unique local supply and demand situations. Sulfur, on the other hand, mined through a drill hole, is related to petroleum in its exploration and recovery techniques and in its economic and legal problems.

Many diverse companies are showing interest in future operations due to the variety of potentially profitable situations. Some companies are oriented

---

[16] Statement by Stanley A. Cain, Assistant Secretary of the Department of the Interior, to the House Committee on Merchant Marine and Fisheries, Sept. 21, 1967.

[17] Charles M. Romanowitz, Michael J. Cruickshank, and Milton P. Overall, "Offshore Mining Present and Future," presented at National Security Industrial Association-Ocean Science Technology Advisory Committee (OSTAC) Ocean Resources Subcommittee meeting, San Francisco area, April 26, 1967.

solely to entrepreneurial opportunities in ocean mining, but many are corporations well established in land mining or petroleum. Offshore exploration and drilling companies, aerospace firms, and shipbuilding companies are among others involved. It is not yet clear what kinds of corporations will constitute the offshore mining industry of tomorrow, but the industry need not be restricted to the traditional mining companies.

Nearshore operations, such as placer mining for gold, could be undertaken by small companies. Deep-sea mining, however, probably will be conducted by large corporations or consortia because of high capital requirements. It has been estimated, for instance, that recovery of manganese nodules on a scale large enough to be economically feasible will require a capital investment of about $100 million. The traditional mining industry has one of the highest capital asset-to-employee ratios of any industry.

## D. Problems and Recommendations

Industry has stated, in effect, that it is willing to take the substantial risks required by ocean mining ventures if Government will provide well defined and reasonable laws relative to property rights, crew regulations, import duties, and taxes. In addition, Government-sponsored services, especially surveys, and equitable treatment in many potential multiple use conflicts will be required if this new industrial potential is to be realized in the near future.

### 1. Leasing Procedures

In accordance with the Outer Continental Shelf Lands Act of 1953, the Department of Interior is responsible for the management of the mineral resources on Continental Shelf lands within Federal jurisdiction. Rights to utilize these petroleum and hard mineral resources are awarded through a competitive bidding and leasing procedure defined by the Act. Many State laws for assigning the resources of submerged lands follow the principles incorporated in the Act.

This system has worked well for oil, gas, and sulfur because of the great demand for utilization rights and the bidding system allocates public resources justly under such circumstances. The present bidding system, however, is inappropriate

for allocation of mining rights at the current development stage for two reasons: so little is known about hard mineral resources or the technology for exploration and exploitation that informed bidding is effectively precluded before a great deal of exploration; second, exploration is inhibited by the financial risk that is greatly increased when a chance exists that exploitation rights may not be granted to the explorer. Until there is sufficient knowledge of the ocean's mineral resources, the panel recommends adoption of a method of property allocation that encourages the maximum private investment in exploration; namely, a method that awards exploitation rights to the prospector who makes a discovery.

One reason that hard minerals from the ocean are not more actively sought is that little is now known about them. This points up two major differences between petroleum and hard minerals—exploration techniques and costs. Initial exploration for oil is based on the extrapolation of known geological information and relatively inexpensive geophysical surveys. In contrast, the complexity and cost of exploration for hard minerals to establish confidence in an exploitable discovery are many times greater.[18] Therefore, by the time the prospector has gained sufficient knowledge to arouse his desire for more detailed exploration (hopefully leading to exploitation), he has made a considerable investment. He will be reluctant to make this investment if, in spite of his initiative, exclusive rights may be awarded to another party.

The panel feels that the highest priority should be given to encouraging hard mineral exploration through private initiative and that every consideration should be given to a system that will encourage this exploration by reducing investment risks. The prospector who has made a large investment leading to an exploitable discovery should be guaranteed the right to exploit it.

Whatever method is finally adopted for assigning hard mineral rights on the outer continental shelf, the following should be considered:

—The method should provide an atmosphere that will attract many searchers. Competition is desirable from the standpoints of stimulating explora-

---

[18] A complete discussion of the differences in methods and cost for petroleum and hard mineral exploration is found in the Reports of the Marine Resources Panel and the Marine Engineering and Technology Panel.

tion and maintaining our traditional economic principles.

—The method should rely on the stimulus of private initiative. However, in rare cases it may be in the National interest for the Government to sponsor exploration. Since there would be no private investment in such exploration, leasing procedures similar to those in the OCS Lands Act appear appropriate.

—A degree of flexibility in management must be allowed, because so little is known about the pattern of future developments and because the potential resources are so different in character. This will enable policies to be adjusted for different minerals or for special situations; however, the policies must be clear and certain.

—The high risk inherent in hard mineral exploration should be mitigated by assuring that prospectors may exploit their discoveries.

—The method should provide a reasonable economic return to the public for the use of public lands and data, but its primary objective should not be to maximize income from rents, royalties, or bonuses, but rather to maximize ocean mining activity. A greater ultimate return to the Nation will result from the development of a healthy industry contributing to employment, tax revenues, foreign exchange, and the Gross National Product.

—The method should recognize that the Bureau of Land Management, the lessor of U.S. outer Continental Shelf lands, faces competition with other nations offering development rights to their offshore lands on terms attractive to U.S. capital.

Recommendation:

**When deemed necessary to stimulate exploration, the Department of the Interior should be permitted to award rights to hard minerals on the outer Continental Shelf without requiring competitive bidding.**

The panel recommends that any U.S. citizen or company should be free to conduct preliminary exploration on the continental shelves for minerals on a non-exclusive basis. A requirement to give the Department of the Interior notification of intent, however, will allow this freedom while still permitting Interior to carry out its responsibilities as manager of the resources. A system that inhibits early reconnaissance exploration should be avoided.

If the prospector's interest is kindled by his preliminary exploration or by other means, he should be able to obtain exclusive rights for further exploration convertible to exploitation rights. A concession system similar to those successfully practiced in several foreign countries appears to be a suitable method for awarding such rights while protecting the public interest. Such a concession system should:

—Assign exclusive exploration rights for hard minerals that could be converted to exploitation rights at the prospector's option. Normally concessions are awarded to the first qualified applicant.

—Clearly define the terms of exploration and exploitation before exploration begins.

—Discourage speculative holding of offshore lands through various combinations of such requirements as: an initial fee; minimum investment in exploration or development within specified periods of time; rental payments increasing at periodic intervals during the exploration phase; and stipulation that a given acreage be returned periodically until exploitation commences.

—Provide for rental or royalty payments during the exploitation phase.

—Provide for return of any portion of the concession acreage at the option of the concession holder.

The preceding discussion has centered around the Federal lands on the outer continental shelves. The State methods for assigning property rights to submerged lands are of equal and perhaps greater importance, since early mining activity probably will take place predominantly in the shallow waters close to shore.

Some coastal States now have a reasonable system for assigning exploration and exploitation rights. Most States, however, have no laws at all or have inappropriate laws drafted for other purposes. It is recommended that the States adopt methods to assign offshore solid mineral rights that will encourage industrial exploration. It is further recommended that such a system be similar to the type of concession system described above. Uniformity in State laws is not considered a necessity at this time, but efforts to work toward uniformity are highly desirable. When changes in the Federal system are adopted, they could serve readily as a model law for the coastal States.

The panel does not believe that the lack of international agreement as to sovereign rights over deep sea mineral resources is a major factor preventing mining operations at this time. However, a clearer definition of the limits of National jurisdiction and an international agreement for the deep ocean will be needed as conflicts arise. Accordingly, the panel concurs with the International Panel in its recommendation that the United States take the initiative in proposing a new international legal-political framework for exploring and exploiting the mineral resources underlying the high seas.

Only with strong U.S. participation can the best interests of domestic industry and the world community be served. Due to the length of time normally needed to establish such a complex and important framework, the panel recommends that the United States take this initiative immediately. Until such a framework is established, the U.S. Government should encourage and protect private investment in the deep ocean.

## 2. Surveys

Geological knowledge of the U.S. continental shelves is insufficient to provide a basis for wise management of the mineral resources and is insufficient to assist industry in selecting target areas for detailed exploration.

Obtaining an adequate understanding of the geologic structure and composition of the continental margins is a vast job. Companies expect to spend large sums of money conducting surveys to delineate deposits, but first need some indication where to concentrate their efforts. Broad, reconnaissance scale surveys are too expensive for individual companies, considering the vast area to be covered and the low probability of discovering economically exploitable minerals. Yet these surveys are a critical first step in determining the basic character of the shelf and in pointing the

way for eventual utilization of the offshore mineral resources.

Earlier in the report a survey program was recommended to provide new bathymetric, geophysical, and geological information on the Continental Shelf, slope, and rise. Completion of this task was suggested in 15 to 20 years, but because certain areas are of more immediate interest, it is recommended that priorities be carefully selected to reflect user needs and that the survey of these more important areas be completed much sooner. Except in special cases, the surveys should remain reconnaissance in scope, and the actual delineation of commercial deposits should be left to private industry. A significant portion of the survey work should be contracted to qualified organizations in the private sector in order to build a National capability and speed up data acquisition.

## 3. Other Recommendations

Before a thriving offshore mining industry can exist, an enormous capital investment will have to be made. The resulting risk levels are within boundaries acceptable to industry, but the pace of investment will be slow in the early stages. There are several ways the Government can assist industry in facing the initial risks:

—Nominal rentals and low or non-existent royalty payments have been mentioned as ways to encourage ocean mining. In addition, there are precedents in foreign countries for encouraging mining through special tax incentives. The panel has not made a recommendation for a specific type of tax incentive, but urges consideration of one or more of the following:

(a) A tax moratorium for a specified number of years.

(b) Extremely rapid depreciation for ocean mining equipment, which can be justified on the basis of rapid technological advances and on swift deterioration from the harsh environment.

(c) Longer periods, perhaps 10 years, to carry net operating losses forward for tax purposes.

(d) Implementation of a special tax differential as presently applied to some high-risk mining operations in South America.

(e) Extension of the investment credit against income tax.

Such incentives would encourage industry to undertake initial, high risk ventures and also make enterprise on U.S. continental shelves more competitive with that of foreign countries providing such incentives. Special tax compensations should be discontinued gradually as the offshore mining industry becomes self-sustaining.

—Minerals mined by U.S. companies in international waters should not be subject to import duties and restrictions. To consider such minerals to be of foreign origin would impose an undue burden on the infant industry.

—The existence of multiple use conflicts poses a possible barrier to ocean mining. Because no strong industry represents offshore mining activities, established interests probably will voice strong objections to such ventures. Problems will arise not only from existing regulatory policies, but from traditional users of the ocean for navigation, fishing, and recreation, from conservation groups, and from owners of pipelines and communication cables.

Encouragement from Federal, State, and local governments will be needed in a variety of such multiple use conflicts. For example, water quality standards now being set by States rarely consider the possibility of offshore mining operations. A time may arise in the future when pollution regulations inadvertently prevent a company from carrying out a profitable offshore mining venture simply because mining was not considered when the law was formed.

—The Coast Guard should review its requirements for operation of special vessels at sea. Indications are that the present regulations, particularly with regard to minimum crew size, are unrealistic where applied to offshore mining operations. The regulations may burden the operator with an additional and perhaps unnecessary cost.

—Navigation systems sponsored by the Federal Government, although extremely useful to offshore mining companies, do not provide sufficient accuracy for some types of exploratory surveys. In many types of delineation or recovery, extreme precision is required. Perhaps this degree of precision is more properly obtained by installation of private systems; however, there is more general need for a National system that will allow survey data to be obtained with much more accuracy and that will be economic for many users.

Three other topics important to offshore mining have been discussed at length in different places: the industry's technological needs are found in the report of the Panel on Marine Engineering and Technology; the importance of environmental data and prediction services is discussed in the petroleum section of this chapter; and the need for clarification of jurisdiction in offshore areas is emphasized in Chapter 3 of this report, in the Panel Report on Management and Development of the Coastal Zone, and in the International Panel Report.

## V. FISHING

### A. Fundamental Position

Fishing as an occupation is as old as mankind. In this country it has evolved through the years with the Nation's economy and politics. Two important U.S. fisheries, tuna and shrimp, are economically strong and healthy; several other segments of the industry are almost as vigorous; and still others are marginal. The industry often has been called sick, but this description is misleading. It is not a single industry, but a group of diverse industries, each with its own peculiar problems and economic situation.

These industries have some serious common problems which probably will lead to progressive deterioration if not checked. Some are world problems, common to all sea-fishing nations. Others are strictly domestic problems which place the U.S. fishing industry in a weak international competitive position. In some areas the industry is subject to international treaties as well as a maze of U.S., State, and local regulations.

Fish are a freely available, renewable resource. Although found at all depths and throughout the world's oceans, most desirable species are concentrated near coasts.[19] Even the coastal fisheries,

[19] The ratio of U.S. catch beyond coastal fisheries to total catch is about 10 per cent in tonnage with about 15 per cent in value. If statistics on U.S. flag tuna landed in Puerto Rico were included, the percentage would be somewhat higher.

however, may be impaired by operation of foreign vessels in adjacent waters because fish migrate between zones. The definition and protection of U.S. rights within various fisheries constitute a major responsibility of Government.

A second major Government obligation is to establish measures to develop and conserve fisheries resources. Often this requires difficult choices between the rights of groups of commercial and sport fishermen and between fishing and other uses of the marine environment. Within coastal waters, abatement of pollution and preservation of natural habitats are matters of major concern.

To further orderly fisheries development, U.S. and State governments for many years have conducted programs to locate and define fisheries resources, improve basic understanding of marine life, and improve catching, processing, and marketing technology. The budget of the U.S. Bureau of Commercial Fisheries for these activities totaled $50.5 million in fiscal year 1969. In addition, State and local governments spend sizable amounts on fisheries development.

In some fisheries, conservation legislation has been used to curtail competition and stifle innovation such that an excessive effort is required to take the available catch. The efficiency of some fisheries subject to potential depletion could be improved by establishing in advance the rights of participants to shares of a given fishery, enabling each to take his share in the most efficient manner.

Fishing is an international business. Many U.S. processors depend heavily on foreign sources of fish, permitting economies which would be unavailable if the industry were forced to operate within the strictures of a high tariff or nontransferrable national quota system. However, foreign competition in domestic markets has contributed to the diminishing proportion of the total world catch taken by U.S. vessels.

Ten years ago the U.S. ranked second in the world in tonnage of fish landings. Currently it ranks sixth behind Peru, Japan, Red China, the Soviet Union, and Norway. Even though U.S. fishermen concentrate on high value species, the United States still ranks only third or fourth in value of fish landed.

The United States has the world's second largest fishing fleet, consisting of 76,000 powered craft of which 12,000 are over 5 tons. Unfortunately, about 60 per cent of the vessels were built over 16 years ago. There are about 128,000 fishermen in the United States.

The law requires fishermen to use U.S.-built vessels to make domestic landings. Capital investment in the industry has been low in spite of a vessel subsidy program, a Fisheries Loan Fund, and a Mortgage Insurance Program (under which the Government guarantees repayment of fishing vessel mortgages).

Widely disparate trends exist within this diverse industry. America's large integrated food companies are able, within the present legal/regulatory environment, to manage highly efficient operations for processing and distributing fish for domestic needs. On the other hand, many U.S. fishermen, small independent companies, and small cooperatives operating U.S.-flag vessels off this Nation's coasts have not participated successfully in the growing U.S. demand for fish products. This has diminished employment opportunities and placed a drain on foreign exchange. The panel urges that the domestic industry be assisted in achieving a higher level of efficiency to enable it to compete more effectively and serve a larger share of the U.S. market.

## B. Investment, Sales, and Production

### 1. Investment and Sales

The total domestic investment in fishing vessels and processing plants is estimated at $1.5 billion.[20] In addition, U.S. corporations have substantial investments in fishing vessels and plants in foreign countries.

The U.S. commercial catch at dockside was valued at approximately $438 million in 1967 with shellfish (primarily shrimp), tuna, and salmon comprising about 70 per cent. This compares to 1966's $472 million and 69 per cent. The 1967 retail value in the United States of all fishery products (both domestic and imported) was almost $2.6 billion.[21]

---

[20] Bureau of Commercial Fisheries.
[21] Office of Program Planning, Bureau of Commercial Fisheries.

## 2. Fish Production Versus U.S. Consumption

Profound changes have occurred since World War II in the utilization of the world's fishery resources. World catch has tripled from 43 billion pounds to 125 billion pounds,[22] yet catch by the U.S. industry has remained relatively stable, between 4 and 6 billion pounds (round weight) despite U.S. consumption nearly tripling in the same period. Fishing activities by many nations, especially Japan and Russia, have been extended to U.S. coasts. Total foreign catch in waters fished by U.S. fishermen now far exceeds the U.S. catch from these waters and is expected to increase considerably.

Imports to meet the rising U.S. demand have increased dramatically from 26 per cent of total supply in 1960 to 71 per cent in 1967. Yet, the U.S. coasts are adjacent to some of the most productive and abundant fishery resources in the world and the U.S. market is the largest and most lucrative in the world. Expectations are that U.S. consumption will grow steadily, reaching 21 billion pounds by 1985 and 31 billion pounds by the year 2000.[23]

Statistics on fisheries *supply* available to domestic fishermen are not generally well known because the research required for reasonable stock assessment has been done on only a few species. Conservative estimates indicate that fishery resources off the U.S. coast are adequate to support a total annual sustainable yield (available to all fishermen) of about 30 billion pounds, including marketable species not being fished now. Depending on the definition of marketable species, some estimate this total to be as high as 45 billion pounds.

The production and consumption statistics for the domestic fishing industry are compiled in Table 3, covering the period back to 1945. Summarizing, the picture is as follows: annual production of four to six billion pounds, static for nearly 30 years; market for about 14 billion pounds, growing at a much more rapid rate than population; and resources available for a total catch of at least 30 billion pounds per year. The question then arises as to how the domestic fishery can begin to take advantage of the growing demand by fully utilizing the wealth of available resources.

## 3. Foreign Trade

In 1967 the United States imported $708 million of fish and exported $84 million, for a net dollar outflow of $626 million.[24] Seventy-six per cent by value of the fish products imported are food fish, most of which comes from Canada, Japan, Mexico, and South America.

Many U.S. processors depend heavily on foreign sources of fish. In fact, fish processing in the United States increased the import product value by $430 million last year. Thus any analysis of the foreign trade problem should consider the value added to the food product within the United States as well as the price paid to foreign fishermen.

The U.S. fishing industry is expanding foreign-based operations. Some reasons for this include diversification, better profits than at home in many cases, and encouragement by foreign governments.

## C. Nature of the Industry

### 1. Components of the Industry

The industry consists of several segments, including fishermen, vessel owners, wholesale dealers and brokers, and processors. The fishermen crew the vessel. Particularly when small vessels are involved, the captain may also be the boat owner. With larger and more expensive vessels the owners usually will not be the fishermen. The processors usually do not own their own fleet and are not tending to become boat owners. The wholesalers and brokers handle a great deal of imported fish and often add some processing, functioning as distributors and merchandisers. In general, the fishing industry is substantially fragmented into many fishing, processing, and distributing firms in port cities with a number of merchandising firms in the interior as well. Processing companies often extend credit to selected fishermen to purchase gear, construct new vessels, or renovate old ones.

---

[22]*Ibid.*

[23]Department of the Interior, "Commercial Fisheries Federal Aid to States," Circular No. 286, Washington, D.C., February 1968, p. 8.

[24]Office of Program Planning, Bureau of Commercial Fisheries.

**Table 3**

**UTILIZATION OF FISHERY PRODUCTS IN THE UNITED STATES, SELECTED YEARS, 1945-67**

| | 1945 | 1950 | 1955 | 1960 | 1965 | 1967 |
|---|---|---|---|---|---|---|
| Population, Millions[1] . . . . . . . . . . | 129.1 | 150.2 | 162.3 | 178.2 | 191.9 | 195.7 |
| | | | **Edible Fish (round weight)** | | | |
| Domestic Catch, Million lbs. . . . . . | 3,167 | 3,307 | 2,579 | 2,498 | 2,586 | 2,385 |
| Imports, Million lbs. . . . . | 680[3] | 1,128 | 1,332 | 1,766 | 2,576 | 2,683 |
| Total, Million lbs. . . . | 3,847 | 4,435 | 3,911 | 4,264 | 5,162 | 5,068 |
| Per Capita Use, lbs. . . . | 29.8 | 29.5 | 24.1 | 23.9 | 26.9 | 25.9 |
| (meat weight)[2] . . | (9.9) | (11.8) | (10.5) | (10.3) | (10.9) | (10.6) |
| | | | **Industrial Fish (round weight)** | | | |
| Domestic Catch, Million lbs. . . . . . | 1,431 | 1,594 | 2,230 | 2,444 | 2,190 | 1,677 |
| Imports, Million lbs. . . . | 31[4] | 639 | 980 | 1,515 | 3,182 | 7,442 |
| Total, Million lbs. . . | 1,462 | 2,233 | 3,210 | 3,959 | 5,372 | 9,119 |
| Per Capita Use, lbs. . . | 11.3 | 14.9 | 19.8 | 22.2 | 28.0 | 46.6 |
| | | | **Total Fish (round weight)** | | | |
| Domestic Catch, Million lbs. . . . . . | 4,598 | 4,901 | 4,809 | 4,942 | 4,776 | 4,062 |
| Imports, Million lbs. . . . | 711 | 1,767 | 2,312 | 3,281 | 5,758 | 10,125 |
| Total, Million lbs. . . | 5,309 | 6,668 | 7,121 | 8,223 | 10,534 | 14,187 |
| Per Capita Use, lbs. . . . | 41.1 | 44.4 | 43.9 | 46.1 | 54.9 | 72.5 |

Source: Compiled by the Office of Program Planning, Bureau of Commercial Fisheries.
[1] July 1 population eating from civilian supplies, excluding armed forces overseas: beginning 1950—50 States.
[2] Computed per capita consumption on edible or meat weight basis with allowances for exports and changes in beginning and end-of-year stocks.
[3] Estimate based on 1946 relationship of round to imported product weight.
[4] Estimate based on 1946 ratio of round weight to industrial product weight.

There is no National organization representing all the interests of the processing, distributing, and marketing sections of the industry, although most firms are members of either the National Fisheries Institute or the National Canners Association, or occasionally both. A number of local trade organizations are in the larger fisheries, such as salmon, tuna, shrimp, menhaden and lobster.

Vessel owners group together in local associations, mostly on a port or regional level, organized under the Fishermen's Cooperative Act of 1934. Functions of such associations vary greatly from marketing to the provision of such benefits as discounts through group purchasing. Several attempts have been made to create a National vessel owners association, but without success.

## 2. Recent Trends

As recently as 1960 only one U.S. firm engaged in the fish trade with as much as $100 million of business per year; a few had $50 million per year; the majority had $10 million or less per year. Around 1960 food firms began diversifying through purchase or amalgamation with fish firms. Today principal firms in the fish trade have sales between $0.5 and $1.5 billion a year.[25] These developments are giving the U.S. fishing industry a new character—more adequate access to capital; National and international scale thinking; merchandising rather than production orientation; and better management.

Large U.S. fish firms customarily have avoided ownership of fishing vessels, although the practice has differed in various sections of the industry. All segments, however, extend credit to fishermen for seasonal operations, vessel acquisition, new vessel construction, and other purposes. The changing character of the industry is diminishing this practice.

Many large firms now beginning to predominate in the fish trade have extensive holdings in foreign operations. They buy raw material to their quality standards from that source having the optimum combination of cost and reliability. However, recent history does not indicate a strong trend to total integration of the fishing industry from the ocean to the supermarket.

The trend to emphasize products having National distribution is increasing. The fish products involved must be obtainable in large volume from a sound resource base and also must have broad customer acceptance.

## D. Problems and Recommendations

The Marine Resources Act sets among its objectives the "rehabilitation of our commercial fisheries." The panel believes that in attempting to achieve this objective the Nation should build on strength. However, the panel also believes that steps taken to solve critical problems can yield substantial gains for weaker segments of the industry, enabling them to take a larger portion of the available catch off U.S. shores.

## 1. Access to Fisheries Resources

Fish are treated in both National and international law as a common property resource. The law of the industry has been: "First come, first served." Action taken to moderate the ill effects of this situation has often been aimed toward maintaining the position of large numbers of individual fishermen by restricting fishing techniques. Consequently, excessive, uneconomical harvesting effort now is applied to many species.

A more rational approach to achieving reasonable competition in taking common-property resources is recommended in the Resources Panel report. In that report an effort to apply the limited entry principle to those U.S. fisheries subject to potential depletion is recommended. Policies should be adopted to restrict fishing units to a certain number, each of maximum efficiency. Controlling entry of fishing vessels should permit more effective management of the resource. Over the long term, production costs should be reduced and earning power improved. This panel concurs in such recommendations. Mechanisms through which shares of the resource could be assigned include license fees and bidding for rights.

Recommendation:

**A quota or limited entry principle should be pilot tested in selected fisheries. The U.S. Government should provide both opportunities and incentives for States and regions to carry out these tests.**

---

[25]Examples: Castle and Cooke acquired Bumble Bee, Inc.; H. J. Heinz bought StarKist Foods, Inc.; Consolidated Foods bought Booth Fisheries; Ralston Purina bought Van Camp Sea Food Company.

## 2. Fleet Renovation

Inefficiency of the present fleet is a serious industry problem. Although the U.S. fishing fleet is the world's second largest, about 60 per cent of the vessels are over 16 years old and 27 per cent have been in service over 26 years.[26] Advances in fishing technology during the past few years have made most of the U.S. fleet economically, if not physically, obsolete.

In the heterogeneous U.S. fishing industry, some fisheries, such as tuna and shrimp, have fairly modern fleets. Some fleets are antiquated and rapidly declining for several reasons.

The reduction of profits due to reasons of foreign competition and/or a declining resource stands out among the various reasons for the decline of some segments of the fleet. The prices U.S. fishermen must charge to make a profit can be undercut by foreign fishermen for one or more of the following reasons: lower labor costs, more advanced technology, and subsidies from their governments. In the case of a decreasing resource, overfishing and reduced yields soon result from the inability of vessels and fishermen to adapt to other, underutilized species. This reduction of profits tends to diminish the ability of those in the fishery to afford technological improvements or new vessels of greater utility.

Where U.S. fisheries are overfished, consideration should be given to retirement of old vessels as new ships are introduced. The new ships, in turn, should be designed for ready conversion to other fisheries whose stocks are not being depleted. Obstacles to this goal are State laws limiting the length of vessels for a particular fishery, possibly reducing the vessel's adaptability to other fisheries. Such laws should be reconsidered.

Application of better vessel and gear technology to overfished stocks will result in a greater rate of depletion. Fishermen taking such stocks can be helped far more through biological research. Such research can help ensure that conservation laws and treaties are based on scientific findings and can assist in determining more abundant stocks.

Where fisheries are not in danger of depletion more modern gear, vessels, and vessel accessories such as detection and navigation equipment, new propulsion systems, and processing and storage

facilities should be introduced. This modernization may particularly aid in developing the much underutilized species as Alaska shrimp, tanner crab, and Pacific hake.

### Recommendation:

**U.S. and State Government policies should be aimed at upgrading the U.S. fishing fleet through introduction of vessels with modern equipment.**

## 3. High Cost of Vessels and Gear

An important legal barrier in several fisheries is Federal legislation requiring U.S. fishermen to use U.S.-built vessels to land fish at a U.S. port. Until 1948 the law was not of major consequence because the U.S. fisherman often had tariff protection and rarely competed in the domestic market with foreign fishermen.

By 1948 domestic inflation contributed to the drastic change in the competitive situation. Tariff protection became inconsequential in many fisheries and foreign policy prohibited increased protection. Imports of fish from allies were encouraged to bolster their dollar earning capacity. Lower shipyard costs abroad accentuated the vessel cost difference. Rapid rebuilding of war-destroyed fleets, often financed through U.S. aid programs, resulted in new, more efficient vessels in principal competing countries. Improved freezer facilities made long distance shipment practical.

Because of the domestic vessel construction law, most U.S. fishermen could not buy an efficient new vessel at prices paid by foreign competitors. The tuna and shrimp industries, an exception, have introduced new technology and purchased new vessels in sufficient quantity to enable domestic shipyards to become competitive with those of foreign countries.

Congress has grappled with the problem of foreign hull restrictions for many years, but varied interests have vigorously opposed repeal of the old law. A vessel subsidy bill was passed to attempt to alleviate the problem but proved ineffective; hence the 88th Congress passed a more practical bill that remains in effect until June 1969.

The present vessel subsidy act still has shortcomings. Statutory limitations on annual expenditures prevent subsidy payments to all qualified applicants. Although the law requires that a vessel's operation will not cause economic hard-

---

[26]Bureau of Commercial Fisheries.

ship to efficient operators already engaged in the fishery, no provision exists to retire an older vessel replaced by the subsidized vessel. Thus, the law generates inequities as it corrects others.

The law has worked to the disadvantage of some aspects of the work of the Bureau of Commercial Fisheries. In addition, the Bureau has not had much control over which fishery would receive subsidy funds. The long-range solution to the vessel cost problem probably will come from increased use of advanced technology and mass production techniques.

Regarding the subsidy program, the Government should develop guidelines to establish priorities in handling subsidy applications. For example, a major portion of the program should be directed to those fisheries not in danger of depletion. It also should help those in overfished fisheries move into underutilized fisheries. When appropriate, the subsidy should be applied to distant-water fisheries. In all cases modern technological developments should be incorporated into the subsidized vessels and gear.

U.S. fishermen should be permitted to buy equipment anywhere in the world where they can find the best combination of price and performance. At present, import duties often prevent acquiring such equipment.

Recommendation:

**Restrictions on the purchase of fishing equipment abroad should be removed. Legislation should be enacted to permit U.S. fishermen to purchase vessels in foreign shipyards; if it is decided not to repeal the restrictive laws, the vessel construction subsidy program should be expanded and modified to provide for retirement of older vessels.**

### 4. Availability of Capital and Credit

The credit problems of fish processing, distributing, and marketing are no different than those of any other industry and the normal financial institutions have served these segments well. However, the fishing segment of the industry has not been so fortunate, witnessing a relative scarcity of capital since World War II. Following the war, bankers everywhere became reluctant to finance fishing vessels. During the low-profit period from 1948 through 1960, and still existing in several fisheries, fishing vessel financing problems were

among the worst handicaps to fisheries development.

Congress recognized this and by 1956 began to ease the fishing industry's credit problem through U.S. Government loan programs. The Fisheries Loan Fund Program has been a very effective incentive for U.S. flag fishing at a nominal cost to the Government. It also has removed the fishing vessel owner from dependence on his customers for capital.

This program is supplemented by a Mortgage Insurance Program. Whereas the Fisheries Loan Fund enables a direct cash loan to the fisherman, under the Mortgage Insurance Program the Government guarantees mortgages used to finance construction, reconstruction, and reconditioning of fishing vessels. The program provides a vehicle through which the Government can extend assistance without making a direct capital outlay.

The fisherman ordinarily will seek a loan from his customer or from a bank under the Mortgage Insurance Program. If reasonable financial assistance applied for commercially is not available, financial assistance may be provided under the Fisheries Loan Fund. The existence of the fund thus provides a fisherman with an alternate source of credit.

The fund has been very helpful to hard-pressed fishermen. Some in the industry contend that the fund is so popular it frequently "runs out of money." Authorization for the fund is $20 million; however, $13 million was appropriated in 1968. On various occasions lending has been restricted to an even lesser amount because of overall Government expenditure limitations.

Both the Fisheries Loan Fund and the Mortgage Insurance Program should be retained. Favorable consideration should be given those fishermen who are or intend to become involved with underutilized species having commercial potential.

### 5. Legal/Regulatory

Among the most serious problems facing the U.S. fishing industry are the laws and regulations that prevent increases in efficiency. These restrictions have resulted from a combination of attempts at conservation, competition among fishermen for limited supplies of particular species, and competition between commercial and sport fishermen for certain species.

Except for fisheries managed under international convention, U.S. fisheries are regulated by the States under a maze of regulations adopted over the years, many for reasons long-forgotten. Numerous State and local laws and regulations were designed to protect established small-boat fishermen by restricting the use of efficient devices.

Such laws increase fish production costs in the United States. For example, laws and regulations forbid the use of traps to capture salmon; prohibit the taking of herring or anchovy for reduction purposes; limit the size and nature of nets; and forbid the use of sonar to detect fish schools. Such restrictions must be eliminated. The States' interest in the problem is beginning to grow and must be encouraged.

Several avenues are available to foster repeal of outmoded State laws and regulations. One is to develop improved knowledge and understanding of the ocean and its living resources to guide State legislators and administrators in improving conservation regulations. The Sea Grant Program should help augment the technical capabilities of State fishery officials, through support of fishery sciences and education in State universities, which, in turn, should provide better advice regarding fisheries regulations.

Problems of conservation and preservation of natural habitats are not always local, but rather are often interstate in scope. As indicated in the Marine Resources Panel report, the tendency toward parochialism in the individual States has led to fragmented solutions to fishery problems. For example, the East Coast States are unable to agree on a management program in the menhaden fishery despite evidence of depletion. In such cases a comprehensive unified management plan is required.

Accordingly, this panel recommends that a mechanism be established under which the U.S. Government can require the development by the States of coordinated management measures for interstate fisheries subject to potential depletion if and when the States fail to meet the responsibility themselves. Similar Federal-State mechanisms have been established in the past.

### 6. Surveys

U.S. coastal waters contain some of the richest fishing grounds in the world. Seven billion pounds are caught each year (U.S. and foreign) and the maximum sustainable yield is at least 30 billion pounds per year. Some estimate the potential yield of underutilized resources as high as 45 billion pounds annually. Given proper incentives, within three years the industry should be able to increase its present annual catch by 20 per cent and within 10-20 years by several hundred per cent. Much of the increased yield would include species presently used and close relatives not yet utilized. Examples of underutilized species include Alaska shrimp, scallops and tanner crab; Pacific and Gulf anchovy; Gulf and Atlantic thread herring; Pacific hake; and Tropical Atlantic and Pacific skipjack tuna.

These fish could be exploited more economically if comprehensive surveys were initiated and kept up to date to establish the parameters of the resource. Rapid action and strong financial support are required. The last survey was authorized by Congress in 1944 and completed in 1945. Depending upon the fishery stock in question, the new surveys proposed may review existing knowledge and/or study the resource itself to acquire new knowledge. Sport fisheries also should be included because of the ecological interaction between all stocks in a given area.

Recommendation:
**The Government should initiate and sponsor continuing surveys of U.S. coastal and distant-water fishery resources, including sport fisheries.**

### 7. Pollution

Pollution of the Great Lakes, estuaries, bays, and certain offshore areas has a serious and increasingly critical impact on domestic fisheries. The panel endorses the pollution abatement proposals made in the Panel Report on Management and Development of the Coastal Zone and in the Marine Engineering and Technology Panel Report and emphasizes that these actions can help to achieve the goal of rehabilitating commercial fisheries.

### 8. Information Exchange[27]

Before scientific research and discoveries can become an operational part of an industry's knowledge and capability, the industry must be

---

[27]The subject of fishing technology is discussed in further detail in the Report of the Panel on Marine Engineering and Technology.

able to use the technology. This ability may be limited by such factors as lack of technical knowledge and capital, marginality of profits, lack of available peripheral equipment, environmental and institutional peculiarities, obsolete laws and regulations, and tradition.

In the past 20 years, and increasingly so in the last few years, new materials and techniques have been incorporated in a few fishing vessels, including improved propulsion units, greater refrigeration capabilities, better location and catching gear, and better sea-keeping qualities. The summation of all these new discoveries could have had a revolutionary effect on the construction of fishing vessels and the reduction in the cost per ton of fish production had they entered the fishing industry more rapidly.

The governments of such countries as Russia, Japan, and West Germany have programs to adapt new technology to fishing industry needs which have helped their industries thrive. Only minimal programs have been sponsored by the U.S. Government. However, the panel notes and commends the recent exchange agreement between the Navy and the Department of the Interior to study advanced acoustic technology in fish detection and adapation of fleet environmental prediction techniques to forecast fish location. The panel urges that similar steps be taken, within the constraints of security, to accelerate the adaptation of other pertinent military research to the domestic fishing industry.

In addition, much information gathered by scientists in work in biological and conservation research has potential to reduce fishermen's production costs substantially. There is, however, no satisfactory mechanism to readily translate the results of Government technology or scientific information to the fishermen.

Recommendation:

**A field service mechanism should be established by the U.S. Government analogous to the cooperative State-Federal extension service administered by the Department of Agriculture in order to facilitate transfer of technically useful information to fishermen at the local level.**

## VI. AQUACULTURE

### A. Present Status

Aquaculture in the United States today consists of a small, scattered but growing effort to raise aquatic plants and animals in a controlled environment or a modified ecological system. Modifications to the natural ecology include those due to temperature, artificial feeding, use of barriers for containment or predator control, and selective breeding. Although the prevailing concept of aquaculture is growing selected species of fish in fresh-water ponds, operations exist in rivers, estuaries, and marshlands, and there is definitely a potential for the open ocean.

In the United States the present level of activity is low compared with that in Asia, especially China and Japan, but nevertheless a variety of plants and animals is being cultivated. Reliable and comprehensive statistics on sales of aquacultural products in the United States are available only in a few selected instances.

The panel estimates that the total U.S. wholesale value was in excess of $50 million in 1967, but this can vary widely with the definition of aquaculture. Sales of farmed trout and catfish in 1967 each exceeded $7 million wholesale, bait minnows exceeded $8 million, and oysters from managed, private lands exceeded $13 million.[28]

In addition, a variety of operations involve salmon, black bass, pompano, mullet, clams, scallops, prawns, lobsters, shrimp, and other animal species, as well as several kinds of seaweed.

Statistics on capital investment in U.S. aquaculture projects are elusive due to the great variety of situations and the often proprietary nature of the information. Both expanding research efforts and reduction of labor costs in commercial operations will result in a sharp increase in the demand for capital. The companies involved are generally small, but the situation is changing rapidly as some of the largest companies in the United States now are beginning to explore aquaculture opportunities. This trend will bring some needed capital as opportunities for profit are discovered. One State recently estimated that several companies have considered investments in fixed facilities in excess of $100 million in different aquaculture projects; the commitment awaits favorable outcome of present research efforts and removal of some political, legal, and regulatory barriers.[29]

---

[28] Bureau of Commercial Fisheries.

[29] Florida Development Commission, Tallahassee, Florida, October 1968.

The panel's interest in the growth of aquaculture is from the standpoint of its potential for profitable industrial ventures. It has been stated frequently that aquaculture can help solve the world hunger and malnutrition problem; however, in the United States early emphasis will be on the most profitable species, clearly the high-valued finfish and shellfish.

There is a rapidly growing demand for seafood in general, but the greatest growth is for the high priced species. As the demand grows, some traditional fisheries are declining, and many of the natural grounds for shellfish are being destroyed by such other uses as waste disposal, land-fill, and dredging. At the same time, research has shown many areas where vast improvements are possible in the technology of aquaculture. Examples include genetic control to improve the quality, growth rate, and adaptability of various species to different environmental conditions, and the possibility of using presently wasted sources of nutrients and heat to effect economical control of local environments.

Thus, with a growing demand for seafood, an uncertain natural supply of some species to meet this demand, and potential for vast improvements in aquacultural technology, prospects for profitable ventures are increasing.

Aquaculture has many advantages for food production. A major impact of aquaculture lies in its extreme productivity per acre—a capability that can lead to considerably larger yields of high-grade animal protein than fertile dry land.

The advantages of aquaculture for food production arise in part from readily available nutrients and water. A basic problem, however, is proper management of these resources. Research has shown that the combination of these ingredients can be very productive due especially to the fact that there is inherently a constant supply of water. If nutrients are in the water, marine organisms have a continuous opportunity to use them as contrasted to most land organisms that can absorb nutrients only when carried to them intermittently by water. In addition, most marine animals are poikilotherms (cold-bloods), and because less energy is wasted in heat production, they are often more efficient in conversion of their food intake to edible weight. Finally, forms of aquaculture that use the water column obviously have added a third dimension that can improve productivity per unit of surface area.

Aquaculture also has some advantages over conventional fishing that enable it to supplement the catch of fish and shellfish. Since most areas desired for aquacultural use are within U.S. jurisdiction, there is no foreign competition for the resource as in some fish stocks. Because a degree of exclusive rights can be assigned to the "aquafarmer," and thus he need not rely on a common property resource, the incentive is increased to improve profits through gaining proprietary knowledge leading to greater efficiency. In addition, in aquaculture there is a potential to harvest more frequently, to harvest in seasons that do not compete with the marketing of natural stocks, and to control the environment, assuring greater reliability in the quantity and quality of the supply.

## B. Problems and Recommendations

The growth of this industry is influenced by many factors, many of which center around a widely-scattered and insufficient knowledge of an extremely complex ecological system.

Lack of thorough understanding of ecological systems is usually the first problem. Research in marine ecology is expensive, and its performance requires trained personnel and considerable time. The task's magnitude and the unknown probability of finding commercial applications generally places this research beyond the limits of industry's risk tolerance. There are many exceptions to this, but developing sufficient ecological knowledge to stimulate commercial interest remains an appropriate area for Federal and State government support. An important parallel lies in the large amount of publicly supported agricultural research. Government funds for basic research, channeled mostly through the Bureau of Commercial Fisheries, are not adequate to truly stimulate this industry. The panel therefore recommends that the modest funds[30] presently available for aquaculture research be increased several fold within the next five years.

Industry is much more willing to undertake applied research programs, and many are in progress. Often they are funded by a combination of industry, university, State, and U.S. Government

_____

[30]Bureau of Commercial Fisheries budget devoted to aquaculture was $2.7 million in FY 1968.

money. The National Science Foundation's Sea Grant College Program, in fact, has reviewed many more applications for applied aquaculture research than it could fund. The panel recommends that the Sea Grant College Program be given greater funding to enable sponsorship of a larger percentage of qualified applications.

Work in estuarine or ocean areas encounters another serious obstacle—ownership or rights to exclusive use of the water column or seabed. Exclusive rights usually are essential to any aquaculture project, but often difficult to obtain. The problem is acute within waters under State jurisdiction and will in time become so in waters under U.S. Government control. Few provisions or precedents assign exclusive rights to the seabed or water column for such uses, and many established interests, such as fishing, recreation, and conservation, regard aquaculture as a conflicting use of given areas. The panel identified several cases where investments in aquaculture were thwarted for either legal or political reasons although conflicts of use were minimal. In these cases the degree of exclusivity required was not great and the area involved was infinitesimal compared to total water resources available.

It is recommended that the State and Federal governments encourage the use of marine waters for aquaculture projects when they do not interfere with more important uses. Seasteading (see Chapter 3) is a means to encourage such projects in U.S. territorial waters by making provisions for granting exclusive use rights.

Inadequate technology also is a deterrent to many types of aquaculture. Mechanical, physical, chemical, or biological methods of containment, of excluding predators, and of harvesting have not been developed to the point of being economically acceptable in many proposed aquaculture systems. Many of these problems will be solved in conjunction with the basic and applied ecological studies, and others will be solved by industry through engineering development programs when basic research indicates potential and identifies specific needs.

Pollution threatens or already has destroyed many attractive sites for aquaculture as well as natural spawning grounds. However, possibly some present-day forms of chemical and thermal pollution may actually enhance certain programs. Increased knowledge of the effects of various pollutants on the ecology of nearshore areas and stronger efforts to control the harmful factors are urgently needed. Vigorous Government support through studies and provision of controls is clearly necessary. Water is often polluted because the cost of abatement is greater than the readily measured economic value of alternative uses; as aquaculture increases in importance, it may provide much of the positive economic impact needed to counter pollution.

Some forms of aquaculture have existed for many years, but relative to the potential, aquaculture is a new and exciting field. In the United States the effort is widely scattered, not only in States with seacoasts but throughout the Nation. At present there is no strong central effort for aquaculture either within the industry or within the U.S. Government. The creation of such a focus is essential to improve communication among governments at all levels, the academic community, and industry. It will assist guidance of research efforts and documentation and dissemination of technology, and prevent unnecessary duplication of effort.

The Bureau of Commercial Fisheries (BCF) would be the appropriate focus in the U.S. Government. BCF already performs some research and provides funds to States for extension programs under the Commercial Fisheries Research and Development Act of 1964. However, BCF never has been in a position to fund a strong aquaculture program because its primary responsibility was for commercial fishing which, indeed, requires much attention.

Therefore, the panel recommends that the Bureau of Commercial Fisheries be given more specific responsibility for investigating aquaculture programs; this must be backed with sufficient funds as recommended earlier. Pilot projects to establish research facilities and develop basic techniques appear warranted, and BCF well might contract such projects to industry or universities. Without increased support of this type, the commercial potential for aquaculture may not be realized as soon as this panel considers possible and desirable.

## VII. SEA TRANSPORTATION

### A. Present Status

The primary components of the U.S. sea transportation industry are the merchant marine and the private shipyards. Merchant marine operations are augmented by such activities as port cargo handling. Annual revenue accruing to the U.S. merchant marine, which encompasses U.S.-flag vessels operating in coastal and world trade, amounts to approximately $1.5 billion. If U.S.-owned, foreign-flag vessels were included in the definition, the revenue figure would be increased by as much as $4 billion, the bulk attributable to tankers owned by U.S. oil companies.[31]

The other main segment of the sea transportation industry, the U.S. shipbuilding industry, includes conversion, repair, and construction of both naval and merchant vessels. The yearly value for this activity exceeds $2.2 billion.[32] Various shipyards also have been engaged in designing and constructing oil rigs, mining vessels, dredges for the Corps of Engineers, and oceanographic vessels, cutters, and other ships for the Coast and Geodetic Survey and the Coast Guard.

Over the past 5-10 years, the small volume of cargo carried under U.S. flag and the decreasing number of merchant vessels built by domestic shipyards have been the subject of considerable concern. Several highly respected study groups have analyzed the problems of the U.S. merchant marine, especially such questions as operating and construction differential subsidies and foreign construction of U.S.-flag vessels. These problems are extremely complex and deserve more careful, concentrated thought than the panel was able to contribute in light of the broad scope of the Marine Resources and Engineering Development Act.

The panel unequivocally believes that strong U.S.-flag shipping and private shipbuilding industries are vital to the National interest. The importance of domestic shipping and shipbuilding becomes paramount during times of emergency or National crisis. In such circumstances, heavy reliance on foreign-flag shipping is not advisable though many of the ships may be under nominal U.S. ownership.

Furthermore, although ships under the flags of Panama, Honduras, and Liberia, the so-called "flags of convenience," are deemed within effective U.S. control, the international political implications of U.S. attempts to wrest these ships from their sponsor nations during peacetime emergencies are great. Therefore, the panel believes that the rapid decline of the U.S.-flag merchant marine hinders the Nation's ability to support overseas military operations and maintain vital imports in time of war.

It is important to realize that U.S.-flag shipping in the foreign trade is an export commodity. The U.S. balance of trade is reduced every time a foreign-flag ship carries trade from a U.S. port.

Shipbuilding also is essential as a domestic industry during a National emergency, since the need for ships increases rapidly. In terms of emergency needs, many believe the Navy building program, constituting more than 75 per cent of total construction in private yards, keeps the domestic shipbuilding industry sufficiently active to maintain the needed industrial base. In addition, the unused potential in U.S. shipyards can be mobilized readily in time of war.

## B. Trends

Shipbuilding in the United States is a sizable industry, becoming more technologically-oriented because of the complicated equipment and design required for naval vessels which are more complex than merchant ships. However, the industry does not operate at peak capacity or optimum efficiency because most types of vessels are ordered in very limited numbers. Thus, the pace of capital investments in updated ship construction facilities has been in almost direct proportion to the available level of orders.

However, the recent Navy trend toward multi-year, multi-ship procurement already has stimulated capital equipment improvement in shipyards. If contracting practices for merchant ship construction also followed this pattern, further modernization could be expected. When a shipyard receives an order for several ships of a particular design, the experience and learning acquired in constructing the first few vessels of the series greatly reduces costs and improves efficiency for the remaining vessels.

[31]Laird Durham (A.D. Little, Inc.), "The United States Ocean Industries," April, 1966, p. 13.

[32]This figure reflects the value of work done during a year. Because most shipbuilding contracts extend over several years, "value of work done" is considered superior to "total cost of ships delivered" as an indicator of shipyard productivity. Shipbuilders Council of America.

One U.S. shipbuilding company has followed the lead of Japan by successfully marketing its own standardized design for a medium-sized tanker. As of mid-1968, this company had obtained nine contracts for nearly identical vessels. The design-marketing practice has been adopted by at least one other major shipyard.

Other ways to minimize costs in sea transportation are to build larger ships and utilize nuclear power. The total energy required to carry a ton of cargo at a given speed decreases as a vessel's cargo capacity increases, reducing cost per ton-mile. Although huge tankers and bulk carriers of more than 100,000 deadweight tons are more efficient on the high seas, many harbors around the world are incapable of accommodating such immense vessels. In fact, programs to deepen ports now are encountering serious physical obstacles, such as bedrock or highway and railroad tunnels that limit dredging depth. Where a harbor cannot be adapted to handle superships, it may be necessary to build remote terminals offshore or relocate harbor complexes.

Nuclear power is another potential way to increase operational efficiency at sea, especially for long-distance, high-speed travel. One big advantage of nuclear power is that ships can operate much longer without refueling. Thus, during normal conditions nuclear ships benefit in time savings from less frequent stops, and under wartime pressures they need less logistic support for continued operations.

In addition, nuclear vessels require much less space for the combination of fuel and power plant and thus have a greater percentage of their displacement available for cargo. Some nations are not yet willing to receive nuclear vessels in their ports for fear of radiation, but it is believed that this will be only a temporary deterrent to the progress of nuclear merchant shipping.

Construction of nuclear-powered passenger and cargo ships can be accomplished readily by U.S. shipyards. The industry has considerable expertise from building nuclear submarines, cruisers, guided missile frigates, and aircraft carriers for the Navy, not to mention the first nuclear-powered merchant ship, the *N.S. Savannah*.

At present, the most heartening recent development in the shipping industry is containerization. Two non-subsidized U.S. companies have set the pace in this area and have been able to compete successfully in international shipping. The concept involves technology no more complicated than computerized inventory and traffic control. Its most outstanding feature is simplicity. Prior to containerization, a typical overseas cargo shipment was handled at least eight times before secured aboard ship. Containerization has resulted in much less handling, which in turn has led to lower handling costs and less pilferage.

Containerization also enables a new systems approach to global transportation. Truck and railroad flatcar scheduling can be coordinated with scheduling for containerized ships, thus allowing large containers to be quickly unloaded and transferred. By minimizing the time a ship spends in port, containerization results in great savings to the operator and permits ports to handle more ships and a much greater volume of cargo.

The impact of containerization can be seen in the fact that 12 per cent of all 1968 foreign commerce handled at New York's piers is containerized, compared to 3 per cent only two years ago. Furthermore, the Port of New York Authority estimates that by 1975 half of all cargo brought into New York Harbor will be handled via containers. In view of this projected boom in containerized shipping, port facilities will have to be updated.

## VIII. INSTRUMENTS

### A. Present Status

The operation, as well as the monitoring of the operation, of oceanographic platforms, test ranges, equipment, and data systems (in fact, all aspects of marine science and technology) depends on the availability of diverse types of instrumentation with adequate cost-performance and reliability characteristics. Most important, much of the National investment in ocean programs now and in the foreseeable future will be devoted to measuring the characteristics of the marine environment. Reliable, accurate instruments that can be maintained in proper calibration are a vital factor in the ultimate usefulness of data obtained from ocean survey programs.

Recognition of the importance of reliable ocean data resulted in the establishment of the National Oceanographic Data Center (NODC). The data are available to the academic, industrial, and government sectors and data exchange also has been established with certain foreign countries. Concern over proper data processing, archiving, and retrieval also should be applied to its collection—both to instrumentation and methods employed to gather data.

Most ocean programs have been limited in both staff and budget. As a result, specific program objectives are often compromised and only limited instrumentation is procured. Unlike conditions in many other non-oceanographic programs, such as the space program, ocean instrument specifications are often minimized, meaningful quality assurance programs are largely nonexistent, and service and maintenance manuals and other documentation are often inadequate to meet basic user needs. In addition, statistical information defining conditions of use, maintenance and repair cycles, and modes of failure are seldom documented and made available to the manufacturer. This, in turn, slows down the correction of problem areas and prevents the upgrading of performance and reliability in a logical manner.

Past experience shows that user demand for a particular type of ocean instrument is generally for a limited quantity of highly complex instruments, often requiring custom design. In such cases, manufacturing does not lend itself to mass production, one factor that has allowed the small, technically oriented firm to compete favorably with large corporations. Although large capital facilities are not always essential to *produce* marine instruments, expensive facilities are often necessary for development and qualification testing.

## B. Specific Problem Areas

The most valid complaints about oceanographic instruments are their lack of reliability and lack of user confidence in the data gathered. Many articles have been written and symposia sponsored to examine the diverse sources of unreliability. One recent meeting identified two primary factors:[33]

---

[33] Government-Industry-University Symposium on Instrument Reliability, May 6-7, 1968, Miami, Florida, sponsored by the National Security Industrial Association-Ocean Science and Technology Committee (OSTAC) Ocean Platform and Instrumentation Subcommittee.

—Lack of a common instrument performance "language" and satisfactory communciations between instrument producers, procurement agencies, data collectors, and data users.

—Present ocean instrument procurement policies.

## 1. Language and Communications—Need for Specification Guidelines

Producers, procurement agencies, and users require standards and specification guidelines encompassing the following:

(1) Performance requirements, (2) environmental conditions, (3) test procedures, (4) quality assurance requirements, (5) design requirements, (6) interfacing and/or installation requirements, (7) terminology, (8) formats for specification and data, and (9) documentation.

Performance requirements should indicate types of functions an instrument must perform and how well these functions must be carried out. Thus, tests will have to measure such items as repeatability, stability, data rate, accuracy, and precision.

Additional specifications should be related to an instrument's interaction with various environmental conditions during operation, storage, and shipping. Therefore, testing would have to ascertain the instrument's ability to withstand such environmental aspects as temperature, shock and vibration, pressure, noise, salt spray, and humidity. Case histories have been compiled showing the seriousness of time lost through equipment failures from such sources as corrosion and shock and vibration. Developing laboratory tests to simulate environmental conditions is difficult, quite complex, and expensive.

For a test procedure specification, for example, it is necessary to define precisely what constitutes an acceptance test to determine if each performance and environmental specification is met satisfactorily by the manufacturer.

Furthermore, oceanographic instruments and important components should be classified by type, and standard specifications should be developed for each classification.

The foregoing indicates types of specifications that could be standardized by Federal agencies responsible for procuring oceanographic instruments. However, it is imperative that the specifications be reasonable. Current military specifications, for instance, would often require instruments that are overdesigned or overpriced for commercial applications. These specifications should provide technical guidance and *should not restrict or freeze a design*. Rather, such specifications should simplify communications among segments of the oceanic community.

A large number of independent organizations gather and contribute oceanographic data to NODC. Often substantially different experimental results are submitted because their instruments, or sensors, while similar, may have been calibrated to different standards, operated in a different manner, or their output data may have been processed differently.

Some specification guidelines already in existence can be applied, with or without modification, to ocean instruments. However, the establishment of standard ocean instrument specifications is a major problem that will require considerable effort in man-hours and money over a long period until agreement is reached on the acceptability of such specifications. Voluntary groups have attempted to write specification guidelines, but have generally failed due to the enormity of the task.

The panel recommends establishing a permanently staffed and adequately funded focal point in the Government, preferably in a marine-oriented agency, to recommend measurement standards, prepare standard specifications, and perform tests on oceanographic instruments. Some efforts of this kind are in progress in the Navy and the Bureau of Standards.

## 2. Procurement Philosophy

Measuring characteristics of the marine environment absorbs a major part of the National investment in oceanography. The present Federal policy for developing and acquiring oceanographic instrumentation appears to *minimize initial capital* cost rather than total data cost. Thus, inadequate consideration has been given to the total cost of obtaining required data, namely the cost to the data collector, processor, and user. It has often been demonstrated that a more expensive instrument, by virtue of its versatility and reliability, can effect reductions in the ultimate cost of data.

Procurement policies have frequently over-emphasized initial cost because no dependable economic and operational performance criteria exist to determine the quality and usefulness of a given instrument. In addition, procurement specifications often fail to take into account the total economic implication of each specification. A typical example is the requirement for a much higher degree of instrument accuracy than is required.

Under present conditions, instrument manufacturers frequently do not have adequate incentive to develop equipment or systems that will be more cost-effective to the user. This need not be, since industry can produce reliable equipment at costs commensurate with high quality. Until procurement policies are changed, many instruments of inherent poor quality will continue to be procured on a low-bid basis.

In summary, many instruments perform poorly under operational conditions and thus cause needless repairs and delays. This latter expense is growing rapidly due to ever increasing vehicle operating costs. In addition, these instruments often are not designed to minimize the total data cost.

## C. Recommendations

### 1. Guidelines

To foster Government procurement of reliable, cost-effective ocean instruments, the panel recommends:

—Federal procurement policies should emphasize lifetime cost, recommend reasonable performance standards, and require complete, adequate quality assurance programs by instrument producers.

—General guidelines should be developed for preparing technical specifications for instrument procurement, taking into account each category of the specifications listed earlier.

—The Government should recognize the cost implications of particular technical specifications for data collectors, data processors, and data users.

—Continuing, effective communications should be established among the data users, procurement agencies, and instrument manufacturers, encompassing full exchange of information on operational economics, performance, reliability, and testing procedures.

## 2. Implementation

—The need for oceanographic instrument specifications is urgent. Since the Navy purchases a large number of such instruments and presently has a lead role in this area, it is recommended that their role be strengthened and broadened. The panel encourages the Navy, working in conjunction with the Bureau of Standards, to act as an interim focal point for tests and standardization activity.

—This function should ultimately be transferred, if necessary, to a civilian marine agency.

Many persons were contacted by panel and staff members during the preparation of this report. The following list includes those who made important contributions through interviews, conferences, submission of written materials, and review of report drafts.[1] There may have been other persons who made such contributions, and the panel apologizes for their inadvertent omission. Although the report reflects in part these contributions, its recommendations are those of this panel and are not necessarily the views of any specific individuals or organizations.

| Name | Organization |
|---|---|
| Abel, Robert B. | National Science Foundation |
| Adams, C.F. | Raytheon Company |
| Allan, Robert M., Jr. | Litton Industries |
| Allen, Louis | Allen Weather Corporation |
| Allen, Sheldon | Freeport Sulphur Company |
| Arnold, K. | Shell Oil Company |
| Asplin, L.I. | Shell Oil Company |
| Barrow, Thomas D. (R) | Humble Oil & Refining Co. |
| Bascom, Willard (R) | Ocean Science & Engineering Inc. |
| Bauer, Robert V. | Global Marine Exploration Co. |
| Bavier, Robert N., Jr. | Yachting Publishing Corporation |
| Beckman, Walter C. | Alpine Geophysical Associates, Inc. |
| Beesley, E.N. | Eli Lilly & Co. |
| Benoit, Richard (R) | General Dynamics Corp. |
| Berman, Bernard | Bissett-Berman Corporation |
| Boatwright, V.T. | General Dynamics Corporation |
| Bolin, L.T. | Brown and Root, Inc. |
| Borch, F.J. | General Electric Company |
| Bowen, Hugh M. | Dunlap and Associates, Inc. |
| Bramlette, W.A. | Humble Oil & Refining Co. |
| Briggs, Robert O. | The Dillingham Corporation |
| Britain, Kenneth E. | Tennessee Gas Pipeline Co. |
| Brockett, E.D. | Gulf Oil Corporation |
| Brown, Fred E. | Tri-Continental Corp. |
| Brown, Herschel | Lockheed Aircraft |
| Burden, William | Wm. A.M. Burden & Co. |
| Burgess, Harry C. | Kennecott Copper Corporation |
| Burk, Creighton (R) | Mobil Oil Corporation |
| Callaway, Samuel R. | Morgan Guaranty Trust Co. of New York |
| Campesi, Nick S. | Divcon, Inc. |
| Carney, Thomas | G.D. Searle Company |
| Carsola, Alfred | Lockheed Aircraft Corp. |
| Caubin, Paul J. | Irving P. Krick Associates, Inc. |
| Cawley, John H. (R) | A.D. Little, Inc. |
| Chamberlin, Theodore (R) | Ocean Science and Engineering Co. |
| Chambers, Leslie A. | Allan Hancock Foundation |
| Chambers, R.R. | Sinclair Research Company |
| Channel, R.C. | Dunlap and Associates, Inc. |
| Chapman, W.M. (R) | Van Camp Sea Food Company |
| Charles, Raymond A. | Prudential Insurance Co. of America |
| Cima, Norman E. | $CM^2$, Inc. |
| Clark, Robert | Hayden, Stone Incorporated |
| Clarke, William D. | Westinghouse Electric Corp. |
| Cleaver, John C. | Aqua-Chem, Inc. |
| Clements, William P., Jr. | Southeastern Drilling Co. |
| Clewell, Dayton | Mobil Oil Corporation |
| Clotworthy, J.H. | National Oceanography Association |
| Coates, L.D. (R) | Lockheed-California Company |
| Coene, G.T. (R) | Westinghouse Electric Corp. |
| Collyer, James | Raytheon Company |
| Conant, Melvin | Standard Oil Company |

| Name | Organization |
|---|---|
| Connelly, Will | Marine Acoustical Services, Inc. |
| Conner, Don E. | Kelco Company |
| Convers, Charles C. | Management Consultant |
| Cornell, Mel | Bull Head Marina |
| Cornwell, C.G. | American Hull Insurance Syndicate |
| Cotton, Donald B. | D.B. Cotton & Associates |
| Crapo, Stanford T. | Marine Acoustical Services, Inc. |
| Crawford, John E. | Crawford Marine Specialists, Inc. |
| Crawford, W.D. | Consolidated Edison Company |
| Cretzler, Don J. | Bissett-Berman Corporation |
| Cullison, James S. II (R) | Florida Development Commission |
| Danforth, Peter | Payson & Trask |
| Danhof, Clarence (R) | George Washington University |
| Davidson, William H., Jr. | Transcontinental Gas Pipeline Corp. |
| Davis, Berkley | General Electric Company |
| Dean, Gordon (R) | Bureau of Mines, Department of the Interior |
| Dean, Robert | University of Florida |
| De Norme, Roger | Belgian Mission to the United States |
| Derr, Earl D. | Royal Globe Insurance Companies |
| Doan, H.D. | Dow Chemical Company |
| Dockson, Robert R. | University of Southern California |
| Doig, Keith (R) | Shell Oil Company |
| Dole, Hollis (R) | Oregon Department of Geology and Mineral Industries |
| Dorsey, B.R. | Gulf Oil Corporation |
| Drain, J. | Joy Manufacturing Company |
| Duncan, C.C. | American Telephone & Telegraph Co. |
| Dunlap, Jack W., Jr. | Dunlap and Associates, Inc. |
| Dunlap, Jack W., Sr. | Dunlap and Associates, Inc. |
| Edgerton, Harold | E.G.&G., Inc. |
| Ensign, Chester (R) | Copper Range Company |
| Felando, August | American Tunaboat Association |
| Fisher, Frank R. | Sinclair Oil and Gas Co. |
| Flowers, W.W. | Sinclair Research Company |
| Fortenberry, Jerry P. (R) | Tennessee Gas Transmission Co. |
| Foster, William C. (R) | Ralston Purina Company |
| Fox, Joseph M. | Merck and Company, Inc. |
| Francis, Thayer, Jr. | Sippican Corporation |
| Franklin, J.M. | U.S. Lines, Inc. |
| Frautschy, Jeffery D. | Scripps Institution of Oceanography, University of California, San Diego |
| Freeman, N.W. | Tenneco, Inc. |
| Frensley, Herbert J. | Brown and Root, Inc. |
| Fuller, Richard C. | Bendix Corporation |
| Fulling, Roger W. | E.I. duPont de Nemours & Co. |

[1](R) denotes those persons who reviewed portions of preliminary drafts of panel material.

*Deceased.

| Name | Organization |
|------|-------------|
| Gaden, Elmer L., Jr. | Columbia University |
| Gagnebin, A.P. | International Nickel Co. |
| Galerne, Andre | International Underwater Contractors |
| Gaul, Roy D. | Westinghouse Electric Corp. |
| Gentry, Robert C. | Environmental Science Services Administration, Department of Commerce |
| Gerstacker, Carl | Dow Chemical Co. |
| Gherardi, Walter R. | Chubb and Son |
| Gilman, Roger H. | Port of New York Authority |
| Ginzton, Edward L. | Varian Associates |
| Gordon, William G. (R) | Bureau of Commercial Fisheries, Department of the Interior |
| Gottwald, F.D. | Ethyl Corporation |
| Graves, C.L. | J. Ray McDermott |
| Hait, James M. | FMC Corporation |
| Hallamore, R.G. | Lear Siegler, Inc. |
| Halstead, Bruce W. | World Life Research Institute |
| Harden, M.L. | Standard Oil of N.J. |
| Hastings, Charles E. | Hastings-Raydist, Inc. |
| Haughton, Dan | Lockheed Aircraft Corporation |
| Heath, Wallace G. (R) | Western Washington State College |
| Henry, Vernon J., Jr. | University of Georgia |
| Hills, R.C. | Freeport Sulphur Company |
| Holden, Donald A. | Newport News Shipbuilding & Dry Dock Co. |
| Honsinger, Leroy V. | Todd Shipyards, Inc. |
| Hood, Edwin M. | Shipbuilders Council of America |
| Horrer, Paul L. | Marine Advisors, Inc. |
| Howe, Eugene E. | Merck, Sharpe and Dome |
| Howe, Richard J. (R) | Humble Oil and Refining Co. |
| Hydrick, Gardner | Scudder, Stevens & Clark |
| Isaacs, John | Scripps Institution of Oceanography, University of California, San Diego |
| Isbrandtsen, Jakob | American Export Isbrandtsen Lines, Inc. |
| Jamieson, J.K. | Standard Oil of N.J. |
| Jenkins, George | Metropolitan Life |
| Jobst, Louis F., Jr. | City and Port of Long Beach |
| Johns, Lionel S. (R) | Ocean Science and Engineering Co. |
| Jones, Albert | Bureau of Commercial Fisheries, Department of the Interior |
| Jones, Robert E. | National Association of Manufacturers |
| Jordan, Arthur | Cape Fear Technical Institute |
| Jordan, S.A. | Westinghouse Electric Corp. |
| Jorgenson, John H. (R) | National Security Industrial Association |
| Joyner, H.H. | American Telephone & Telegraph Co. |
| Jurow, Irving H. | Schering Corporation |
| Kahl, Joseph | Kahl Scientific Instrument Corp. |
| Kane, Eneas D. | Chevron Research Company |
| Kaufman, Alvin (R) | Bureau of Land Management, Department of the Interior |
| Kaufman, Otto | Aetna Life Insurance Company |
| Kennedy, Joseph B. | Sinclair Oil Corporation |
| King, Lyle | Port of New York Authority |
| Kirby, George F. | Ethyl Corporation |
| Kirkbride, Chalmer G. (R) | Sun Oil Company |
| Knowlton, Hugh | Smith Barney & Co., Inc. |
| Kushner, Harvey D. (R) | Operations Research Inc. |
| Laborde, Alden J. | Ocean Drilling and Exploration Co. |
| LaQue, Francis L. (R) | International Nickel Co., Inc. |
| Laverty, William J. | The Sippican Corporation |
| Lenagh, Thomas H. | The Ford Foundation |
| Lenz, Winthrop C. | Merrill Lynch Pierce Fenner & Smith, Inc. |
| Lesser, Robert M. | Lockheed-California Company |
| Lockwood, William | First National City Bank (New York) |
| Ludwig, Daniel K. | National Bulk Carriers |
| Luehrmann, W.H. | Teledyne, Inc. |
| Lynch, John | Sea-Land Service, Inc. |
| Maloney, Walter E. | Bigham, Englar, Jones & Houston |
| Maness, Irving | Small Business Administration |
| Menzel, Daniel | Battelle Northwest |
| Martin, George | North American Rockwell Corp. |
| Martin, William R. | Aquasonics Engineering Co. |
| Maton, Gilbert L. | John I. Thompson Co. |
| May, T.P. | The International Nickel Co., Inc. |
| Maybeck, Edward B. | The Chase Manhattan Bank |
| Mayer, Raymond W. | $CM^2$, Inc. |
| McDonald, Capt. C.A.K., USN (R) | Department of the Navy |
| McDonald, Joseph | Public Land Law Review Commission |
| McIlhenny, W.F. (R) | Dow Chemical Company |
| McKeen, John E. | Charles Pfizer Company |
| McLean, Noel B. | Edo Corporation |
| Mero, John L. | Ocean Resources, Inc. |
| Miller, Leonard A. | Columbia Gas System Service Corp. |
| Miller, O.N. | Standard Oil of California |
| Miller, Paul | First Boston Corporation |
| Milliken, Frank R. | Kennecott Copper Corp. |
| Mole, Harvey | U.S. Steel Corp. |
| Montgomery, W. Saxe | Geodyne Corporation |
| Moody, John D., Sr. | Mobil Oil Corporation |
| Moore, J. Jamison | Modern Management |
| Moore, John | North American Aviation |
| Moore, W.T., Sr. | Moore-McCormack Lines |
| Morris, W.T., Jr. | Lykes Brothers Steamship Co., Inc. |
| Morrish, Thomas M. (R) | Oceanic Foundation |
| Muys, Jerome C. | Public Land Law Review Commission |
| Nemec, F.A. | Lykes Brothers Steamship Co., Inc. |
| Nickerson, Albert L. | Mobil Oil Corporation |
| Oberle, Frank | Murphy-Pacific, Merrit Salvage Division |
| Ochacher, Donald M. | Columbia Gas System Service Corp. |
| Officer, Charles B. | Alpine Geophysical Associates, Inc. |
| O'Keefe, Bernard J. | E.G.&G., Inc. |
| O'Leary, John F. | Bureau of Natural Gas, Federal Power Commission |
| O'Malley, Hubert J. | ESSO Exploration, Inc. |
| Oppenheimer, Carl H. | Florida State University |
| Orlofsky, S. (R) | Columbia Gas System Service Corp. |
| Osborne, William | Lehman Brothers |
| Paige, John | International Nickel Co. |
| Paine, F. Ward (R) | Ocean Science Capital Corp. |
| Palmer, R.B. | Texaco, Inc. |
| Pearson, A.S. | Consolidated Edison Company |
| Peterson, C.E. (R) | Bureau of Commercial Fisheries, Department of the Interior |
| Phillippe, G.L.* | General Electric Co. |
| Phillips, T.L. | Raytheon Company |
| Power, John J. | Charles Pfizer & Co., Inc. |
| Prior, William W. | Trunkline Gas Company |
| Purdon, Alexandria | U.S. Lines, Inc. |
| Ramo, Simon | TRW, Inc. |
| Rebikoff, Dimitri I. | Rebikoff Underwater Products, Inc. |
| Richardson, William S. | Nova University |
| Ricker, J.B., Jr. | Marine Office of America |
| Rolfe, Briney | Sinclair Research Company |
| Root, L. Eugene | Lockheed Aircraft |
| Rorer, Gerald F. | William H. Rorer, Inc. |
| Rudiger, Carl E. (R) | Lockheed Missiles & Space Co. |
| Rutledge, Carleton (R) | Westinghouse Electric Corp. |

Ryan, William R. . . . . . . . . . . . . . . . . . . . Edo Corporation
Salladay, Steve . . . . . . . . . .Insurance Company of North America
Sampson, Charles M. . . . . . . . Freeport Sulphur Company
Sarett, L.H. . . . . . . . . . . . . . . . . . Merck & Company, Inc.
Schafersman, Dale A. . . . . . . Natural Gas Pipeline Co. of America
Schenck, Herbert H. . . . . . . . U.S. Underseas Cable Corp.
Schmidt, Benno C. . . . . . . . . . . . . . . J.H. Whitney & Co.
Schoales, Dudley N. (R) . . . . . . . Morgan Stanley & Co.
Scott, John . . . . . . . . . . . . . . . . . Mobil Oil Corporation
Shapiro, Hymin . . . . . . . . . . . . . . . . Ethyl Corporation
Sheets, H.E. . . . . . . . . . . . . . . . . . . . General Dynamics
Shepard, Hardy . . . . . . . . . . . . . . . . . . . Payson & Trask
Shephard, Robert J. (R) . . . .Westinghouse Electric Corp.
Sherwood, Robert . . . . . . .International Nickel Co., Inc.
Shigley, C. Monroe (R) . . . . . . . Dow Chemical Company
Shykind, E.B. (R) . . . . . . . .CMREF, National Council on Marine Resources and Engineering Development
Siebenhausen, C.H. (R) . . . . . . . . . . . .Shell Oil Company
Simons, Merton E. (R) . . . . Phillips Petroleum Company
Singleton, Henry E. . . . . . . . . . . . . . . . . . Teledyne, Inc.
Smith, A.C. . . . . . . . . . . . . . . . . . . . .Ocean Systems, Inc.
Smith, Warren Lee . . .Kidder, Peabody & Company, Inc.
Snodgrass, James (R)Scripps Institution of Oceanography, University of California, San Diego
Snyder, A.E. . . . . . . . . . . . . . . . . . . . . . . Colt Industries
Snyder, Capt. J. Edward, USN . .Department of the Navy
Soloman, Herbert L. . . . . . . . . Uris Building Corporation
Spangler, Miller B. . . . . . . . National Planning Association
Stephan, Charles R. . . . . . . . .Florida Atlantic University
Stephan, J. Stan . . . . . . .First Bank and Trust Company, Bryan, Texas
Stewart, Harris B. . . . . . . . . . . . . .ESSA, Department of Commerce
Stoddard, George A. . . . . . . . . .Scudder, Stevens & Clark
Stoddard, George E. . . . . . . . . . Equitable Life Assurance Society of the United States
Stowers, H.L. . . . . . . . . . . .Texas Gas Transmission Co.
Strohmeyer, D.D. . . . . . . . .Bethlehem Steel Corporation
Sutton, Paul A. . . . . . . . . . . . . . . . . Alpine Geophysical Associates, Inc.

Swan, Dave . . . . . . . . . . Kennecott Copper Corporation
Symonds, Gardiner . . . . . . . . . . . . . . . . . .Tenneco, Inc.
Tajima, George (R) . . . . . . . Bissett-Berman Corporation
Taylor, J.F., Jr. . . . . . . . . . . . . . . . . . Decca Systems, Inc.
Thayer, Stuart . . . . . . Lykes Brothers Steamship Co., Inc.
Thomas, Charles (R) . . . . . . . . . . . . . .Sun Oil Company
Thornberg, Russell B. . . . .Global Marine Exploration Co.
Tibby, Richard B. . . . . . . Catalina Marine Science Center
Tishman, Robert . . . . . . . . . . . . . Tishman Realty Corp.
Tonking, W.H. . . . . . . . . . . . . . . . . . . . Brown & Root, Inc.
Topping, Norman . . . . .University of Southern California
Torrey, Thomas . .Insurance Company of North America
Treadwell, Capt. T.K., USN . . . . . . Naval Oceanographic Office
Turman, S.B. . . . . . . . Lykes Brothers Steamship Co., Inc.
Tuthill, Arthur H. (R) . . . . .International Nickel Co., Inc.
Vance, Jack O. . . . . . . . . . . . . . . .McKinsey and Company
Wakelin, James H., Jr. (R) . . . . . . .Ryan Aeronautical Co.
Walthier, Thomas N. (R) . . . . . Occidental Minerals Corp.
Ward, David M. . . . . . . . . . . . . . . . . . . . Ward Associates
Ware, T.M. . . . . International Minerals & Chemical Corp.
Warm, W.F. . . . . . . . . . . . . . . . .Marine Office of America
Warner, Arthur J. . . Bureau of Mines, Department of the Interior
Warner, R., Jr. . . . . . . . . . . . . . . . Mobil Oil Corporation
Waters, Rear Adm. Odale D., Jr., USN . . . . . Department of the Navy
Weber, Ernest M. . . . . . . . . . . . .Charles Pfizer & Co., Inc.
Wedin, John (R) . . . .Staff, Senate Commerce Committee
Weiss, A.M. . . . . . . . Natural Gas Pipeline Co. of America
Wheaton, Elmer P. (R) . . . . . . . . . Lockheed Missiles and Space Co.
White, N.C. . . . . . . .International Minerals and Chemicals
Williams, L.M. . . . . . . . . . . . . . Freeport Sulphur Company
Wilson, Roger W. . . . . . . . . . . . . . . . .J. Ray McDermott
Wingate, H.S. . . . . . . . . . . . . . . . .International Nickel Co.
Wright, Donald L. . . . . . . . . . . . . .Jersey Enterprises, Inc.
Wright, Edward W. . . . . . . . . . . . . Dillingham Corporation
Zimmerman, Edwin M. . . . . . . . . . . . Anti-Trust Division, Department of Justice
Zimmerman, Jack . . . .Hydrospace Research Corporation

Part VI

Report of the Panel
on Marine Engineering and Technology

# Contents

This report assesses the present national effort in marine engineering and technology and provides broad guidance for the economical and rational development of a strong U.S. capability in the marine environment.

The following objectives, stated in subparagraphs of Section 2(b) of the Marine Resources and Engineering Development Act of 1966, were felt to be applicable in establishing the scope of activities of the panel:

*(1) The accelerated development of the resources of the marine environment . . . .*

*(4) The preservation of the role of the United States as a leader in marine science and resource development . . . .*

*(6) The development and improvement of the capabilities, performance, use, and efficiency of vehicles, equipment, and instruments for use in exploration, research, surveys, the recovery of resources, and the transmission of energy in the marine environment.*

*(7) The effective utilization of the scientific and engineering resources of the Nation, with close cooperation among all interested agencies, public and private, in order to avoid unnecessary duplication of effort, facilities, and equipment, or waste . . . .*

The panel has endeavored to delineate the Nation's future course in the marine environment in terms of engineering and technological feasibility, to assess its present structure, to point out inhibitions to progress, and to relate the necessary input to the obtainable output. It stresses areas where engineering and technology have a bearing on the growth and development of industry and the solution of defense problems.

The panel was particularly cognizant of the need for *national* participation as opposed to a predominantly government approach, in future ocean activities. Achieving a strong marine engineering and technology capability can be accomplished best by the cooperative efforts of the States and regions, private enterprise, the academic community, and the U.S. Government.

The material presented in this report represents the effort of the panel Commissioners, staff, and the beneficial guidance of many consultants during the course of the panel's deliberations. The Panel Executive Secretary was:

Lincoln D. Cathers

Under sponsorship of the Oceanic Foundation additional staff was assembled to support the panel. This staff, the Marine Commission Support Group, was comprised of:

Amor L. Lane
Carl E. Rudiger, Jr.
Carleton Rutledge, Jr.
Robert J. Shephard
R. Lawrence Snideman II
Robert M. Lesser (part-time)

A special note of thanks is made to the agencies and companies who generously provided the time of the Commissioners, Executive Secretary, staff personnel, and consultants.

The panel contacted existing organizations (the National Security Industrial Association, the National Academy of Engineering, numerous technical societies, universities, commercial and defense industries, regional authorities, and non-profit organizations) to solicit and involve the private sector in defining problems and recommending solutions. Coordination was maintained with other panels through personal contact, monthly Commission meetings, and distribution of draft materials.

In Appendix A is a complete listing of individuals and organizations contributing to the development of this report.

John H. Perry, Jr., *Chairman*
Charles F. Baird
Taylor A. Pryor
George H. Sullivan

## I. PROGRAM AND GOAL

The development of the ocean as a resource is a major concern closely linked to the solution of the problems of urban development, transportation, public health, foreign aid, and world hunger.

An essential element of the national commitment to the oceans is the technology to explore and utilize them, to occupy the U.S. territorial sea, and to utilize and manage the resources of the U.S. Continental Shelves. This country's position of technological leadership requires it to take an active role in developing the earth's resources, especially those of the undersea frontier.

Technological development has been the foundation of U.S. strength and national growth. Its extension into the oceans is necessary to continue national development, including creation and protection of employment, a more enjoyable way of life, and maintenance and improvement of the national environment for the future. Economic and social benefits, continuing acquisition of scientific knowledge, and military necessity justify the commitment.

## II. MAJOR OBJECTIVES

The panel proposes, as the major objectives of an increased national commitment to the oceans, that the United States should develop the technological base and capability to:

—Within 10 years: **occupy** the U.S. territorial sea; **utilize** the U.S. Continental Shelf and slope to depths of 2,000 feet; **explore** the ocean depths to 20,000 feet.

—Within 30 years: **manage** the U.S. Continental Shelf and slope to depths of 2,000 feet; achieve the capability to **utilize** the ocean depths to 20,000 feet.[1]

The depths of 2,000 feet and 20,000 feet for technological development of the undersea frontier are dictated by the bathymetry of the oceans and

[1] Key definitions are given in Figure 1.

the state of technology. Both depths are reasonable targets. The two major objectives are workable for U.S. ocean activities and may be carried out within an acceptable international legal framework.

---

**Figure 1 Key Definitions**

**Ocean engineering**—The application of science and engineering to describe the marine environment and to develop and operate systems for its utilization.

**Marine technology**—The total capability to utilize the ocean environment, including knowledge, equipment, techniques, and facilities.

**Occupy**—To inhabit a volume of ocean or an area of seabed to observe, make decisions, and take action. Occupation includes the element of permanence.

**Explore**—To search, probe, map, and chart systematically the ocean environment, including the water column, floor, and subfloor features for the purpose of enhancing subsequent action.

**Manage**—To direct effort to conserve depletable resources, achieve continued and improved yield of regenerative resources, modify the environment to facilitate these efforts, and resolve multiple use conflicts.

**Utilize**—To carry out a useful purpose or operation; to obtain profit or benefit by using.

---

The earth's continents are fringed by shallow, sloping shelves varying in width from a few yards to hundreds of miles. The shelves and a limited area of the steeper continental slopes beyond lie within the 2,000 foot contour, an area totaling nearly 10 per cent of the earth's ocean floor—approximately as large as North and South America combined. The 2,000-foot depth is within reach of present U.S. technology and closely relates to current estimates of diver working potential. As a primary technological goal it is realistic, attainable, and immediately rewarding.

The continental slopes, especially beyond the 2,000 foot contour, are quite precipitous. For example, the next four 2,000 foot increments to the 10,000 foot contour each provide only about three per cent more bottom area. For depths from 10,000 down to 20,000 feet, increased depth capability is rewarded with access to an additional 75 per cent of the total ocean bottom area, while depths beyond 20,000 feet (two per cent of the total) are found only in a few trenches. Therefore, a natural deep ocean technological development goal exists for 20,000 feet. (See Figure 2.)

The promising characteristics of advanced structural materials, new concepts of external machinery and equipment, and better engineering make operations at 20,000-foot depths a practical objective. Twenty thousand feet is a logical, realistic, yet challenging goal for technology.

## III. MAJOR RECOMMENDATIONS

The panel's report is summarized in this list of recommendations:

### A. General

1. A National Advisory Committee for the Oceans to guide national marine efforts.
2. An oceanic agency concentrating in one agency appropriate U.S. Government groups with primary roles and missions in the oceans and including a technology development group.
3. A 10-year program of intensive undersea development.
4. National Projects to accelerate progress into the undersea frontier.
5. A strong Navy undersea mission and an improved program in deep submergence and ocean engineeering.
6. An effective national commitment to the ocean requiring understanding and cooperation from all segments of the national economy.

### B. Fundamental Technology

7. A program to advance *fundamental* marine engineering and technology.
8. Development of engineering design handbooks, technical memoranda, and other design data with a system for continually updating this information.

### C. Test Facilities

9. A program to increase the number and quality of test facilities and to reduce testing costs.

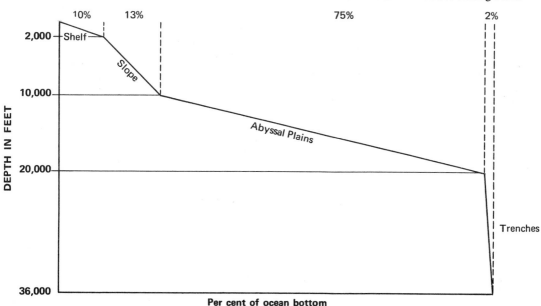

**Figure 2.** *Per cent of ocean bottom that can be explored by various operating depth capabilities.*

### D. Deep Ocean

10. A program to expand 20,000-foot ocean engineering capabilities.
11. Technology priorities in power sources, free flooding machinery, equipment, and materials.
12. Systems priorities in survey vehicles, search vehicles, transfer vehicles, manned stations, and support systems.

### E. Nearshore

13. A program of pollution monitoring and water quality restoration to complement the essential goal to halt effectively the pollution of nearshore waters.
14. A program of coastal biological and engineering efforts.
15. A program to improve port and harbor development technology.
16. A Coast Guard research and development program leading to improved maritime safety.

### F. Great Lakes

17. A restoration technology National Project tailored to the immediate needs of Lakes Erie and Ontario and southern Lake Michigan.
18. An actual restoration project undertaken as soon as technology is available.

### G. Industrial

### 1. Fishing and Aquaculture

19. Development of greatly improved domestic fish production capability.
20. Surveys of promising underutilized commercial and sport fisheries.
21. A program to pursue aquaculture development vigorously.

### 2. Oil and Gas

22. A mechanism for optimum information exchange between the Government and the petroleum industry.
23. Government furnished information on fundamental undersea technology, biomedicine, and reconnaissance mapping and charting, and increased development of environmental prediction and modification technology.
24. A program directed toward reduction of oil spills and combating their effects.

### 3. Chemical Extraction and Desalination

25. Development of new chemical extraction technology in conjunction with desalting research.
26. Government participation in advanced desalting technology projects without its entrance into the business of supplying desalted water.
27. A balanced program advancing desalination technology to convert seawater, inland brackish water, and waste water into usable supplies.

### 4. Ocean Mining

28. A program to advance undersea exploration technology to enable timely delineation of offshore reserves and provide growth of offshore mining.

### 5. Power Generation

29. A developmental program for submerged commercial nuclear power.

## IV. TEN-YEAR PROGRAM OF MARINE DEVELOPMENT

The concept supported by the panel is to advance marine engineering and technology through cooperative participation by State, Federal, academic, and industrial groups.

### A. Fundamental Technology

Fundamental technology is an essential base for future marine endeavors. Particular categories, by definition, have numerous multiple interrelated applications. The quality and scope of fundamental technology must be expanded continuously to assure new developments, reduce costs, increase capability, improve reliability, and afford new ways to solve problems.

Elements of fundamental technology most critical for effective commercial development, scientific exploration, and military operation are listed in Figure 3 in approximate descending order of importance. References in parentheses are to Chapters 5 and 6 of this report where pertinent detailed discussion may be found.

## B. National Test Facilities

The marine environment is not well known, and with today's technology it is a hostile and difficult operating area. History has borne out that adequate testing is required to utilize a foreign environment effectively. Thus, in developing the capability to occupy and manage the offshore areas and explore and utilize the deep oceans, it will become evident that test facilities will be a national resource as important as any other single factor.

There are two prime elements of the national test facility needs—(1) those to test systems, equipment, components, and fundamental developments and (2) those to test man as a diver in the sea. (See Chapter 5, Section II for details.)

## C. National Projects

A series of national facilities, programs, and projects, generically called National Projects, is recommended for consideration during the 10-year program to support technological progress in the oceans. These projects, many having strong inter-relationships, are listed in Figure 4. (See Chapter 7 for details.)

## D. Costs

The result of the national effort will be to establish the technology needed for access to the oceans in a convenient, economical, and reliable manner with a taxpayer investment of less than one billion dollars of new funding per year over the next decade.

Figure 5 is a breakdown of the estimated costs for the 10-year marine development program.

**Figure 5**
**Cost for 10-Year Program**

| Category | Ten Year Cost (billions of dollars) |
|---|---|
| Fundamental Technology[1] | 2.0 - 3.0 |
| Test Facilities | |
|     Simulation facilities | 0.4 - 0.6 |
|     Biomedical chambers | 0.1 - 0.2 |
|     Ocean test ranges | 0.3 - 0.4 |
| National Projects | |
|     Undersea facilities | 0.6 - 1.0 |
|     Marine programs | 0.3 - 0.5 |
|     Marine projects | 0.4 - 0.7 |
| Operational Support | 1.0 - 1.5 |
| TOTAL | 5.1 - 7.9 |

[1]See Figure 2.

The major findings and recommendations of the Marine Engineering and Technology Panel are summarized under the following categories:

A. General
B. Fundamental Technology
C. Facilities
D. Special Deep Ocean Considerations
E. Special Nearshore Problems
F. Great Lakes Restoration
G. Industrial Technology

These categories relate directly to the report's major marine technology discussions, most of which are concerned with surface or relatively shallow operations to 2,000 feet. Such operations are expected to dominate national ocean activities during the remainder of this century. Within each group, findings are presented first, followed by recommendations. This chapter summarizes the current state of marine technology, its potential, and a valid approach to advancing the nation's capability to explore and utilize the oceans fully.

## A. General

The oceans are the promise of future generations; they are the arena for achieving a major advancement in world gross product. Ocean development is a major concern—more compelling to today's national interest than space development—integral to the solution of urban, transportation, health, foreign aid, and world nutrition problems—and vital to national defense.

The present overall undersea capability of the United States is extremely limited relative to the potential of marine technology. Given a fundamental technology program and a commitment to the oceans, the United States could produce systems in 10 to 15 years that would duplicate on the continental shelves many productive terrestrial functions while attaining substantially improved operating capabilities throughout the oceans at all depths.

Industrial, scientific, and military undersea technology are closely linked. A properly managed, balanced, comprehensive, dynamic marine engineering and technology development program over the next 10 years could provide the United States a wide range of industrial, scientific, political, and military technological options.

Without such an accelerated undersea exploration and development program, a critical national technological deficiency will develop. Moreover, instead of an orderly development, a crash reaction would become necessary should some other nation demonstrate an internationally important undersea capability.

The goals stated in this report will not be achieved unless a much greater national commitment to the oceans is made. U.S. ocean activities presently include substantial private, State, and regional efforts. Therefore, the oceans deserve a different approach than military and space endeavors which have been strictly Federal responsibilities.

Overall undersea capability could advance more rapidly if affirmative efforts were made to publish government-developed technology. Unclassified research and engineering data are sometimes not released because funds are insufficient to prepare public reports, manpower limitations hamper extraction of unclassified technological data from classified documents, or the U.S. Government (especially the military) chooses to withhold unclassified data from general distribution.

Recommendations:

**1. A National Advisory Committee for the Oceans (NACO) should be established with representation from the States and regions, private enterprise, the academic community, and the U.S. Government. Its principal functions would be to (1) advise all U.S. Government agencies with missions in the oceans on the planning and implementation of the national marine efforts, (2) inform the Congress, (3) assist the States and private interests, (4) guide the fundamental marine technology development program, and (5) submit a periodic report assessing the national ocean program. Advice should be given in such areas as national goals and long-range plans, facilities, manpower, National Projects,**

scientific investigations, and oceanographic operations.

2. A new, adequately funded oceanic agency should be established within the U.S. Government to concentrate in one agency appropriate civilian groups with primary missions and roles in the oceans. An important part of the new agency should be a technology development group responsible for conducting and supporting a fundamental marine technology program and providing engineering support to the agency's operating groups.

3. A 10-year program of intensive undersea development should be undertaken. Such an effort would give the Nation the technological base and capability to: (1) occupy the territorial sea, (2) utilize and manage the resources of the U.S. Continental Shelf and slope, (3) explore and utilize deep ocean resources, (4) meet needs for undersea military operations, and (5) determine intelligently future national undersea programs.

4. A series of National Projects should be established to support advancement into the undersea frontier of industry, the States, the academic community, and the U.S. Government agencies in an economic manner. These projects should receive government support and, where applicable, be available to all users on a cost reimbursement basis. Principal use of these National Projects will be to test and evaluate the economic and technical feasibility of advanced marine developments.

5. Navy undersea development efforts in deep submergence and ocean engineering should be increased. The program outlined by the Deep Submergence/Ocean Engineering Program Planning Group appears to reflect realistically future Navy needs. In addition to this program, an expanded Navy mission in support of the applicable national technology goals should be recognized to take maximum advantage of existing capabilities and facilities. Cooperative efforts between the Navy program and the civilian program should be pursued to the fullest extent.

6. An effective national commitment to the oceans will require understanding and cooperation from all sectors of the economy—general public, industrial, academic and scientific, and military and civilian government.

General Public Requirements:

—Total national involvement including efforts of States, regions, and private enterprise.

—An awareness by the American people of the importance of the oceans to the Nation and the world.

Industrial Needs:

—Extensive survey information on marine resources on which to base investment decisions.

—Sufficient Government ocean engineering development funds to stimulate substantial private investment in operational systems.

—A better appreciation of the complexities and costs of operating in the oceans.

—A solid base of fundamental technology and operating experience.

—A legal and political framework that fosters ocean exploration and production activities.

Academic and Scientific Needs:

—Sufficient funds allocated to scientific projects to provide improved engineering support of at-sea scientific operations.

—A close interaction between scientists and engineers in applying engineering capabilities to the conduct of scientific projects.

—More emphasis in engineering institutions on ocean problems.

Military Needs:

—Establishment within the Department of Defense of a strong primary military mission in undersea technology to meet present and future threats.

—A clearly stated Navy mission in support of national marine programs evoking support of the Congress, civilian leaders, and the general public.

—A recognition of the contribution that can be made by use of Navy capabilities in international, economic, political, scientific, and technological fields.

—Funds in addition to those required for military commitments sufficient to allow use of Navy capabilities and management expertise in support of the overall national goals.

Civilian Government Needs:

—A concentration of agencies having ocean roles and missions.

—A marine and undersea technology development capability.

## B. Fundamental Technology

Critical advances in fundamental technology are required to improve undersea operating capabilities and reliability. Examples include: reliable, efficient, compact power sources; machinery and equipment capable of ambient operation; corrosion and fouling resistent, high strength-to-weight materials; subsurface navigation and precise positioning devices; underwater communication and viewing systems; and biomedicine.

Knowledge of ocean environmental variables, particularly such features as temperature, salinity, depth, biological effects, bathymetry, acoustic properties, bottom and sub-bottom geology, is insufficient to establish valid engineering design criteria for undersea systems.

Recommendations:

7. A fundamental marine engineering and technology program should be vigorously pursued to expand the possibilities and lower the costs of undersea operations.

8. Handbooks, technical memoranda, and other engineering design data should be developed, continually updated, and made available to the ocean engineer to provide critical information on undersea environmental conditions and the behavior of systems, materials, and components in the environment.

## C. Test Facilities

The necessity for adequate test facilities to permit safe, orderly, and rapid advancement into the undersea frontier parallels the history of strategic test facility needs for development of high altitude, supersonic, and space flight. Ocean test facilities are a national resource as important as any other single factor in the development of technology.

Insufficient and often unsuitable test facilities today are seriously impeding advancements in submersible, habitat, equipment, and instrumentation development.

Facilities for physiological research, medical training, diver equipment development, and saturation diver training are grossly inadequate.

Recommendation:

9. A national program should be initiated to increase the number and capability of undersea research, development, test, and evaluation facilities and to oversee efforts to improve facility design technology to reduce costs. A two part approach is needed for systems and equipment development and biomedical development.

## D. Special Deep Ocean Considerations

The bathymetry of the world's oceans is such that approximately 88 per cent of the ocean floor lies between the 2,000 and 20,000 foot contours, with 10 per cent less than 2,000 feet deep and only two per cent greater than 20,000 feet deep.

Marine life and high grade mineral resources exist at 20,000 feet. Sedimentary deposits which may contain oil are known to exist on the continental rises at depths from 6,000 to 14,000 feet.

The deep sea is of great interest to scientists concerned with such fields as ocean circulation, climatology, nutrient supply, marine biology, geophysics, and geology.

A technological deficiency in systems designed to operate below 2,000 feet exists because of the lack of a national commitment to understand, explore, and utilize the deep ocean. Deep ocean operations in general are restricted severely by equipment failures and the lack of ability to do useful work.

Military systems with deep operating capability will provide such advantages as better concealment, improved location for acoustic systems, expanded tactical coverage of systems operating above, and larger absolute margin of safety during dives and submerged maneuvers. Deep operating systems would be required for undersea arms control inspection and enforcement.

Recommendations:

**10.** The United States should undertake immediately a dynamic and comprehensive advanced development program leading to a greatly expanded ocean engineering capability. The deepocean goal should be set at the working plateau of 20,000 feet to gain access to 98 per cent of the world's oceans. This is consistent with the projected status of deep ocean technology. Development of 20,000-foot systems to explore and utilize the ocean as a whole is more rational than to advance incrementally at greater overall cost.

**11.** The deep ocean development program should give highest priority to:

—Compact power sources for vehicles and habitats.

—Reliable free flooding external machinery, electrical systems, and equipment.

—Materials for low weight-to-displacement ratio structures; high-strength, corrosion and fouling resistant components; and supplemental buoyancy.

**12.** The United States should undertake a program to gain knowledge and experience in the deep ocean, focusing on technology to develop:

—Efficient long-endurance exploration submersibles and associated instrumentation.

—Logistic support and rescue vehicles for crew transfer and resupply.

—Manned stations capable of submerged support by deep submersibles.

—Submersible mother ships and stable surface platforms to support undersea operations safely and efficiently.

### E. Special Nearshore Problems[1]

Pollution is the most serious problem in the nearshore area, having detrimental and often dis-

---

[1] In this panel report, the emphasis is on the engineering and technology to support activities in the coastal and estuarine zones. Another panel report deals with the overall problems of these zones.

astrous effects on recreation, fish and wildlife, water supplies, natural beauty, commercial development, and scientific study. Pollution in some areas is so critical that the use of nearshore waters for additional waste disposal cannot be tolerated. A technology base exists to produce more effective waste treatment techniques, monitoring devices, and to introduce preventative and restorative measures.

So much critical U.S. coastal land has been lost to the sea that improved coastal engineering technology becomes increasingly important. Extensive erosion protection projects have been undertaken, but due to a lack of basic understanding of shore processes there often have been both unexpected failures and undesirable results.

Progress in marine transportation is leading rapidly to larger, deeper-draft bulk carriers and high speed ships with such improved cargo handling systems as containers and lighters. Containerization is growing especially fast. The New York Port Authority estimates that by 1975, 50 per cent of its general cargo will be containerized compared to 12 per cent at present and only 3 per cent in 1966.

Port design in addition to ship design will pace future progress. Deepening of harbors to accommodate large bulk carriers is encountering such severe physical barriers as bedrock, manmade tunnels, and long shallow approaches. In general, terminals for bulk and containerized shipping must be totally new. Utilization of land made available by obsolete facilities can make valuable contributions to urban development. Increased ocean activity will require government emphasis on safety and regulation. Nearshore activities place prime reliance on dependable navigation and communications.

Recommendations:

**13.** Disposal of wastes in coastal waters must not be considered an acceptable alternative to pollution abatement and control without full prior knowledge of its effects. A goal should be set to halt substantially any further pollution and to improve the quality of nearshore waters. The goals of this program should be enforced by joint State-Federal ultimate standards to be fixed immediately. These standards should be tailored for incremental future compliance until the desired standards are attained. In addition, detailed research and development programs should be pursued to improve technology of monitoring devices to help determine pollution sources and distribution.

14. To increase the quality and quantity of usable coastal land, a program of coastal biological and engineering efforts should be pursued vigorously and adequately funded to perform such tasks as:

—Coastal process studies.

—Prototype developments of new erosion prevention systems.

—Applied research on nearshore ecology.

15. Port and harbor development should be based on a total systems approach to marine transportation. Such development should concentrate on design of offshore bulk cargo terminals and improved methods of intermodal (air-land-sea) transfer to allow more effective use of coastal land.

16. To protect life and property better, the Coast Guard should pursue a research and development program to strengthen capabilities for traffic control, monitoring, and search and rescue (including underwater divers, submersibles, and habitats). A study should be made of present and potential underwater acoustic requirements. Frequency and power level allocations should be established and enforced.

## F. Great Lakes Restoration

The major problem faced by the Great Lakes is aging (eutrophication) accelerated by water pollution leading to:

—Over-enrichment of the Lakes

—Build up of dissolved and suspended solids in the Lakes

—Oxygen depletion of the Lakes and tributaries

Lake Erie, Lake Ontario, and southern Lake Michigan are in the worst condition of the five Great Lakes, but none is beyond restoration. Technology can reverse the aging process. Pollu-tion abatement is required to make restoration efforts effective.

Recommendations:

17. A National Project tailored to the immediate needs of Lakes Erie and Ontario and southern Lake Michigan should be funded to test such promising restoration schemes as artificially induced destratification. Existing facilities should be used to the fullest extent.

18. A restoration project for Lakes Erie and Ontario and southern Lake Michigan should be undertaken as soon as the technology is available. The program should complement the implementation of effective pollution abatement technology in all the Great Lakes and must be managed to accommodate Federal, State, community, and private interests.

## G. Industrial Technology

### 1. Fishing and Aquaculture

The total annual production of the U.S. fishing industry has been static at four to six billion pounds for nearly 30 years, although the U.S. market is three times the U.S. catch and is growing rapidly. Further, the sustainable yield adjacent to the United States is estimated to be greater than 30 billion pounds. The U.S. fishing fleet is mixed in quality—partly antiquated, such as the New England ground fish fleet, and partly modern, as the West Coast tuna fleet and parts of the Gulf Coast shrimp fleet.

Fishermen spend an average of half of their total time at sea hunting fish, and in some fisheries considerably more. Nevertheless, government efforts to assist the industry have given greater emphasis on biological science, and less on search, location, and harvesting technology development.

Freshwater aquaculture of catfish and trout and estuarine aquaculture of oysters are examples of successful local U.S. industries with good growth potential. A strong market exists in the United States for quality sea food products many of which are adaptable to aquaculture. Open sea aquaculture, however, does not yet exist commercially.

Recommendations:

19. Fisheries production technology should be developed through greater emphasis on engineering to permit U.S. fishermen to supply a much greater fraction of the domestic market. An expanded program should be undertaken to improve vessels, fish catching gear, and methods. Laws governing fisheries management should focus on controlling the total catch rather than restricting the use of improved equipment and harvesting methods. For overfished stocks, emphasis should be placed on technical support of biological research and on modification of existing fishing equipment for use in other fisheries. For stocks not in danger of depletion, efforts should be concentrated on gear development, vessel design, survey, and fish location technology. A substantial share of the program budget should be used for contract studies by industry and private institutions.

20. The U.S. Government should sponsor continuing surveys of promising coastal and distant fishery resources, including sport fisheries, to determine the potential of under-utilized species, to provide information for fish location and harvesting equipment design applicable to these species, and to support negotiation of international fisheries agreements and treaties.

21. The promise of aquaculture should be pursued with such development efforts as selective breeding, control of temperature and nutrients, and containment techniques. Aquaculture projects should be established, in existing laboratories where feasible, to emphasize engineering applicable to freshwater, nearshore, and open sea systems.

## 2. Oil and Gas

Offshore oil and gas industry initiative has developed a major nongovernmental marine science and engineering program. Much of the resultant technology will be applicable to future Government and other industry ocean programs.

Offshore production continues to move into progressively greater depths. During 1969, exploratory drilling is expected in water depths of 1,300 feet and production established in as deep water as 400 feet. Within 10 years, such systems as remote control undersea core drilling rigs may be in

operation. Mainly because of power requirements exploration and production wells will continue to be drilled from the surface. An increasing number of production wells and fields will be completed beneath the surface, making increasing use of acoustically controlled undersea equipment.

Technology has so advanced that specially designed barges can weld, X-ray, externally coat, and lay pipelines. Five thousand miles of pipe, from small 2-inch flow lines to 26-inch trunk lines, now traverse the floor of the Gulf of Mexico. To date, pipe laying has been limited to 340 feet in medium diameter (12 inch) pipe and 100 feet in large diameter (48 inch) pipe.

Major oil spills from tankers have been a costly hazard, in some cases disastrous and causing international repercussions. Even such lesser oil discharges as cleaning tanks or pumping bilges on the high seas have detrimental effects on beaches and coastlines.

Recommendations:

22. A mechanism should be established to ensure optimum information exchange between the U.S. Government and the petroleum industry.

23. Results of such Government undersea technology programs as biomedicine to support advanced diving, fundamental undersea technology, and reconnaissance mapping and charting should be available to the petroleum industry to help expand operations to deeper water and reduce operation risks and costs. Technology efforts should be expanded to improve Government services in environmental prediction and modification, particularly regarding hurricanes and sediment behavior and transport.

24. The government must ensure development of improved methods to minimize the possibility of oil spills, optimize clean-up measures, and identify the responsible polluters. Contingency plans should be prepared to permit immediate action to contain and clean up major oil spills.

## 3. Chemical Extraction and Desalination

Magnesium metal, magnesium compounds, and bromine are extracted from sea water commercially, supplying 90, 34, and 50 per cent respectively of the U.S. market. Desalination effluents and high concentration anomalies, such as the Red Sea hot spots, may make it practical to extract other elements of even lower average concentrations. Worldwide, salt is the most important product extracted, with almost 30 per cent of the total world production being derived from sea water.

Desalination processes can be used for multiple purposes including the conversion of sea water and brackish water and for purification of polluted water. No single process is optimum for the divergent types of input water and output quantity and quality needed. Energy and capital investment costs dominate the economics of desalted water.

Recommendations:

**25. The present program to develop alternate desalting methods for differing applications should be expanded. Attention should be given to new chemical extraction technology which can be used with concentrated brines.**

**26. The U.S. Government's prime objective in its saline water program should continue to be the advancement of desalting technology, in contrast to the business of supplying water. The final step in developing promising new or improved processes should be based on two major approaches, both in cooperation with private industry: (1) sponsorship of construction and operation of prototype or demonstration plants and (2) participation with water supply agencies in constructing and operating such plants. Thus, State, municipal, and private water supply agencies would have an opportunity to utilize new desalting technology in a first-of-a-kind plant wherein the risk is shared through Government financial support.**

**27. The Government's desalination research and development program should be balanced to develop techniques to supply large-scale regional water needs, including metropolitan coastal facilities and ultimately agriculture; to develop more reliable and efficient small plants for beachfront hotels and islands and for small inland communities which must make use of brackish or polluted water supplies; and to develop systems to permit industrial and municipal re-use of waste water.**

## 4. Ocean Mining

Solid minerals exist in the form of deposits on the seafloor and within the bedrock. In each category the resources are extremely diverse in nature and value. Bottom deposits include shells, sand, phosphorite and manganese nodules, and gold and tin placers. Bedrock deposits include coal, sulphur, and iron ores. Technology for exploration and recovery of each is substantially different.

The only mineral recovery operations on the U.S. Continental Shelf are sand, gravel, and oyster shell dredging plus sulfur extraction. Deep ocean manganese nodules are known to contain substantial concentrations of nickel, copper, and cobalt. The technology for commercial nodule mining, however, has not yet been demonstrated. Future ocean mining may require submersible exploration vehicles and dredges; seafloor production, boring, and drilling rigs; ocean accessible installations in the bedrock; and high capacity vertical and horizontal transport systems.

Recommendation:

**28. Although the worldwide supply of land based mineral resources may be sufficient to the year 2000, it is essential for U.S. industry to make an early start in offshore exploration and production. To delineate offshore mineral reserves and provide the fundamental technology for future growth, the U.S. Government should establish a program to (1) prepare and publish reconnaissance scale bathymetric, geophysical, and geological maps of U.S. Continental Shelves and deeper areas, (2) establish favorable legal, political, and economic incentives to encourage industry to delineate further exploitable deposits and develop its own extraction technology, and (3) cooperate in developing undersea mineral exploration devices emphasizing more rapid geophysical exploration tools and improved deposit sampling equipment.**

## 5. Power Generation

Tides, waves, currents, and thermal differences are theoretically feasible sources of power in certain locations. Although some developments show promise, as yet no plant in the world is profitably generating power from these sources. Principal use of the sea in power generation probably will continue to be for dissipating waste heat from fossil or nuclear fueled power plants.

Recommendation:

**29. The Atomic Energy Commission and the new oceanic agency in cooperation with private industry should sponsor development and construction of an experimental continental shelf submerged nuclear power plant. The technology developed** would permit later construction of relatively small (5,000 to 10,000 kw) power sources to support undersea operations. A possible subsequent development would be huge stationary electric generating facilities (thousands of megawatts). Such large facilities will become increasingly important as coastal land grows scarce and expensive and as it becomes necessary to shift thermal pollution loads from the nearshore areas.

This chapter presents a number of important non-technical aspects that will influence the course of marine technology in the United States. These include (1) opportunities for the future, (2) importance, urgency, and rationale for U.S. leadership, (3) trends influencing marine development, (4) interrelationships among economic segments, (5) interrelationships of technical influences, and (6) influence of technology on the law of the sea.

Experience shows that forecasts of the near future tend to be overly optimistic and forecasts of the far future lack boldness. A look at the distant future and the benefits of a national ocean program envisions communities working and living in the oceans.

The importance, urgency, and rationale for U.S. leadership in ocean science and technology require that a national program be pursued vigorously. Although timing is critical, a crash program is not needed. The complexities of the undersea frontier require a modern store of knowledge for operations both on the continental shelves and in the deep oceans. In the progress to the shelves and the deep, science and technology will be constantly challenged. Well conceived and executed endeavors in science and technology have proved worthwhile in the past. National security, water pollution, and international affairs are important motives for U.S. leadership.

Several influences strongly pressure the Nation's advancement into the waters of the continental shelves and deep ocean. Just to maintain, nonetheless to improve, living standards of an increasing world population requires progressively more food, shelter, water, energy, and recreational resources. National needs include areas for further peaceful expansion, new opportunities to earn profits and establish new tax bases, reliable military security, and means for assisting developing nations to become self-supporting.

Although not always distinctly defined, science, engineering, and technology have interrelations essential to the national program, and they require reinforcement. There is an important interrelationship among the government, industry, and academic communities which requires an exchange of information and skilled personnel. The interrela-

tionship of the civilian and military sectors of society has problems relating to planning, information exchange, and security classification. Ocean activities will stimulate new international relationships; they can benefit this Nation and others.

Current law of the sea relates only to the ocean's surface. Inevitable technological progress will compel new legal codes when present surface-oriented laws fail to satisfy the needs of the undersea activities.

The rise and fall of great nations has invariably included a period of territorial expansion and acquisition. Nations failing to extend frontiers often fell victim to neighbors who pursued policies of expansion. The United States originated with 13 colonies on the Eastern seaboard and through purchase and settlement spread the American culture from the Atlantic to the Pacific.

Except Antarctica, no important land area today remains for peaceful expansion and settlement. Overpopulation and undernourishment are rapidly becoming a specter of the future, and man will turn to the sea for additional nourishment, material resources, and perhaps living space. Future generations may dwell on continental shelves, going ashore only to market the products of their undersea community and to procure items not available in the ocean. Atlantis may become not a myth of the past but a civilization of the future.

Complete, well planned exploration and intensive utilization are needed to establish firmly this new frontier. The United States should proceed now with this planet's final peaceful expansion.

## I. OPPORTUNITIES FOR THE FUTURE

The engineering and technology program recommended is aimed principally at opening the undersea frontier. Particularly important is the element of economical and continuous access, with strong emphasis on reducing the costs of at-sea operations to make ocean resources more available.

From the first, the Commission was directed to pioneer, experiment, and look to the future. Its mandate was to outline activity for the foreseeable future and to give guidance to the U.S. Government.

Fulfillment of technological potentials is a difficult task. It is hoped that the following two mission objectives will provide the guidelines to achievement. The United States should develop the technological base and capability:

—Within 10 years to **occupy** the U.S. territorial sea, **utilize** the U.S. Continental Shelf and slope to depths of 2,000 feet, and **explore** the ocean depths to 20,000 feet.

—Within 30 years to **manage** the U.S. Continental Shelf and slope to depths of 2,000 feet and **utilize** the ocean depths to 20,000 feet.

The two objectives are interrelated. The first provides the improved understanding and capability basic to ocean systems development. The second, during the period 1980 to 2000, visualizes extensive use of new techniques on U.S. Continental Shelf areas. In the deep oceans development of long-term operating capability will be stimulated by needs formulated from exploration.

By the year 2000, colonies on the sea floor will be commonplace because industries will operate profitably at sea and people will be there to support them. It is not difficult to conceive of fish harvesting systems or perhaps open water aquaculture. Much of the offshore oil and gas industry will be operating completely submerged, and very possibly mining will have overcome ocean exploitation problems. Chemical processing plants may well find deeper ocean conditions compatible with the needs of high pressure processes.

Although it may be easy to overestimate near-term progress, it is equally easy to underestimate the long term potential. By the year 2000, the U.S. industry with the highest sales volume, employment, and earnings may well be one intimately associated with the oceans.

Beyond the economic considerations of a commitment to the oceans, there are tremendous social, political, scientific, and military implications for the 1980-2000 period. Water pollution can be checked; water quality restoration—initially in fresh water areas and later in coastal regions—will have a firm beginning. Although during this period the problem of thermal pollution will become fully apparent, technology will permit

placement of heat generating operations at sea where adequate cooling capacity is available. Moving large stationary power plants to sea will free high value urban land for other use.

During this same period the knowledge will be acquired upon which to establish reasonable water quality standards satisfying both commercial and recreational interests. Beaches once closed because of pollution may be reopened, and coastal engineering technology will be available to restore damaged beaches, construct artificial islands, and otherwise enhance the usefulness of coastal lands.

Improved technology will benefit greatly scientific effort, perhaps allowing basic discoveries to be made that will profoundly affect the future. The scientist will have convenient and economical access to entire oceans.

Finally, the stage will be set for a new period of 21st century seapower, a period characterized not only by a powerful Navy in the military sense, but an internationally strong and respected Nation. If the Nation accepts the challenge of this report, there will be established an increased opportunity to solve some of the difficult social problems of population, poverty, and malnutrition. The United States should lead in meeting the challenge of the undersea frontier.

## II. IMPORTANCE, URGENCY, AND RATIONALE FOR U.S. LEADERSHIP

There is little question that mankind eventually will make massive use of the oceans for natural resources, transportation, recreation, and national security. A well-conceived program is needed—a national program that is thoughtfully scheduled, carefully executed, and wisely balanced with other national interests. The rate at which man becomes economically involved with the oceans may be debated, but the need for his involvement is a certainty. The United States must learn to court the oceans, eliciting responses which reinforce the material, aesthetic, and social ends the Nation is striving to achieve.

Offshore oil has demonstrated its viability. With initial success, the industry can look forward confidently, and an increasing industry contribution to the economy can be expected. Although the world supply of mineral resources on land appears generally sufficient to the year 2000, leadtimes require an early start. Offshore exploration and pilot production are required to delineate the more accessible reserves and to develop the technology base to meet accelerating needs.

Gradually ocean industries collectively will generate a larger and larger fraction of the gross national product and will help the United States maintain its competitive position in the world marketplace. It is easier and cheaper to maintain a position of leadership than to regain lost initiative.

More intelligent stewardship of resources will be required as utilization of the oceans increases. This implies improved knowledge, best achieved through an aggressive basic marine science program. Improved scientific understanding of the oceans also is needed to support a continuing advance in technology, to make longer-term weather predictions, to realize food production potentials, and to determine future military usefulness. Science has returned dividends in the past, and will in the future.

Now is the time to reverse the trend of degradation of the environment. Beaches have been closed on Lake Erie; ocean beaches have been rendered useless by oil slicks; oyster beds have been condemned; and city water front areas have been blighted by raw sewage and chemicals dumped into harbors. Technology should be extended so these problems can be solved economically.

The state-of-the-art is such that it is possible to consider a law requiring municipal and industrial intakes to be installed downstream from their outfalls, in effect putting the water user in the same position as others downstream. There is no reason why a user cannot return water of a quality equal to that which he takes from a stream.

The world's richest Nation need not live in its own filth, but should set an example by directly facing these problems rather than leaving greater problems to future generations. The technology should be developed to eliminate the economic penalty of waste treatment, making it possible for many activities to profit by reprocessing wastes into marketable products. This quantitative benefit would be in addition to the qualitative values of beauty, clean water, and recreation.

The net effect of modern communication and transportation has been to deny the oceans their historic role as natural barriers. Interaction between nations will increase as technology allows

more ocean resources to be harvested economically.

A stable and predictable legal environment will be required. Technology should be considered in framing laws to ensure their enforceability and realistic applicability to prospective activities. The latter quality is particularly important because development and utilization of ocean resources involve major capital investment.

In some cases, the most valuable assistance the United States can give less advanced nations is the technological knowhow to develop their own industry. Technology can be expanded to support profitable ocean exploitation and meaningful international scientific programs.

National security is much more than classic military might—submarines, missiles, aircraft carriers, and destroyers. In its broadest sense, it is the action a nation must take to maintain its position in world affairs. The United States does not and should not fulfill all its needs from resources within its boundaries. More than 98 per cent of U.S. international commerce is carried by ships. Control to assure free use of the seas is basic to national security. But such control of the sea is relative, not absolute, applying equally to friend and foe.

Seapower is best built on a sound base of industrial and commercial ocean development, providing knowledge and trained manpower for times of military need. This emphasis would minimize Navy expenditures for in-house development, yet would provide a viable foundation for the future. The Navy must keep informed constantly of non-military ocean activity. Its development program should emphasize long range items necessary to national security, such as deep submergence systems, which do not now attract a large amount of commercial activity.

## III. TRENDS INFLUENCING MARINE DEVELOPMENT

The marine environment will become increasingly important, and national interest in and emphasis on the exploration and utilization of the undersea frontier will increase accordingly. Effective planning of technology development must be based on estimates of future trends and needs induced by both natural and man-made influences.

Barring a major war, world requirements for such basics as water, food, housing, and energy can be estimated reasonably well to the year 2000.

However, it is difficult to make long-range projections of such qualitative factors as consumer tastes, political and legal arrangements and economic progress. It is essentially today's technology that will be employed to meet such requirements during the next 10 years. Beyond that period planning becomes more difficult because of the unpredictability of technological advancements, especially real breakthroughs. Yet, when national interests have dictated the need for both adequate funding and high priority emphasis, solutions to difficult technological problems have been more rapid than most conceptual planners visualized.

Technology can provide a better way of life. A higher standard of living for a doubled world population in the year 2000 will require more than twice the power, fresh water, and raw materials consumed today. The material demands of higher living standards are vividly illustrated by the fact that the United States with five per cent of the world's population consumes almost half the power and raw materials produced by the entire world. So that the United States cannot be accused of taking a disproportionate share of world resources, it is prudent to encourage development of technology for new offshore petroleum, mineral, food, and other resources, in effect greatly expanding the world resource base.

For the near term, national security will be the most compelling influence forcing advancement of marine technology. However, offshore petroleum expenditures are growing more rapidly than defense expenditures. A large portion of the effort will have both civilian and military application, suggesting a need for strong cooperation between the two.

The quest for wealth and profit will help advance marine technology. Advanced technology will provide the key to more economic utilization of the undersea environment. Such assets of the sea as buoyancy, sound transmission, and a limitless heat sink will influence technological development.

Technology development has allowed concurrent achievement of a shorter work week and a higher standard of living. As this trend continues, Americans will earn higher disposable incomes and more leisure time. These will accelerate the need for additional coastal recreation areas.

Impairment of activities by pollution will become more obvious and will motivate increased programs of abatement, enforcement, and restoration. Pollution, like inflation, goes relatively unheeded for a time but has enormous long term implications. Before the end of the century, a significant amount of national energy must be directed to protecting and enhancing the environment.

Technological knowhow incorporated in most U.S. products gives the United States a great advantage in the world market. To retain this advantage the United States must commit itself to the development of the technology needed to open the undersea frontier as a new source of products and materials.

## IV. INTERRELATIONSHIPS AMONG PARTICULAR SEGMENTS

Technology development must be accomplished in a realistic environment subject to economic, social, political, scientific, international, and military pressures. Decisions on program activity should be preceded by objective discussions carefully weighing technical and policy features. Important areas of interrelationship have been identified among economic segments: (1) government - industry - academic, (2) civilian - military, and (3) relationships among nations.

### A. Government—Industry—Academic

Government's traditional role in industrial development has been to provide protection for business investments and information of a scientific or technical nature. The State Department, Department of Defense, U.S. Coast Guard, Department of the Interior, and the U.S. Patent Office provide protection for marine industries in many forms: physical survey data pertinent to mineral deposits, general environmental information, and statistical data.

Protection of business investments is of particular concern to those industries interested in exploiting the continental shelves. Because exploration and survey information must precede exploitation of the shelves, broad surveys of the shelves must be given high priority in any national ocean program. Legal rights of industries operating on the continental shelves are particularly vague. Conflicts over jurisdiction among individuals, States, and the U.S. Government and between the United States and foreign nations over sovereignty on the shelf have created a climate of legal uncertainty hindering private investment and technological development.

Various agencies of the U.S. Government have programs in ocean research and development. In particular the Navy has recently increased its efforts through establishment of the Deep Submergence Systems Project and the Deep Ocean Technology Program. The Sea Grant Program, under way in 1968, is expanding Federal Government support of applied marine sciences.

The present relationship among the government, industry, and academic world in marine programs needs strengthening. Expanding interests of industry in the ocean environment and the importance of these interests to the economic well-being of the United States argue for a strong non-military Government ocean services program and a guarantee of offshore protection. Government-sponsored technology development efforts should emphasize improved and less costly methods, thereby enabling ocean industries to operate profitably and also provide increased tax revenues.

Fundamental technology development cannot be effective without close coordination with the industrial and academic sectors. A continuing mechanism should be established through which the industrial, financial, and academic communities readily can advise on marine science, engineering, and technology. Advice is needed in fundamental technology, facilities, manpower, and national goals and projects. More specifically, a relationship similar to that which existed between the National Advisory Committee for Aeronautics (NACA) and its advisory panels would be desirable.

## B. Civilian—Military

Effective civilian-military interchange of technology is obviously useful to both parties. Independent research and development programs conducted by defense contractors normally have two objectives: (1) keeping a company's products and components technically advanced to maintain a competitive position and (2) applying technical skills and experience to solving known military problems. Military technology developments often are applicable to civilian endeavors.

Often a simple solution to a technical problem can open the door to major systems applications. However, because of security classification, advances in the state-of-the-art can be withheld from other potential users. Overclassification unnecessarily slows communications and can cause unintentional duplication of effort when civilian industry is not apprised of military developments.

Devising means of transferring technology and bringing about utilization of that technology for purposes other than those for which it was developed have become activities of national importance requiring continued high level attention. The transfer problem can occur within either the civilian or military sector as well as between them.

Research and development in the marine sciences constitutes a rapidly increasing and relatively unexploited resource. Effective transfer of technology can increase the rate of economic growth, create new employment opportunities, and aid the international competitive position of American industry.

Furthermore, technology is a tool that the United States can use to aid other nations striving to improve their standards of living. Ocean technology is particularly suitable to technology transfer. First, marine activities are global in perspective and application. The Gulf Stream that washes Florida shores eventually influences the climate and ecology of England, Norway, and the North Sea. Second, marine problems are relatively new to the community of advanced science and engineering, and few institutional barriers have been erected.

Traditional means of transferring technology include the movement of knowledgeable people and technical literature coupled with the normal activities of libraries, technical journals, professional symposiums, corporations, and governments. These are key activities, but because of the extreme technical diversity of the oceans and the large numbers of present and potential users of marine data, more is needed. It is necessary to construct and implement channels of distribution and methods of retrieval of these technical data, particularly from government to industrial users.

A special problem exists with small business which historically has had difficulty obtaining security clearances and need-to-know on classified programs. Small companies often lack general knowledge of information sources of the Federal Government. Progressive companies prepare unsolicited proposals to demonstrate their expertise. However, unless industry is aware of project needs, time and money may be wasted in submitting proposals for duplicative efforts.

The U.S. Government role in technology transfer must be based on (1) a positive policy that the release of marine science and technology is a legitimate function and (2) an implementation of the policy in the agencies concerned with fundamental technology, ocean exploration and survey, and ocean services. For example, the National Aeronautics and Space Administration has accomplished the transfer of technical data by establishing technology utilization officers at its various activities, placing responsibility in an identifiable office or individual. However, great care must be taken in the treatment of patentable data to assure an incentive through ownership for the developer who risks funds in furthering his invention.

The Navy role in dissemination of technical data is particularly important because of the magnitude of its ocean research and development program. It should be recognized that there are penalties to both under- and over-classification. What is most needed is a consistent classification policy directed toward optimizing the technical and military superiority of the United States. Since only the Navy can judge the implications of its data, it must carry out this function with the utmost care.

## C. Relationships Among Nations

From the earliest times the oceans have supported bonds of commerce and culture. However, historic relationships are changing, accelerated by advances in marine technology, enabling nations to conduct activities farther from home and in deeper water. Multinational communication is necessary to the beneficial utilization of the sea because of the international character of marine science, the sheer magnitude of the unexplored undersea frontier, and the free use tradition of open ocean areas. The size, complexity, and variability of the marine environment emphasize the importance of international cooperation.

As a basis for harmonious international marine exploration and resource development, certain premises should underlie national policies and programs. Excellence, experience, and capabilities in marine science and technology exist in several nations and cooperation can be beneficial to the United States.

In the development of ocean resources, major capital investments must be protected. Uncertainties in interpretation and application of existing international law may result in conflicts between nations, particularly with regard to the width of territorial seas, rights of innocent passage, and the exploitation of ocean resources. A legal framework is required to prevent conflicts and to preserve the traditional freedom of the sea.

U.S. marine technology developments should consider both international competition and cooperation. Where consistent with the national interest, programs should encourage increased cooperation and data exchange among ocean scientists and engineers of all nations. The U.S. should consider advanced marine technology as a prime export product and as a foreign aid tool to assist developing countries to strengthen their capabilities for using the ocean and its resources as a means to economic progress. The International Panel proposes an international framework for ocean exploration in its report.

## V. TECHNICAL INTERRELATIONSHIPS

In addition to economic, social, political, international, and military pressures, interrelated technical areas also influence marine technology development. Included are those among science, engineering, and technology and those between outerspace and hydrospace development.

### A. Science—Engineering—Technology

Using modern technology, man can explore and understand increasingly greater portions of the marine environment. Improvements in technology lead to an ability to monitor, measure, and predict environmental phenomena more accurately. Designs for and operations of such complex undersea military systems as those employed in an anti-submarine warfare and undersea command and control are dominated by acoustical conditions. In fact, almost all undersea activities are heavily influenced by environmental considerations.

A great scientific effort is needed. There should be close interaction of the scientist with the engineer to facilitate the effort. The overall development of marine science has suffered from the lack of communication between the two, and the present relative paucity of knowledge stems in large measure from the past lack of adequate equipment. Essential in studying or exploiting the ocean for any purpose are the necessary tools. Despite the need for improved marine engineering and technology support, engineering institutions have not emphasized problems of the oceans.

Oceanographic research operations are costly in terms of manpower, especially considering the limited number of oceanographers. In 1966, the United States graduated only 24 doctorate level oceanographers compared to 100 for the Soviets. Since manpower resources are limited, improved tools and equipment should be emphasized. Both parties, the scientist and engineer, are responsible for better cooperation in the future.

Insufficient funds allocated to scientific projects have generally made impossible improved engineering support. It is probable that the scientist will demand the better tools and equipment technology can provide. This is underscored by the fact that scientists at the Woods Hole Oceanographic Institution waited in an almost endless line to use the *Alvin* submersible.

The science-engineering interaction also works the other way. Although Sir John Baker may have been correct when he said, "Science earns no dividends until it has been through the mills of technology," development of new technology often waits for scientific breakthroughs. For example, aquaculture will benefit from scientific advances in fish genetics. Deep sea nodule mining will benefit from understanding the ocean mineral precipitation process.

## B. Outerspace—Hydrospace

Much has been said about the fallout of space technology applicable to the ocean environment. Meteorological satellites continuously observing global weather patterns obtain critical forecasting data from unpopulated oceanic regions. Communications satellites have spanned vast ocean areas.

Unfortunately, observations are limited to ocean surface features. The totally different subsurface environment usually means totally new solutions to problems. Aerospace talents and philosophy of approach can and are being applied to ocean problems, especially in fundamental technology, systems engineering, and systems management. Although many problems such as navigation and communication have technical similarities, actual hardware solutions are often very different.

Operational designs cannot be assessed without environmental data. Instrumentation, sensor, recording, storing, and processing systems are essential for environmental profiling. For example, determining effects of marine life on acoustical properties requires special marine test equipment. Bottom bearing strength, shear and plastic flow strength, core samples, turbidity susceptibility, bottom stability, and seismic activity data are needed to establish design criteria. Space instrumentation cannot serve these needs. Also, space simulation facilities which emphasize low pressures have little application to the high pressure needs of hydrospace.

Aerospace power source needs have brought fuel cells out of the research laboratory and transformed them into practical devices. They have advanced considerably the state-of-the-art and have provided impetus to the fuel cell industry for lower cost construction, standard sizes, and mass production techniques. These advancements have provided a technological base from which development of undersea power systems can proceed at a greatly reduced cost. However, specialized development is still necessary to adapt this basic development to the marine environment.

Aerospace technology has contributed structural design techniques, high strength-to-weight metals, and composite structures. This technology has been applied to design and fabrication of submersible pressure hulls and hard tanks, outer hull or fairing structures, and flotation spheres. Advanced pressure hull design entails the use of detail stress analysis, shell buckling theory, and experimental stress analysis techniques largely developed in the aerospace industry. Rocket motor technology involving flaw detection, alloying, and processing of materials has been used in development work for deep submersibles.

Titanium is an example of a high-strength metal developed by the aerospace industry, but it requires substantial modification before application to deep ocean vehicles. Space technology has not concerned itself with the unique ocean needs of resistance to stress corrosion and crack propagation. Fabrication and welding techniques for thick sections, critical to deep submergence programs, have not been an aerospace requirement.

Deep ocean vehicles are limited in pressure hull volume, requiring many electrical components mounted externally. Those retained inside the pressure hull must conform to strict requirements on heat generation, size, weight, and electromagnetic interference. Aerospace technology in the areas of solid-state devices and switches, miniaturization and packaging design, circuit design, and reduction of interference effects is applicable to ocean vehicle problems. However, space technology does not provide answers to such electrical system requirements as penetration of pressure hulls and water-tight electrical connectors.

Frequently, aerospace-developed hydraulic pumps, motors, and valves have been utilized directly off-the-shelf, but usually these have been unreliable in the undersea environment. Aerospace technology has led to advances in viscosity index, oxidation and corrosion inhibition, long term storage, and high and low temperature characteristics bearing on the successful application of hydraulics to marine systems. However, there are no hydraulic systems or qualified hydraulic fluids currently functioning at high pressures up to the 16,500 psi required for deep ocean systems.

Reliable communications is critical to effective diver and submersible operations. Unlike radio and telemetry methods and equipment available worldwide for surface communications, undersea operations depend upon acoustics and cables as the primary means of information transfer. Underwater sound transmission suffers from refraction, attenuation, and limitations of spectral range.

For rendezvous and mating of submerged vehicles, six degrees of freedom are involved, just as for a Gemini-Agena docking. However, an additional complication under water is variable ocean currents. Controllers have been developed from lessons learned in aircraft and spacecraft to provide submersible pilots with controls for rotation in pitch, roll, and yaw and translation in surge, sway, and heave. Aerospace technology has led to the use of a modified computer and a modified inertial

guidance system from the Polaris program in the Deep Submergence Rescue Vehicle.

A parallel is readily apparent between space and undersea life support requirements. Work in submarine non-regenerable life support systems served as the basis for the original systems for spacecraft, resulting in advanced non-regenerable systems. This knowledge is now being used to provide sophisticated life support systems for small deep submersibles with comparable volume and power limitations.

Space technology can contribute little to the special certification requirements and procedures needed for undersea vehicle pressure hull materials, hard tank structure, penetration fittings, and piping. However, common safety requirements exist for crew protection from toxic fumes, fire, smoke, and atmospheric contaminants.

Indeed, aerospace technology has been useful in solving ocean systems problems. However, the degree of applicability should not be over stressed since once the undersea environment is penetrated, new technological solutions are usually needed.

## VI. INFLUENCE OF TECHNOLOGY ON THE LAW OF THE SEA

Although the trends and relationships discussed above will affect technology development, probably the reverse will be true in the law of the sea. Society tends to move as an organic whole and the advancement of technology is inevitable.

Laws must be tailored to the needs of society and to the technology which is integral to their enforcement. The technology of the sea will undergo drastic change and that change has barely begun. Saturation diving, submersible vehicles, and undersea habitation will become commonplace. The essence of the change will be the replacement of present ocean surface technology with totally submerged technology.

There will be critical problems to solve, but when they are solved, the ability to work in the subsea environment will become increasingly easy.

In the undersea area, law must respond to a rapidly developing technology. The law will be greatly challenged to keep pace.

The following ideas on organization represent the input to the Commission from its Panel on Marine Engineering and Technology. An effort has been made to emphasize only comments that relate to the organizational needs to promote and encourage progress in marine engineering and technology. However, it is recognized that several thoughts would affect much broader areas of future marine programs.

## I. NATIONAL PERSPECTIVE

Overall national management of ocean resource development and the related supporting marine engineering and technology need strengthening. Because of the decentralized character of ocean activities, the important contributions of the States and regions, private enterprise, and the academic community must be recognized. These complement the well-established role of the U.S. Government.

To date major Government contributions in marine engineering and technology have come from the Navy, chiefly because of its requirements for knowledge and skills associated with the oceans. However, the past two decades have seen efforts of the private sector, led in this area by the petroleum industry, expand such that their expenditures are greatly in excess of non-military Government efforts.

The need for national participation as opposed to a predominantly Government approach to marine programs became clearly apparent during the panel's investigations. The States and regions, private enterprise, the academic community, and the U.S. Government all have vital roles to play. These roles can be responsive and coordinated only if they are provided with a means for cooperative long-range planning and National guidance.

## II. NATIONAL ORGANIZATIONAL STRUCTURE

### A. General

With the diverse scope of national activities in the ocean it is unwise and impractical to consolidate all U.S. Government activities associated with the oceans into one organization. Rather, it is necessary to take advantage of the competence that presently exists and to selectively cluster where appropriate to provide additional strength. Regardless of the amount of clustering, the Navy should remain separate to support its military obligations. In the civilian sector several organizations have limited interests in the ocean and therefore could not fit logically into a single civilian marine agency.

The panel feels two basic principles must be satisfied to respond to the diverse character of marine activities and the critical need for advanced technology to support future activities. First, a mechanism must be established to provide national perspective and guidance to the Nation's engineering and technology efforts. Second, recognition must be made of the necessity of continual additions to fundamental technology. This latter principle leads to the importance of assuring that funds to support fundamental technology development are adequately distinguished from agency general operating funds so that a steady and continuing fundamental technology program can be assured without interruption.

### B. National Advisory Committee for the Oceans (NACO)

It is essential that a mechanism be established that can ensure orderly development and execution of a national ocean program. Such a mechanism should be responsible for providing advice on the planning and coordination of a national program including ocean science, technology, environmental services, and ocean resource development. It would be concerned with the marine programs of all U.S. Government agencies, States and regions, private enterprise, and the academic community and would provide a continuing statutory means for furnishing a representative input from all sectors. Specifically, the panel recommends a National Advisory Committee for the Oceans. Regardless of action taken to consolidate Federal Government agencies, this committee is needed.

## 1. Functions

The panel believes the committee could most usefully focus its advice in such areas as the following:

—Review and advise on updating the 10-year objectives of national ocean programs.

—Assess current levels of activity in terms of accomplishing the 10-year objectives.

—Identify deficiencies and recommend assignment of responsibilities to rectify them.

—Recommend means to eliminate unintentional duplication of effort.

—Review and offer a national perspective to the plans and budget requests of the U.S. Government agencies by taking into account efforts outside the Government.

—Recommend lead agencies for marine programs having multi-agency interests, and recommend whether specific marine programs can best be undertaken by the Navy, by the new consolidation of appropriate existing agencies, or by an agency not included in the civilian consolidation.

—Offer guidance and recommend important new ocean programs and facilities for the overall national program, making effective use of the competence of both private and Government organizations.

—Promote means for collecting, processing, and disseminating pertinent technical information.

—Recommend an adequate level of programs and facilities for marine education and training.

—Anticipate, focus attention on, discuss, and recommend the resolution of multiple-user conflicts.

—Respond to requests for advice from the President and U.S. Government agencies with marine activities.

—Help to ensure that the national program has proper and continual visibility to State and municipal governments, private enterprise, the academic community, and especially to the Congress and the public.

—Serve, when appropriate, as a channel of communications and a focal point in the plans and arrangements for international programs.

—Submit to the President and the Congress an assessment of the national ocean program, including a review of the activities of the oceanic agency. The report is to be made at intervals not less frequently than every two years.

—Generate pertinent activities on its own consistent with its overall responsibilities.

As can be seen from the above list, a primary function of this organization would be to advise (1) the new oceanic agency, (2) the Navy, (3) the Army Corps of Engineers, and (4) other U.S. Government agencies with marine interests. Advice should be provided on such matters as fundamental technology, facilities, manpower, National Projects, scientific investigations, and oceanographic operations. The unique feature of the committee will be the ease of reciprocal information transfer among the U.S. Government, States and regions, private enterprise, and academic institutions.

## 2. Membership

It is recommended that this advisory committee consist of 15 official members representing private enterprise, the States and regions, and the academic community. The chairman should be selected from outside the U.S. Government. In addition to the 15 official members, U.S. Government representatives should be designated official observers. This would assure that the committee was aware of the programs and problems of the U.S. Government marine agencies. All members would be appointed by the President with the advice and consent of the Senate and would serve fixed overlapping terms. This committee would be supported by a full-time executive director and appropriate staff.

The members from industry should be drawn primarily from the users of the sea such as those engaged in the transportation, petroleum, fishing, mining, desalination, and recreation industries. Those industries that supply hardware and services also should be represented.

The State and region members should be drawn from the Pacific, Atlantic, Gulf Coast, and the

Great Lakes areas. The members from the academic community should be drawn from universities with ocean programs. The U.S. Government members should be chosen to represent its diverse marine interests.

## 3. Structure

The advisory committee should be supplemented by as many subcommittees or panels as might be required to deal with specific topics or areas of national concern requiring specialized knowledge. It is recommended that the parent committee form an executive board comprised of the chairman, and one member from each of the four groups—industry, U.S. Government, States and regions, and the academic community—to expedite operations between the formal full committee meetings.

The advisory committee should be established by statute and provided with funds for its administrative operations and for accomplishing the functions listed above.

The panel considers the formation of this committee a critical requirement. The recommendation is intended to enlist a cooperative relationship between all sectors of the economy and is characteristic of programs utilized in opening new frontiers. Indeed, it is intended to include key characteristics of the historic programs so successful in developing the American railroad, agriculture, and aircraft industries.

## III. U.S. GOVERNMENT ORGANIZATIONAL STRUCTURE

### A. General

To ensure optimum and continuing contributions from the U.S. Government to the development of a national program, a stronger non-military input is needed. A new marine program would be advanced and strengthened, if it could build upon a consolidation of those appropriate existing agencies with primary missions and tasks in the ocean. This consolidation would support the very important new civilian technology development group and would complement the Navy deep submergence and ocean engineering programs. In many cases the existing competence, facilities, and experience of the Navy should be drawn upon to support missions of national importance.

### B. New Civilian Ocean Agency

A new, adequately funded civilian oceanic agency should be established within the U.S. Government to concentrate in one agency appropriate civilian groups with primary roles and missions in the oceans.

A new civilian technology development group should be created within the agency to support fundamental technology. The fundamental technology program should be managed by this new marine technology group and should utilize when appropriate the resources and facilities of existing agencies and the private sector.

### C. Interagency Coordinating Mechanism

To complement and support the efforts of the agency and NACO and to recognize the fact that many marine activities would still be located outside any consolidation, it is recommended that an interagency coordinating mechanism be established and chaired by the head of the new civilian agency. This mechanism would ensure the inclusion of the interests of all Federal agencies with marine programs not included in the proposed consolidation.

### D. Navy Role

The Navy is in a position to contribute greatly to advanced marine engineering and technology related to a national ocean program. It is recommended that the Navy be given an expanded role recognizing the support it can provide to the national program in areas closely related to its competence, facilities, and experience.

Even with an increasing involvement of non-military users, the Navy is the logical organization to support many of the overall national needs of marine engineering and technology. The following statements of high ranking leaders of the Department of Defense and the Office of the Secretary of the Navy reinforce this conclusion:

*If national oceanographic objectives require it, the Department of Defense is willing to request funds from Congress for work only marginally related to defense needs, but for which the Department of Defense is in the best position to manage because of technical skills, facilities, or organization. The direction for utilization of these funds could come from a non-Department of Defense organization if this is judged to be the best course.*[1]

*The Navy is proud of the role it played in leading the revolution in oceanography and of the indispensable support it has given so many of the programs directed by other federal and private agencies. The Navy believes that a vigorous, well defined, and multifaceted oceanographic program is clearly in the national interest. It, therefore, is prepared and expects to participate in all areas where Navy experience and facilities may be of value to the nation.*[2]

*In my mind these programs (undersea technology programs) can best be described as the development of technology leading toward the occupation and exploitation of the ocean bottom and the deep ocean. Although our primary objectives are military exploitation, the technological knowhow developed by these programs is identical for all types of exploitation.*[3]

The above statements were used to guide the Navy Deep Submergence/Ocean Engineering Program Planning Group. This group recommended a substantial increase in the Navy undersea efforts. It is also apparent that a more fully responsive Navy contribution to the national effort in the oceans requires:

—Establishment within the Department of Defense of a strong primary military mission in undersea technology to meet present and future threats.

—A clearly-stated Navy mission to support national marine programs which will evoke the support of the Congress, responsible civilian leaders, and the general public.

—A recognition of the contribution which can be made by the use of Navy capabilities in international, economic, political, scientific, and technological fields.

—A definition of security requirements that will enable the civilian sector to derive maximum advantage of Navy programs in technology with realistic concern for national security needs.

Therefore, to capitalize on the assets of the Navy, selected national missions should be assigned and adequate funds should be allocated to the Navy.

## IV. FOCAL POINT IN THE LEGISLATIVE BRANCH

The U.S. Government's ocean program is within the scope of numerous committees and subcommittees of the Congress,[4] each concerned with a portion of the oceanographic program. Thus, oceanography and ocean engineering have lacked a clear cut channel of effective communication with the Congress. Many committees of the Congress receive fragmentary information on the ocean program, usually small parts of the presentations of the many departments and agencies having some ocean responsibilities and missions in addition to other large responsibilities.

The situation is even worse regarding Congressional consideration of ocean appropriations. Ocean appropriations are a very small part of Defense, Commerce, Interior, AEC, and other department budget requirements. Usually, no specific ocean program is presented to the Appropriations Committee, but when it is, the description is disjointed.

The unsatisfactory Congressional overviews of the ocean program probably will become worse unless changes are made. It is necessary to create a Congressional committee or a Joint House-Senate Committee for Marine Affairs to hear the entire national program—including the parts of the States, industry, and the academic community—as well as the total U.S. Government program with emphasis on its role in the national program. The Congress should be asked to authorize the Government program and endorse the total national program. Presentations should be made to a new oceanic sub-committee of the House Appropriations Committee.

The reports and advice made available by the proposed National Advisory Committee for the Oceans should assist in the development of a clearer focus in the Congress.

[1] Statement of the Honorable John S. Foster, Jr., Director of Defense Research and Engineering, Feb. 24, 1967.

[2] Statement of the Honorable Paul R. Ignatius, Secretary of the Navy, to the Navy League Convention, Honolulu, April 26, 1968.

[3] Statement of the Honorable Robert H. B. Baldwin, Under Secretary of the Navy, at the Fourth U.S. Navy Symposium on Military Oceanography, Washington, D.C., May 11, 1967.

[4] For details, see chart between pages 32 and 33 of hearings of House Subcommittee on Oceanography—National Oceanographic Program, 1965, Serial No. 82-83.

Seapower, defined by Admiral Mahan many years ago, encompasses all elements contributing to national strength—natural resources, industrial capacity, manpower, economic power, geographic situation, and cultural status. These many dimensions serve a nation in both peace and war.

The United States stands on the threshold of a rekindled interest in the oceans. A new age of seapower, important to the United States and the world, can be achieved by technological readiness to utilize the sea.

—*Cultural status.* National prestige is an image of strength or lack of it in the eyes of other nations. This is of major concern, because (1) no nation wants to be a loser, (2) as a nation's prestige falls, other nations begin to suspect it of weakness, (3) other nations do not want to be associated with a loser, and (4) as other nations progressively withdraw their adherence and support, the trend toward becoming a loser accelerates. This is a vicious circle—strength begets strength and weakness, weakness.

A nation's prestige or cultural status adheres closely to the vigor of its research and technological activities. The world community is well aware that today's scientific and technological strength is the direct source of tomorrow's economic and military strength. Space activities have illustrated this truth. However, activities in the marine environment inherently promise far greater economic, military, and prestige rewards than in space. A great nation ignoring this runs the grave risk of falling into weakness.

—*The geographic situation.* Over 70 per cent of the earth is covered by water. The last major dry land frontier was discovered in 1492, when the world population was 350 million. Today with 10 times the population, the world is forced to turn again to the sea for new sources of food, minerals, and energy.

In the undersea frontier, many nations with widely divergent geographies, needs, and technological capabilities are involved. Achieving the technology to occupy new territory and modify world geography would give a nation the potential to make valid and defensible claims with an excellent position to counter claims by those not having the technology. A technology base must be established for the United States to enter the undersea frontier.

—*Economic power.* New technology determines which country will be the world source of various products. U.S. domination of the world aircraft and computer markets is an excellent example; Japanese strength in fishing and shipbuilding is another. New industries have been created in a short time by such technological breakthroughs as xerography, polaroid photography, solid state electronics, offshore drilling, and desalination. Technology and the economics of production and exploration are inseparably linked. A strong technology base will likely lead to new marine industries.

—*Manpower.* An improved technology requires the continual upgrading of the manpower necessary to fabricate, operate, and maintain the systems utilizing the undersea frontier. Manpower of various skills and interests will be required. Some will find employment in the actual marine environment, while many more will provide critically needed support functions that can be accomplished only on the land. The requisite manpower with the tools and equipment provided by technology will rapidly alter the ocean from an area of dreams to a site of action.

—*Industrial capacity.* Volume production can work wonders in reducing costs. American industrial capacity has met great challenges. A highly refined automobile can be bought for less than $2,500. Should it not be possible to build a class of exploration vehicles with 20 horsepower propulsion systems, life support, and unsophisticated communication electronics for $50,000 each?

—*Natural Resources.* Low-cost underwater vehicles could open a prospecting era eclipsing the California gold rush. Exploring and mapping the sea bottom might be accomplished in much less time than now thought necessary. Support of a technology base for low-cost, reliable systems development could hasten the exploitation of the natural resources in the undersea frontier.

*—Technology plateau.* Much has been expressed in the popular press about a technological plateau. To the contrary, the panel agrees with the remarks by Dr. John S. Foster, Director of Defense Research and Engineering, before Congressional hearings in early 1968:

*There is no technological plateau now nor is one about to be created. We are convinced that research and exploratory development effort requires increased support during the next few years to ensure many options—a margin of safety—against any technological challenge.*

Dr. Foster also warned against relying too heavily on technical forecasting instead of sound research and exploratory development. He noted that those predicting the future of science have usually been far too conservative.

In the sections of Chapter 5 which follow, an assessment of the current situation and some ideas on future marine technology needs are presented. Recommendations are made at the end of each subdivision. In most cases, the recommendations are those the panel would like undertaken in the near future. Longer-term recommendations reflect judgments on potentially rewarding advanced technology not necessarily required for today's operations.

The potentials discussed throughout this report are critically dependent on the discoveries and knowhow generated by ocean science and technology. A substantial investment to extend and consolidate this fundamental knowledge promises handsome rewards in terms of sufficient resources, enhanced economic vigor, improved strategic position, a better way of life, and a stronger national defense. All this is the promise—the threat is that it will be underestimated or overlooked.

## I. Fundamental Technology

Step one in the capability development cycle for marine technology is base-building to establish the knowledge and means to explore and utilize the undersea frontier and improve the U.S. world competitive position. A solid program to advance fundamental technology is needed for developing elements and processes that can be combined into useful ocean components, subsystems, and systems.

While an excellent base already exists—so much so that the panel is convinced that the United States can achieve the goals set forth in this report—many categories require further development, a lesser number require extensive effort, and others require little advancement. This section concentrates on the most critical fundamental technology needs, to which the panel has assigned the following order of priority:

*—Survey equipment and instrumentation.* The Nation's most urgent needs in undersea development are for knowledge of the ocean's living and non-living resources and the technology to determine quickly and efficiently their potential. What is generally available must be known before it is utilized, ignored, wasted, or deeded away.

*—Power sources.* No single power source will meet all the power level and endurance requirements of undersea tasks. A variety of power sources is needed.

*—External machinery systems and equipment.* Undersea technology will be abundantly rewarded by developing systems that can operate in the environment without the need for encapsulation.

*—Materials.* Materials advancement can lead to large undersea payloads and more reliable ocean subsystems and components.

*—Navigation and communications.* These are prime requisites to safe and successful operations on and in the oceans.

*—Tools.* Improved diver and vehicle tools are required to do useful work in the oceans.

*—Mooring systems, buoys, and surface support platforms.* Surface support is used for many undersea activities. Stable surface platforms and reliable long-life buoys must be developed.

*—Biomedicine and diving equipment.* Man can operate in the sea safely and efficiently only if supported by a biomedical program determining

physiological limits, medical treatments, and minimum decompression times.

*—Environmental considerations.* Environmental information is critical to the design of reliable, efficient, and economic equipment for use in the oceans.

*—Data handling.* Data are the product of scientific and exploration missions. Technology applied to marine data handling can vastly improve at-sea operations.

*—Life support.* Extended underwater manned operations require advanced life support systems.

## A. Survey Equipment and Instrumentation

## 1. Survey Equipment

**a. Current Situation**  Survey functions required for undersea operations result from needs for (1) measurement and sampling of ocean and sub-bottom parameters for geophysical, chemical, and biological analysis, (2) knowledge of position, and (3) communication of data among undersea stations, surface support locations, and onshore centers.

The current approach to undersea mapping involves use of surface methods almost exclusively. Ocean surveying is limited in accuracy by the lack of precise long-range surface positioning systems. The advent of satellite positioning constitutes an improvement, but does not approach the accuracy required to perform undersea construction and geological evaluation surveys.

The same type of basic reference systems provided by the usual geodetic methods on land—ultimately of comparable accuracy—are required undersea for mapping ocean bottom and sub-bottom features and for recording the location of physical, chemical, and biological measurement taken in the water column. The technology of navigation and bathymetry, mapping magnetic and gravitational fields, and primary sub-bottom tectonics can be combined to synthesize regional geology.

Technological aspects of ocean surveys cannot be considered separately from priorities and types of surveys whether they be scientific, industrial, or military—each having special requirements. This diversity plus the complexity, vastness, and general inaccessibility of the ocean volume make surveys, especially of the continental shelves and suspected anomalies, a first step toward undersea utilization.

Bathymetric measurement systems have been improved markedly in accuracy, speed, and convenience through advancements in echo sounding. For detailed studies in deep water, however, existing systems are not adequate. Measuring and recording profiles of the ocean bottom along selected courses traveled by the survey ship, plane, or satellite omits knowledge of intervening areas that can be compensated only by increasing the number of courses (survey lines).

High endurance submersibles with side-scan sonar and short range echo sounders offer a method for detailed bathymetric mapping essentially independent of subsurface visibility and surface weather. Major obstacles are the lack of precise navigation and limited endurance and payload.

Acoustic profiling with high energy sources, mechanical vibrators, air guns, gas exploders, electric arcs, and explosives can be used for deep reflection and refraction work. Detailed shallow water geology can be defined with high resolution profiling utilizing low energy sources.

For several years, general surveys of limited ocean areas (as parts of the Gulf Stream) have been conducted from aircraft. Some data are being gathered on the sea surface now by weather satellites, and steps are being taken to establish global surveys of the ocean surface by satellite (Figure 1). Aircraft and satellite mounted cameras, infrared radiometers, microwave radiometers, and similar instruments are capable of gathering valuable data on ocean surface temperature, sea state, ice conditions, current and water mass movements, schools and congregations of fish, phytoplankton blooms, water pollution, and other important processes.

**b. Future Needs**  The study of ocean processes and marine species on more than a very small scale will require the availability of data on an automatic or rapid retrieval basis. Ocean engineering efforts will profit greatly from the existence of rapid access to data on the environment. Predictions of fish production and migration to optimize

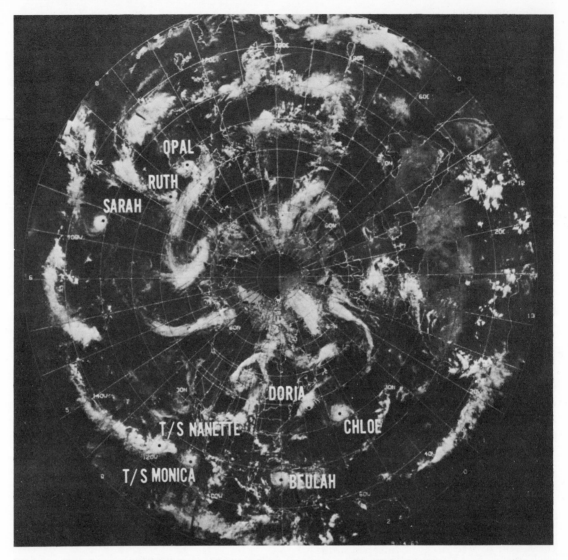

**Figure 1.** *Digital mosaic compiled from analog signals received from satellite ESSA-5. Eight major storms in Northern Hemisphere on Sept. 14, 1967, are displayed. (ESSA photo)*

fish catch require synoptic environmental data and predictions. Knowledge of regional and local bathymetry, circulation, and other environmental factors is needed to design outfalls for desalting and waste disposal operations.

General mapping functions should include measuring and plotting magnetic and gravitational fields. Like sub-bottom profiling, the general resource development interest is in regional features and navigational aids with initial emphasis on continental shelf surveys rather than localized anomalies for substructure analysis. Continuous gravimetric surveys are limited in effectiveness by their slow speed, necessitating improved instrumentation and procedures.

Bathymetric survey methods involving multi-ship operations with centralized data reduction and mapping functions are under evaluation. Component deficiencies and lack of priorities have deterred implementation. The potentials of aerial and satellite color photography and of infrared sensing for subsurface mapping functions should be determined and exploited, especially in shallow waters and coastal areas. The potential of submersibles in such operations should receive more attention.

## 2. Instrumentation

**a. Current Situation** The measurement of underwater physical, chemical, geological, and biological parameters is accomplished predominantly with devices lowered from surface craft or suspended from floating or submerged buoys (Figure 2). Such measurements are limited generally to basic parameters required to identify water masses and determine their movement or to provide gross identification of biological activity and nutrients. Limited measurements from submersibles have included stereophotography for topographic studies, temperature, salinity, and on-site sound velocity measurements in upper sediment layers.

**Figure 2.** *Meteorologic (left) and oceanographic (right) sensor packages of ODESSA system, which gathers data from unmanned buoys over wide ocean areas. (ESSA photo)*

Measurements by divers in the water mass have been limited to a few physical parameters, such as distance and temperature, requiring only such rudimentary devices as bulb thermometers, magnetic compasses, and measuring sticks or cords. *In situ* measurements have been made of sediment shear strength. However, diver monitoring and manipulation of instruments lowered from surface

craft have been an important aid to such measurements as sound velocity in sediments.

Only chemical parameters of very general interest, such as salinity, pH, and dissolved oxygen have been measured with other than sophisticated laboratory instrumentation or methods of volumetric analysis. Some application has been made of fluorescence, spectroscopy, radioactive tracers, and neutron activation analysis in tracing sediment and water movement. Little has been done to adapt instruments for analysis in geochemical surveying, pollution monitoring, nutrient assessment, and other ocean activities of growing interest and concern.

Biological measurements are completely inferential, consisting of chemical and physical measurements that can be correlated with biological concentrations, movement, and activity. Biologically important properties such as oxygen, total organics, salinity, Eh, and pH[1] plus the physically important parameters can be compared with biological observations and bioacoustic measurements to predict response to environmental factors, productivity, and migration.

New developments by the Atomic Energy Commission and the Navy include a deep water isotopic current analyzer, a nuclear sediment density probe, and an *in situ* oxygen analyzer.

**b. Future Needs** New instrumentation is needed to study biological species, their distribution, feeding habits, reproduction, and migration as a function of chemical and physical parameters. In addition, assistance to the biologist in the acquisition of field data can be provided through (1) development of automatic discrimination of acoustic signals generated by marine species, (2) observation of movement of species by acoustic networks, (3) counting marine species migration through fish passes or other constrictions, and (4) other survey techniques.

Submersibles should be particularly well adapted to on-site measurements of physical properties of sea water and sediment. Sediment measurements are needed for basic design criteria for bottom emplacement, construction, tunneling, and laying of pipelines and cables as well as for

---

[1] Eh and pH are defined in the subsection on environmental considerations of this section.

resource surveys. Instruments and procedures for on-site measurement of engineering properties of sediments is needed.

While great progress has been made in developing instrumentation having digital capabilities, further progress is essential before long-range rapid ocean environmental surveillance becomes a reality.

Much instrumentation available has been criticized as being unreliable and unsuited for service at sea. Instrumentation development will flourish to the extent of the commitment to utilize the sea—a commitment in part dependent on the state of undersea technology.

It follows that initial efforts in opening the vast economic potentials of the ocean may be invested best in developing precise, rugged, seaworthy measuring instruments. Calibration and evaluation of new instrumentation is needed to provide the proof-testing leading to dependable use.

## 3. Conclusions

Increased knowledge of the oceans can be obtained through better survey equipment and mapping techniques. Technology and scientific study can provide information for proper exploration and development of ocean resources. New equipment is needed for precise measurement of the ocean environment both for single in-place measurements and for high-speed continuous measurements of variable water and sediment properties.

Except where abrupt topographical changes occur or where a need for detailed studies in deep water exists, the accuracy of vertical dimension measurements by current systems is adequate for mapping. However, surveys are limited in speed and economy, partially due to the lack of rapid data collection and processing capability.

Platforms, equipment, data systems, and such other tools of undersea technology as test range operations depend inherently on instrumentation capable of adequate performance and acceptable reliability. A primary deterrent to equipment development is the inadequacy of facilities for evaluation and calibration.

Ocean simulators and laboratories to evaluate and calibrate equipment are not only scarce, but are not generally available to either manufacturers or users. Because of high capital costs, test facilities should be provided on a reimbursable basis to service the manufacturers and users of both military and non-military equipment.

Properly operating survey equipment is critical to the exploration and development of ocean resources. Separate groups using similar equipments not calibrated to the same standards often obtain substantially different results. At present no mechanism exists whereby uniform standards of measurement can be established. Such standards are essential to efficient evaluation and analysis of data obtained under various conditions.

## Recommendations:

**Highest priority should be assigned to development of survey equipment for detailed mapping of bathymetric, geological, and ecological features; high-speed, wide-path width bottom scanning; and three dimensional plotting. Realtime[2] digital recording and processing systems adopted to oceanic instrumentation should be pursued. Improved equipment should be developed to perform high-speed surveys of (1) shape, thickness, and extent of sediment layers, (2) depth and shape of rock surfaces, and (3) spatial distribution of engineering properties of rock sediment layers.**

**Technology should be advanced in (1) rapid at-sea analysis of chemicals in ocean and estuarine waters and in sediments for pollution monitoring, nutrient evaluation, corrosion control, and geochemical exploration, (2) on-site measurement of microgradients of salinity, pH, Eh, and water and sediment densities, and (3) magnetic and gravimetric survey instruments for use at depths.**

**Consideration should be given to observation, measurement, and sampling functions as integral components of a system including navigation, communications, observation platform, and handling equipment.**

**Programs involving mapping, surveys, exploration, research, and preconstruction engineering functions will be most cost effective by applying a systems approach and automation. The ultimate goal should be to return to shore with data reduced, plotted, and ready for interpretation, or to relay realtime data via synchronous satellites to data processing centers ashore.**

---

[2] Realtime refers to the capability to process data simultaneously with the event being observed, permitting conclusions to be drawn and corrective action to be implemented immediately.

Because of lack of facilities for equipment evaluation and calibration a coordinated program should be established immediately whereby calibration services and development of essential standards and specifications can be made available to all users on a cost-reimbursement basis.

To permit standardized development, fabrication, and calibration of ocean instruments and sensors, studies should be undertaken to determine realistic accuracy requirements.

## B. Power Sources

This nation must develop better undersea power sources. When submersibles with adequate endurance are developed, they need only submerge and surface in the sheltered waters of a harbor. This will provide great cost reduction for future submersible operations—the elimination of surface support.

Within the foreseeable future undersea vehicles and habitats will be limited to the utilization of presently known and identified prime energy sources including (1) nuclear energy systems which require only occasional maintenance and refueling, (2) chemical energy systems replenished by support ships, and (3) ship- or shore-generated electrical energy transmitted by cable.

A portable undersea support laboratory at a depth of 2,000 feet and the continental slope or midocean ridge station at 8,000 feet with crews of 15 to 25 and possibly 100 to 1,000 will require large amounts of energy, many thousands of kilowatts. When the laboratory is relatively near land, the energy can be generated best on shore and transmitted to the habitat through cables.

For remote locations a self-contained undersea power system probably will be required. Submersible vehicles and underwater construction machinery will incorporate nuclear power systems or refuelable or rechargable chemical energy plants, because electrical cables impose serious entanglement and vulnerability hazards.

Extensive work in the space program on the SNAP 2, SNAP 10, and SNAP 8 power systems (Space Nuclear Auxiliary Power developed for 2, 500, and 30,000 watts) may find application in the undersea frontier. Reactors and conversion systems that meet the initial power requirements of anticipated fixed bottom habitats and future deep submergence vehicles have been developed for outer space. Considerable expenditures will be required, however, to redesign these systems for manned undersea applications.

Divers usually will be able to obtain electrical energy through umbilical cords. But free-swimming saturated divers working appreciable distances from base will need reliable, high capacity, portable energy packages. Power demands for tethered operations may extend upward to the multikilowatt range to fulfill life support, illumination, work, environmental protection (especially suit heat), and other demands.

### 1. Chemical Batteries

**a. Current Situation** Deep submersibles have used lead-acid batteries as a primary energy source because of their low cost, established reliability, and adaptability to submerged operation. Silver-zinc batteries have been used in a few applications where improved performance was mandatory and increased cost acceptable. Bottom installations such as Sealab have relied on power generated on support ships or ashore.

Small vehicles with limited mission requirements employ batteries because of their relatively low cost, although payload is reduced by battery weight. Because neutral buoyancy must be maintained, the low overall energy availability per pound of battery system limits greatly the endurance of most vehicles. Weight-to-energy ratios range from 75 to 125 and 25 to 40 pounds per kilowatt hour for installed lead-acid and silver-zinc batteries, respectively.

**b. Future Needs** Use of new battery reactants such as fluorine may offer a two-to-three-fold improvement in weight-to-energy ratios, but the projected costs of such developments are high. Further, the weight-to-energy ratios will be challenged seriously by improved fuel cells and thermal conversion systems. Battery development should concentrate on adapting to undersea use such other known high energy systems as mercury-zinc or nickel-cadmium.

Methods of recharging submersible battery systems at ambient pressure in the deep ocean would enable battery powered submersibles to achieve greatly enhanced endurance. Such techniques would allow the battery powered submersible to rival and perhaps to exceed the endurance of fuel cell powered submersibles.

## 2. Fuel Cells

**a. Current Situation**  Deep submersible vehicles and habitats with power requirements in the 10 to 100 kilowatt range may well use fuel cells in the coming decade. The hydrogen-oxygen fuel cell has by far the most extensive development history, albeit for highly specialized and costly space applications.

Another major fuel cell type being considered for undersea use, hydrazine-hydrogen peroxide, has received relatively less attention but is in an advanced state of development for terrestrial applications by the U.S. Army. It is a much less expensive device probably in part because of less stringent qualification and documentation requirements. Like the battery, the fuel cell is a static energy converter producing electrical energy from chemical energy.

Unlike the battery, the fuel cell can produce energy as long as fuel and oxidant are supplied. Fuel cells produce waste products (heat and water from the hydrogen-oxygen cell or heat, water, and nitrogen from the hydrazine-hydrogen peroxide cell) which may be of use.

The basic concept of the fuel cell has received much conceptual development during the first half of this century. Nevertheless, it took the impetus of the space race and the expenditure of over $100 million to provide the operational hydrogen-oxygen fuel cell systems used in the Gemini and Apollo projects. Such accelerated technology development ultimately may have applications in automobiles, recreational boats, and undersea systems.

A fuel cell is planned as the power source for the Navy's Deep Submergence Search Vehicle (DSSV). The 34-hour DSSV mission time and power consumption rate demand peak power of 50 kilowatts and a 1,000-kilowatt-hour energy supply. The system, including required buoyancy material, will weigh about 10,000 pounds, or 10 pounds per kilowatt hour. A silver-zinc battery system providing the same energy would weigh about 30,000 pounds. The additional vehicle weight and size required to utilize silver-zinc batteries would seriously affect the performance of DSSV.

**b. Future Needs**  Fuel cells appear essential to efficient undersea operations. Hydrogen-oxygen fuel cells for undersea use require hard tanks for both the fuel cell module and the fuel. The fuel could be stored cryogenically as a liquid, but substantial insulation would be required.

Tankage, designed to withstand ambient pressure at operating depth, adds considerable weight to the power system. If a fuel cell could be developed capable of pressure-balanced ambient operation without hard tank protection, system weight would be independent of operating depth, and a weight-to-energy ratio of six to eight pounds per kilowatt hour might be achieved. This could result in important weight improvement in power systems for 20,000-foot submersible operations.

## 3. Thermal Conversion

**a. Current Situation**  Thermodynamic power systems may range from the simplest, using jet fuel and an oxydizer with a reciprocating engine, to very advanced systems, using such high energy sources as the reaction of sodium with seawater. Application of thermodynamic cycle systems most likely will be in the shallow zero to 2,000-foot zone, thereby allowing wastes to be exhausted directly to sea. For covert operations, it would be necessary to condense the exhaust and store it aboard so no trail would be left, and neutral buoyancy maintained.

An extensive engineering effort was devoted to closed cycle thermodynamic power systems in the early 1950's. A complete evaluation was made of long-term submerged operations, and several usable concepts were developed to permit submerged operations of days or weeks. The pressurized water nuclear reactor development in 1955 supplanted the thermodynamic power concept for fleet submarines, and little additional work has been done since.

**b. Future Needs**  Few undersea applications will require a nuclear reactor energy source. Chemical dynamic systems (operating on the Brayton, Rankine, or Sterling cycles and utilizing a reciprocating engine or a turbine driving an electrical generator) could produce electrical energy at much less cost and weight than a nuclear plant and should receive renewed development attention.

Encapsulation quickly raises the specific weight of chemical dynamic systems for operations below 2,000 feet. Important weight reduction for mobile systems could be achieved by employing systems in which the fuel and effluent were maintained at ambient pressure with only the engine and generator enclosed in hard tanks. Ultimate development of a system with conversion equipment and fuel maintained at ambient operating pressures might achieve power sources weighing around 25 pounds per kilowatt hour.

## 4. Nuclear Reactors

**a. Current Situation** The nuclear reactor proved to be a dramatic success on Navy fleet submarines. Units delivering tens of thousands of kilowatts are in reliable service for main propulsion and auxiliary loads of submarines and surface ships. The recent launching of NR-1 is a major milestone in adapting nuclear power to much smaller vehicles.

A concept developed for the Naval Civil Engineering Laboratory of a five man, 6,000 foot undersea station includes a nuclear reactor for main power. A unit recommended for a power demand of 38 kilowatts was the TRIGA Oceanographic Power Supply with a steam turbine generator power conversion system. Total weight of this plant (maximum capacity 100 kilowatts) was estimated at 145,000 pounds, more than half shielding. The Navy and the Atomic Energy Commission are working to develop yet more suitable nuclear reactors for other future deep ocean applications.

**b. Future Needs** There are attractions to placing a nuclear power plant on the ocean floor where it would be away from population centers. If the plant were operated unmanned with most systems at ambient pressures, external pressure might be used to reduce some wall thicknesses. Waste heat removal problems would be reduced in the limitless heat sink of the ocean. If the power plant were remote from manned habitats, shielding might be reduced by relying upon seawater, an excellent shielding material itself. Except for power plant maintenance problems and some materials development, current technology is adequate to provide submerged nuclear power plants.

Three factors will influence decisions to build a nuclear power plant at an undersea site:[3] (1) cost of electricity supplied by a nuclear plant at the site compared with cost of long cable transmission from land or from surface floating plants, (2) the character and priority of the undersea operation, and (3) the leadtime for nuclear power plant construction and operation.

Reactor technology considerations will not greatly influence the decision at shallower depths. For missions at 20,000 feet, there are severe design and engineering problems, particularly in the structural design of the condenser.

Remaining problems may include a variety of materials and operating difficulties. Maintenance, for example, would be virtually impossible at depth. It would be difficult and expensive to raise a plant for repair and maintenance. Maintenance requirements might be minimized if static energy conversion systems such as thermo-electric conversion were incorporated in place of dynamic turbine-generator systems. Several conceptual designs for such power plants have been developed.

Unfortunately, the much smaller power requirements of current saturation diving habitats are not compatible with the characteristics of existing nuclear reactors. Technology derived from development programs to supply small nuclear reactors for space applications may be adapted to the undersea power problem, particularly for manned underwater stations at limited ocean depths.

## 5. Isotope Power

Power up to 10 kilowatts is considered achievable via radioisotope-dynamic conversion power systems, in which the heat of radioactive decay produces steam to drive a conventional turbine-generator or power a thermoelectric converter.

Isotope materials with halflives ranging from four months to 458 years exist in varying quantities and costs. One most promising for long missions, cobalt-60, has a halflife of over five years and an energy density of 1.7 watts per gram in compound form. For shorter missions, polonium-210 with a halflife of 138 days might be selected.

---

[3]There are also reasons to locate power generating stations offshore to serve land needs. See Chapter 6, Section VII, Power Generation.

Since radioisotopes are the product of reactor operations or separation of spent fuel, careful consideration must be given to selection and availability of isotopes when considering them for electric power production. Some isotopes are completely unavailable. With others, price is changeable and reflects many factors, some unrelated to actual isotope demand. A careful survey of information supplied by the Atomic Energy Commission regarding cost and availability is mandatory before planning to utilize such systems.

Isotopes are expensive. With a somewhat optimistic 25 per cent engine cycle efficiency, power output of 15 kilowatts would require 60 thermal kilowatts with an expected cobalt-60 isotope cost of $390,000.

As with reactor systems, radiation and waste heat must be considered. The advantages and disadvantages of deep ocean reactors are similar to isotope systems. The transportation of a radioisotope system is difficult due to the necessity of continuous shielding and heat rejection.

Assuming acceptable weight characteristics and cost considerations, radioisotope systems can provide small-power supplies having low maintenance and high reliability for a number of relatively constant power consumers (such as fixed environmental monitoring systems, transponders, buoys, wellhead controls, and communications and navigation systems).

## 6. Conclusions

Reliable, cost effective, high energy per unit weight and volume power sources are a primary requisite for a wide variety of undersea applications. Existing power sources in various development stages for other applications are potential candidates for underwater service, but each requires considerable adaptation to the ocean environment and to specific underwater applications. Clearly, no single candidate is preferable over the entire energy spectrum in which submersibles, habitats, and other undersea systems may operate.

The current need for suitable power sources for submersibles is urgent. Excluding combatant submarines, only rechargable batteries have been employed for main power in manned, selfpropelled submersibles. The NR-1 will be the first submersible with nuclear power. Batteries impose severe weight, payload, and endurance penalties on small vehicles. Until fuel cells, small nuclear plants, and other power sources can be developed for deep ocean service, submersible capabilities will be seriously limited. Figure 3 is a general presentation of approximate ranges of useful outputs for various power sources for submersible systems illustrating the point that no one type would satisfy all missions. Figure 4 summarizes the comparative usefulness potential for various power sources. The diversity of advantages and disadvantages of each also enforces the need for pursuing diverse approaches in power source development.

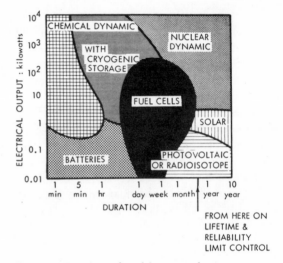

**Figure 3.** *The range of useful outputs for various power sources.*

**Figure 4**
**COMPARATIVE USEFULNESS OF VARIOUS POWER SOURCES**[1]

| Criteria / Type | Low Power | High Power | Endurance | Ambient Pressure Capability |
|---|---|---|---|---|
| Lead Acid Battery . . | 3 | 5 | 5 | 1 |
| Silver Zinc Battery . . | 3 | 4 | 4 | 1 |
| Fuel Cell . . | 2 | 3 | 3 | 3 |
| Chemical Dynamic . | 4 | 2 | 3 | 4 |
| Isotope . . | 1 | 5 | 1 | 3 |
| Nuclear Reactor . | 5 | 1 | 1 | 5 |

[1] 1 is best; 5 is poorest.

## Recommendations:

**While it is not realistic to presume that any one power source will be adequate for all underwater requirements, the design, development, testing, and certification of each new source is both time consuming and expensive. Therefore, it is also unrealistic to conceive of a program wherein all power sources will be developed simultaneously. A more rational approach dictates that development efforts be directed initially to low-cost adaptions of existing power sources to systems specifically designed for the ocean environment.**

**Development of compact, deep ocean power sources ranging particularly between 50 and 5,000 kilowatts for deep submergence vehicles and habitats is most urgent and should receive first priority.**

**Engineering criteria, standards, and performance and qualification specifications for power systems (including components) must be established for nonmilitary underwater applications. Applied research and component improvement programs must be supported. The development of a low-cost 50 kilowatt power source for submersible operations of several days is an example.**

**Fuel cells should receive priority to meet the 10 to 100 kilowatt demand of small submersibles, a requirement that can be met by the DSSV fuel cell project if carried out as planned. Development of both hydrazine and hydrogen-oxygen systems should be supported. Cryogenic underwater technology should be emphasized because of its potential application in fuel cell and thermal conversion systems. In the range for resource utilization on the continental shelves, thermal conversion systems should receive renewed development support.**

## C. External Machinery Systems and Equipment

The sea environment imposes entirely new operational requirements on machinery systems. Mechanical and electrical equipment have been developed for operation in the atmosphere or in the vacuum of space, but the ocean's high pressure and corrosiveness impose more severe demands than have been encountered in most previous applications.

Military submarines operate at relatively shallow depths with most machinery systems inside the pressure hull and a minimum of equipment exposed to the ocean environment. Consequently, little undersea component development has been directed toward external machinery. Yet small submersible hulls generally enclose only the man and the electronic equipment, and in unmanned systems it is desirable to utilize as little heavy pressure-resistant structure as possible. Consequently, efficient design requires the use of new subsystems exposed directly to the ocean environment.

The attempt to use off-the-shelf or slightly modified equipment in submersible systems because of cost has in many cases proved unwise. Few items have worked as planned, and modification has been expensive. The use of off-the-shelf equipment in effect has led to *in situ* testing, often a costly and wasteful procedure. A few hours of operation without any equipment malfunction is the best expected from vehicles in initial stages of operation.

The Circular of Requirements issued in late 1965 as part of the procurement specification for the Deep Submergence Rescue Vehicle (DSRV) specified the use of off-the-shelf equipment. But many subsystems proposed would not operate when tested in the deep environment, requiring added efforts to develop, test, and qualify suitable equipment for the vehicle.

Safety and progress in the undersea frontier necessitate testing, evaluation, and certification of equipment for external operation prior to installation. Because the use of equipment exposed to the environment promises great rewards in the efficiency of undersea systems, external machinery systems and equipment development should receive emphasis in the fundamental technology development program.

### 1. Power Application

**a. Current Situation** A key element of mobile undersea platforms will be the propulsion system. Neutrally buoyant vehicles may have to have mobility in all six degrees of freedom—(1) heave (up and down), (2) surge (fore and aft), (3) sway (right and left), (4) roll, (5) pitch, and (6) yaw. For docking or mating, very precise maneuverability is required. For many activities speeds of five knots or less are acceptable, but in such cases as chasing tuna or potential enemy submarines much higher forward speeds are needed.

The choice of propulsion systems for submersible vehicles depends on their mission. Typical uses—scientific studies, site survey and inspection, object recovery and light salvage, transport of men and equipment, or mobile tool operations —generally demand precise maneuverability, normally more important than high speed.

Other challenges to propulsion system design include protection from entanglement, minimum disturbance of bottom sediments (especially for bottom-sitting vehicles), and creation of large forces and moments at zero speed. Propulsion system selection will involve weight, volume, simplicity, efficiency, reliability, maintainability, and mechanical endurance.

The state of development and features of the most common propulsion systems are:

—*Screw propulsion.* Well defined, with designs available for almost any application. Systems have utilized conventional propellers, ducted thrusters, or rotatable pods. Precise maneuverability in all degrees of motion requires no less than three screw propellers.

—*Tandem propulsion.* In early development, not progressed beyond the analysis and tank-test stages. Has promise for highly maneuverable vehicles.

—*Cycloidal (vertical axis propeller) propulsion.* In use for years on tugs and ferries which require high thrust at low speeds and directed thrust for maneuvering but not three-dimensional control. Only a prototype glass submersible presently employs cycloidal propulsion.

—*Water jet propulsion.* Uses pumps to expel water at high velocity for propulsion. Currently in use on at least two commercially operated deep submersibles. One uses rotatable jets for primary thrust; the other uses jet thrusters for maneuvering control.

Many submersible functions and habitat operations require power transmission by hydraulic pumps and actuators. In theory, complete hydraulic systems placed externally to the hull at ambient pressures can be operated at still higher working pressures. However, such operations have often failed for one or more of the following reasons:

—Characteristics of hydraulic fluids change at extremely high pressures—viscosity may increase 100 times while operating a system from zero to 20,000-foot depths.

—Waxes may form in hydraulic oils and clog the lines.

—Gases may accumulate and block the system.

The mechanical parts of pumps, actuators, and motors normally designed for 3,000 pound per square inch (psi) operation in atmospheric systems must be redesigned for deep submergence.

Most underwater propulsion systems and virtually all hydraulic and seawater pumps are driven by electric motors. Several methods for conditioning motors to resist the operating environment have been developed. These include oil-filling, encapsulation in pressure-resistant housings, and sealing principle parts such as rotors and stators with plastic compounds. None is yet completely satisfactory.

Most undersea electric power sources provide direct current. Since no power conversion is necessary, direct current motors (especially for constant-speed applications) promise high efficiencies. However, problems of commutation and brush wear under high pressure or in oil have restricted their use.

Alternating current motors have the advantage of being brushless, but require DC-to-AC inverters for power conversion and speed control. Although modern inverters have no moving parts, they do not operate reliably in ambient pressures, and their electrical complexity adds weight.

**b. Future Needs** Propulsion system reliability and efficiency must be improved for advanced undersea systems. The tandem propeller concept appears feasible within the foreseeable future. Reduction of vehicle drag to reduce power consumption and increase propulsion system performance holds limited promise.

Solution of the DC motor brush problem appears imminent. The Navy has been testing 3 and 17 horsepower DC motors of a unique brush concept with favorable results. Larger motors are yet to be developed. AC motor inverter-controllers are being refined, but reliability and weight improvements, including possible ambient operation, should be pursued.

Entirely new hydraulic equipment designs are needed for deep submergence. Pumps, motors, actuators, and such power conversion equipment as fluid speed reduction gears that use corrosive, nonlubricating seawater as the working fluid would be a real breakthrough. Entirely new concepts for pump and motor construction and new working fluids may prove a very fruitful alternative.

## 2. Electrical Distribution

**a. Current Situation** Electrical power must be distributed within and outside the pressure hull of undersea systems. Signals to control external machinery must be transmitted through the pressure hull, and outside information must enter for processing, interpretation, and storage. On a relatively simple vehicle, a thousand or more wires may pass through the hull. The Deep Submergence Rescue Vehicle will require more than 1,400 such penetrations. A large bottom habitat may require thousands of such penetrations.

Electrical distribution systems within the pressure hull are similar to those for atmospheric applications, but external distribution systems encounter entirely different problems. Each wire and component is subjected to both pressure and adverse chemical effects. Deficiencies in the state-of-the-art exist in insulation, circuit interruption techniques, and automatic system monitoring equipment.

Electrical hull penetrators contain contacts which complete circuits through the hull. Their selection is important, as number and size determine hull reinforcement requirements and may affect internal and external equipment arrangement.

Penetrators must be reliable barriers to hydrostatic pressure to avoid electrical shorting or hull flooding. Although various configurations containing relatively few contacts have had some success, none is yet satisfactory for extended operations requiring many signals at great depths.

Underwater cables and connectors are a significant problem. Each must resist the high pressure seawater environment and form a reliable pressure resistant connection at the connector-cable and connector-connector interfaces.

Underwater cable must be resistant to mechanical stresses from pressure cycling, vibration, thermal variations, abrasion, and chemical, electrolytic, and biological attack. Extreme pressure changes cause cable insulation to squeeze and withdraw from between conductor strands and to be pinched and chafed. Voids formed in cable during manufacture can result in air bubble accumulation under pressure, subsequently causing rupture due to gas expansion during ascent.

Molded distribution boxes and oil-filled junction boxes have been utilized to distribute electrical power. In a molded distribution box, cable, connectors and wiring are mated in solid rubber or plastic. Inaccessible connecting points are fully protected from the outside environment.

Oil-filled junction boxes, although heavy and bulky, are reliable in undersea systems. Pressure is compensated by an electrically insulating fluid (usually silicone oil) and a flexible diaphragm. When pressure increases, the diaphragm transmits pressure to the fluid in the box, thereby supporting the box's walls. The diaphragm may be spring-loaded to ensure a positive pressure to keep seawater out. Most remotely operated external contactors and relays are placed in oil-filled boxes.

**b. Future Needs** Reliable, multiconductor hull penetrators, cables, and connectors are essential to systems development. Available components have only marginal capability.

Insulations capable of withstanding many pressure cycles must be developed. New techniques of circuit interruption are needed. Reliable automatic system monitoring equipment must be developed. Because undersea maintenance is difficult if not impossible, equipment must be provided to detect, evaluate, and correct equipment faults automatically. Pressure and water resistant switch gear, preferably electronic rather than electro-mechanical, must be developed to avoid bulky protective enclosures and to improve reliability. New methods of hull penetration, using radio or visible light frequencies now being developed for glass hulls, show promise and warrant increased effort.

## 3. Buoyancy and Trim Control

**a. Current Situation** Maintaining neutral buoyancy reliably is important because uncontrolled descent or ascent could be disastrous. A vehicle's weight generally must be controlled through a range as much as ±5 per cent of total weight.

Merely moving from seawater to the fresh or brackish water of a river mouth changes displacement perceptibly.

Descent from warm surface waters to cold bottom waters or transit through several thermal or salinity layers places a heavy burden on buoyancy control systems. Existing systems require constant attention of experienced personnel to compensate for changing conditions.

Buoyancy control is achieved most simply by pumping seawater in and out of hard tanks, changing the ratio of vehicle weight to displacement. This method has proven satisfactory to 2,000 feet, but pumping water against the high pressures of greater depths requires expenditure of much precious energy.

When transporting specimens, minerals, or recovered objects to the surface, it will be necessary to provide buoyancy at least equal to the wet weight of the cargo. Dropping weights may be inexpensive, but pumping seawater ballast is more desirable because it is reversible. Further, systems operating submerged for long periods may not have the opportunity to replace dropped weights.

Trim in undersea vehicles has been controlled by shifting ballast, changing the pitch of fins or vanes, or applying propulsion. In shifting ballast, seawater or mercury is pumped from one region of the vehicle to another, working effectively even at slow or zero forward speeds. However, the system responds slowly, and the ballast, tankage, interconnecting piping, and pumping system add weight, volume, and complexity. The vehicle must have some relative forward or reverse motion to effect trim by the use of lifting surfaces.

**b. Future Needs** New fast and completely automatic buoyancy control must be developed. Chemical propellants may achieve a more satisfactory ratio between the weight of energy storage and the change in vehicle buoyancy. The solution may lie in designing vehicles so their bulk modulus closely matches that of seawater, utilizing materials and devices which vary in displacement to compensate for changes in pressure and temperature, thus providing automatic buoyancy control and minimal requirements for variable ballast.

More efficient trim control methods with quicker response will be needed as vehicles become larger and faster. Automatic trim controls to free the vehicle operator for other duties will be required.

## 4. Conclusions

External machinery systems and equipment not designed for undersea use have proved generally inadequate. However, due to the unavailability of special subsea commercial equipment, equipment designed for other purposes has been used in the oceans. Even equipment specially designed for submerged application requires extensive improvement. The state-of-the-art in external machinery systems and equipment is summarized as follows:

| Propulsion Systems | Problem |
| --- | --- |
| Screw | Maneuverability requires several units |
| Tandem | Not tested on a full-scale vehicle; complex mechanism |
| Cycloidal | Not tested on a full-scale vehicle; complex mechanism |
| Water Jets | Sediment disturbance; low efficiency |
| New Methods | Need to be developed |

| Electric Motors | Problem |
| --- | --- |
| DC Motors | Commutation and brush wear |
| AC Motors | Inverter/controller weight and reliability; flooded operation |

| Electrical | Problem |
| --- | --- |
| Penetrations | Weight; reliability of seals and insulation; continuity of circuit |
| Distribution | Weight and bulk of oil-filled junction boxes; mechanical circuit interruption; cable reliability |

| Control | Problem |
| --- | --- |
| Buoyancy | Ballast pump rates and reliability; automatic control; buoyancy generation at great pressure |
| Trim | System weight and speed; automatic control |

## Recommendations:

**More efficient, reliable, lighter weight external subsystems are critical to deeper ocean operating capability. Development has not received the attention given materials and power sources, although of equal importance. A program specifically aimed at improving reliability and developing new external machinery systems and equipment—propulsion systems, buoyancy, and trim control systems—is needed.**

**The Navy's Deep Ocean Technology Program should be funded to the requested levels.**

**Civilian technology funding levels should allow the development of fundamental knowledge needed to produce low-cost systems for non-military users.**

## D. Materials

Materials problems enter critically into every aspect of underwater technology. The economy and effectiveness of ocean activities are dependent upon development of improved materials for submersible vehicles, underwater structures, equipment, and all types of components. Material development involves not only basic metallurgical and mechanical properties but problems of production, design, fabrication, testing, in-service inspection, corrosion, and marine fouling.

Developments are needed in metallics, nonmetallics, and composites of increased strength with sufficient notch toughness, corrosion resistance, fatigue strength, producibility, weldability, and economy for pressure hulls and other structural applications. Included in the nonmetallic category are fiber-reinforced plastics, glass, and other ceramics.

Neutral buoyancy is an operating requirement for submersibles. Applying a principle that buoyancy is best provided by the pressure hull and auxiliary buoyancy material is used primarily for trim—the pressure hull should have a weight-to-displacement (W/D or buoyancy) ratio of 0.4 to 0.6. This allows for the buoyancy required for external machinery and equipment, outer hull and payload. In the discussions following, a spherical geometry is assumed, because this shape provides minimum W/D ratios.

No currently available production material suitable for pressure hulls can achieve a W/D ratio lower than 0.5 for 10,000-foot operations. For greater depths, supplemental buoyancy material or advanced hull materials will be required. The amount of such material will be a function of the hull's W/D ratio and the density of the buoyancy material.

The pressure hull buoyancy ratio must increase with depth. A recently constructed submersible, for example, with an 8,000-foot operating capability has a pressure hull made of a 190,000 pounds per square inch (psi) compressive yield strength steel and a buoyancy ratio of 0.43.

The Deep Submergence Search Vehicle (DSSV) designed to operate to 20,000 feet would have a pressure hull buoyancy ratio of 0.9 if fabricated of the same material. The buoyancy ratio of the DSSV pressure hull would be reduced to 0.7 if a titanium alloy of 125,000 psi compressive yield strength were used.

Higher yield strength titanium alloys have not been used in deep submergence pressure hulls because of lower toughness and possible susceptibility to stress corrosion. If a titanium alloy with a 180,000 psi yield strength and acceptable toughness became available, a pressure hull buoyancy ratio as low as 0.5 could be attained for 20,000 feet.

Complementary needs include (1) hatches that form an integral part of the structure when closed, but which can open for mating operations at great depth without dangerously degrading the structure, (2) techniques to utilize more than one material in a hull to capitalize on the unique advantages of each, (3) analytical tools to predict and evaluate preliminary design choices, and (4) fabrication techniques.

Development is needed of undersea antifouling coatings to inhibit biological growth (Figure 5), new coatings to protect against corrosion, and cathodic and impressed current techniques for combating corrosion. Materials are required for a variety of underwater applications in addition to pressure hulls:

—Gaskets, sealants, and pressure hull penetrations.

—Rubberized fabrics for pipelines, storage containers, and buoyancy bladders.

—Nylon and other materials for mooring cable, insulation, and protective sheaths.

—Transparent materials for viewports.

**Figure 5.** *Biological growth on hydrolab after one year's submergence off Florida coast near Palm Beach. Inspection of laboratory after removal of growth showed little corrosion had taken place. (West Palm Beach Post-Times photo)*

—Fluids for buoyancy and hydraulic systems, pressure compensating systems, and lubrication.

Technology and knowledge of material performance in the ocean has not progressed to where final decisions can be made as to what materials and construction techniques are to be employed in future systems. Entirely new material concepts may be developed and employed by the year 2000, but only if sufficient effort is expended in analysis, development, and use of a wide variety of materials.

## 1. High Strength Steels

**a. Current Situation** Ferrous materials having a yield strength of 80,000 psi (HY-80) or less have been used in all fleet submarines and in most deep submergence vehicles. HY-140 steels (130,000 to 150,000 psi yield strength) now can be specified for use in noncombatant vehicles, although the use of HY-140 for combatant submarines awaits solution to many problems in forging, fabricating, and welding large segments.

Operations at 20,000 feet will require much stronger steels in excess of 180,000 psi yield

strength or advanced nonferrous or nonmetallic materials.

If many pressure cycles are involved, failure due to fatigue rather than crushing forces must be considered. Unfortunately, as yield strength increases, toughness and fatigue life decrease. Each time a vehicle descends to operating depth and returns, a fatigue cycle is incurred. If a collapse safety factor of 1.5 is incorporated, cyclic loading would vary from zero psi to a maximum of 86,500 psi for HY-140.

Data suggest that HY-80 can sustain 10 times the cyclic loading of HY-140; however, the 10,000 cycle capability for HY-140 steel is likely to be at least three times the cycles a submersible will undergo during its useful life. Since HY-140 fatigue life is ample, it is not correct to imply that an HY-140 vehicle will have a shorter service life than an HY-80 vehicle. This would be true only if service life extended beyond 60 years with dives to maximum depth every other day.

**b. Future Needs** While steel has a higher density than other materials considered for pressure hulls, new ultra-strength steels (yield strength greater than 240,000 psi) may produce in 15 years efficient 20,000-foot pressure hulls (W/D around 0.5) for small, maneuverable noncombatant vehicles.

Although other materials may be used for vehicle and habitat structures, high strength steel may be found the least costly once stress corrosion cracking and brittle failure problems are overcome, and manufacturing and fabrication techniques developed.

Currently HY-80 steel, for which suitable manufacturing and fabrication techniques have been developed, is much less expensive than any other material proposed for pressure hulls. If ultra-strength steel technology were successful, a 20,000-foot hull with W/D ratio around 0.5 would be possible and steel might remain the most economical material.

## 2. Nonferrous Metals

**a. Current Situation** Titanium and aluminum materials, much less dense than steel, show promise for low W/D ratio hulls for deep submergence vehicles. However, fabrication technique and corrosion unknowns have limited such materials to only a few applications. *Aluminaut* uses aluminum forged rings for hull construction, and the *Alvin* employed titanium buoyancy spheres. Aluminum spheres with yield strength of approximately 75,000 psi, and small titanium spheres with yield strength of 120,000 psi have been fabricated.

**b. Future Needs** Extensive development and improvement of fabrication techniques must be done to realize the full potential of nonferrous materials. For example, bottom habitats probably will be manufactured in large sections on shore, transported by surface ship or towed to the site, and lowered. Since most, if not all, structural fabrication will take place on land, dry weight will be extremely important in handling such large structures.

Operating costs of current submersibles are related to vehicle weight due to surface support difficulties. Thus, advanced structural materials and improved supplement buoyancy that reduce vehicle weight can be economically rewarding. In the future submerged support of submersibles could make dry weight a much less important factor. Further, continuing development of nonferrous metals and alloys for ocean equipment and components is necessary. Included are gunmetals, cupronickels, and cast and wrought aluminum alloys.

## 3. Nonmetallic Materials

**a. Current Situation** Operation of vehicles at 20,000-foot depths will require pressure hulls having weight-to-displacement ratios approaching the ideal 0.4. These can be achieved only by using the very high strength steels with yield strengths above 240,000 psi, titanium with a 180,000 psi yield strength, glass-reinforced plastics, advanced composites, or massive glass.

Glass is expected to be developed to a usable compressive strength level of 250,000 psi during 1970-1980. The attractiveness of massive glass lies in its low density and theoretical compressive strength, possibly as high as 4,000,000 psi. Failure generally initiates at the glass surface when tension forces are present and occurs long before compressive capabilities are reached.

Annealed glass spheres up to 56 inches diameter have been fabricated and tested, but results are inconsistent, and adequate fabrication control techniques have not been developed. Unfortunately, the failure of glass spheres is unpredictable and usually catastrophic; once a crack begins, the entire assembly disintegrates. In metallic structures the failure mode is usually buckling; initial cracks and structural anomalies usually can be detected prior to complete failure.

Glass technology is being applied in construction of the Naval Undersea Warfare Center's (NUWC) *Deepview,* a vehicle having a 44-inch glass end hemisphere (Figure 6). Also NUWC's *Hikino* design has a total glass sphere with no penetrations. The sphere incorporates a titanium ring joint between hemispheres and utilizes an acrylic inner and outer lining. Other glass construction techniques include pouring, sagging by heat, sagging by vacuum, and injection molding. The Naval Civil Engineering Laboratory is working on acrylic sphere construction by assembly of 12 identical spherical pentagons.

**Figure 6.** *Artist's concept of* Deepview *submersible vehicle. (Navy photo)*

Properties and performance characteristics of a glass filament, originally developed for Polaris rocket cases, have been evaluated under simulated conditions. Complex ring-stiffened cylindrical models have been tested, demonstrating a capability to withstand short-term exposure to 30,000 feet of hydrostatic pressure and long-term static and cyclic exposures at depths to 20,000 feet.

Glass fiber reinforced plastics (GRP) are of very low density and offer the possibility of compressive strengths of 130,000 to 200,000 psi. Improved matrices, reinforcements, and composites offering higher compressive strength, modulus, shear strength, and environmental resistance can lead to greatly improved weight-to-displacement ratios and reliability. GRP materials now have demonstrated strengths of 100,000 psi; 150,000 psi appears attainable in the next decade.

Oxide ceramics are another potential material for construction of low W/D ratio pressure resistant enclosures. Alumina and beryllia appear the most likely candidates. Current technology does not permit precision manufacture of high strength ceramic parts larger than 18 inches. Spherical pentagonal ceramic plates imbedded in a metallic framework may offer a solution for spherical structures.

**b. Future Needs** Much must be done to develop the nonmetallics into safe, reliable, producible, and fabricable engineering materials for deep submergence applications. Glass work should emphasize reliability, fabrication and penetration techniques, and joint design. Fiber-reinforced plastics need process and quality control improvement.

Promising fibers such as carbon, boron, beryllium, alumina, and others should be developed further. Penetrations for manned hulls must be developed and evaluated. Oxide ceramics deserve extensive investigation with emphasis on mosaic structures to solve the scale-up problem. By the 1980's, nonmetals may be practical for manrated pressure hulls.

### 4. Supplemental Buoyancy Material

**a. Current Situation** Vehicle volume is an important criterion in maneuverability, which improves as volume decreases. Volume is greatly influenced by the buoyancy material employed. Combatant submarines have been of such limited depth capability that buoyancy has generally not been a problem. In fact, they carry lead for weight-growth margin and stability. Because of available pressure hull materials, deep submersibles ordinarily attain neutral buoyancy by carrying extra buoyancy material.

Gasoline is used for supplemental buoyancy in the *Trieste*, which has descended 35,840 feet in the Pacific. But gasoline is inefficient as buoyancy

material, causing the *Trieste* to be quite bulky and unmaneuverable. Its operations with a gasoline-filled buoyancy balloon are analogous to helium-filled balloon or blimp operations in the atmosphere.

Titanium spheres are used on the *Alvin* to provide an effective net buoyancy. Radial fiber spheres, a variation on filament wound rocket motor case development, show great promise for supplemental buoyancy. Spheres with a weight-to-displacement ratio of 0.39 have withstood up to 45,000-foot equivalent depth pressure; an 11-inch sphere with no surface resin coating has been held at 26,000 feet and tested to failure at 56,000-foot pressures. A 32-inch diameter sphere has been proof-tested to pressures equivalent to 22,000-foot depths.

Most vehicles currently under construction will employ syntactic foam for supplemental buoyancy. This is a mixture of very light hollow glass microspheres in a resin matrix. Current technology has yielded syntactic foams with a weight-to-displacement ratio of 0.56 at 8,000-foot pressures and 0.69 at 20,000 feet. Thus, the achievable net buoyancy from each foam is approximately 28 and 20 pounds per cubic foot of material respectively. (One cubic foot of water weighing 64 pounds is displaced by a cubic foot of foam weighing 36 pounds yielding a net lift of 28 pounds, etc.)

The importance of relative density of syntactic foam is evident from analyzing its role in vehicle construction and operation. Every pound of vehicle negative buoyancy when submerged must be compensated by a pound of supplemental buoyancy. If each pound of buoyancy material contributed only one-third pound of net buoyancy, then one pound of negative buoyancy would require the addition of three pounds of buoyancy material.

The result would be that each pound added to a vehicle would compound to a total of four pounds of dry weight. Based on current costs for installed buoyancy material, each added pound of vehicle weight may cost an extra $200 to $300, a cost penalty approaching or exceeding that of excess weight on a jet aircraft.

**b. Future Needs** Volume reductions, and perhaps very significant cost reductions, can result from improved syntactic foams or other supplemental buoyancy materials. Ultimately it will be desirable to develop a buoyancy material providing 39 to 44 pounds of lift per cubic foot for 20,000-foot operations. Syntactic foam improvements may require stronger, lighter resins and microspheres with improved tolerances and fatigue life; the possible combination of glass macrospheres and microspheres in the foam matrix; and castable foams that can be poured into small irregular spaces and set at room temperature. To use glass spheres, techniques must be developed to eliminate the danger of sympathetic implosion, a very serious problem prohibiting their use currently.

A possible assist may come from development of structural members which are themselves positively or neutrally buoyant. For example, an outer skin built of laminated GRP imbedded with glass microspheres might be used both to reduce wet weight and to add stiffness to the outer hull structure. Effort devoted to improving buoyancy materials and developing buoyant structure is sure to be highly cost effective and could even permit less advanced pressure capsule materials in 20,000 foot systems.

## 5. Secondary Materials

There are a great number of critical secondary materials problems for undersea structures, vehicles, and devices. They involve rubber, plastics, fabrics, fibers, insulations, hydraulic fluids, lubricants, etc. The problems are related to such environmental effects as leakage under pressure, temperature embrittlement, corrosion, fouling, scouring, and contamination. Most materials developed for submerged use have been employed only near the surface. Research and development on deep sea materials has barely begun.

## 6. Conclusions

Materials technology development is of critical concern, and upon it the economy and effectiveness of undersea activities depends. Weight-to-displacement pressure hull ratios of 0.4 to 0.6 are exceedingly important due to the fundamental requirement of supporting the remainder of the vehicle to achieve neutral buoyancy.

If the pressure capsule cannot provide needed buoyancy, supplemental material must be added, increasing vehicle weight and cost, and reducing effectiveness. Materials considered for structural

applications include steel, titanium, aluminum, glass, glass fiber reinforced plastics, and ceramics. All have promise of meeting low W/D ratios at 20,000 feet by 1980.

Although such materials as titanium and glass are being improved, once manufacturing and fabricating techniques have been developed the high strength steels might remain least costly for most undersea applications. Materials failures in marine equipment, a major shortcoming of most oceanographic efforts, may constitute a major obstacle to better utilization of the sea. Fatigue life under cyclic stress is important in selecting materials for submersibles, and long-term corrosion is the key consideration for permanent structures.

Extensive use of supplemental buoyancy material for operations below a few thousand feet is likely to be required for many years. Currently for 20,000-foot operations, buoyancy materials give only about one-half pound of buoyancy for each pound of their own weight. Vehicle volume has an important effect on maneuverability, and the buoyancy material has an important effect on vehicle weight, volume, and costs. Hence, improved buoyancy materials and equipment will be very cost effective.

Independent or contractual materials development is not being undertaken to a meaningful extent by industry. For example, 80 per cent of the Navy's exploratory development in deep ocean materials is undertaken in-house.

**Recommendations:**

**Structural materials development must be accelerated along several paths with sufficient funds to reach fair conclusions about the ability to obtain efficient deep submersible and habitat structures. After 10 years, efforts should be narrowed and production choices made. Research must be coordinated and industry initiative encouraged; the approach should be through systems engineering. Efforts should focus on:**

**—*Steel.* High strength steels development and fabrication techniques, including study of fatigue problems, should be pushed to obtain a high-quality, low-cost material.**

**—*Nonferrous metals.* Aluminum and titanium should be developed to provide the basis for efficient (W/D=0.4 to 0.6) 20,000-foot structures**

within 10 years. Emphasis should be given to corrosion resistance, fabrication methods, and cost reductions.

*—Nonmetallics.* Large glass structures for 20,000 feet should be manufactured and tested to prove reliability. Construction methods and quality control techniques should be stressed. Glass fiber reinforced plastic and ceramic structures should be built and evaluated against glass, titanium, and steel; efforts should be dropped if no clear feasibility is shown within 10 years. GRP work should emphasize reliability, resistance to delamination, and reduction of water absorption.

Supplemental buoyancy material should be developed with a major effort to provide a low-density, acceptable-strength product having 39 pounds of buoyancy per cubic foot.

A program to develop secondary materials should be emphasized to provide the needs of new systems exposed to seawater. More vigorous research into ocean causes and effects (Section I, Environmental Considerations) would feed directly into this program.

A more comprehensive program should be organized to ensure proper information transfer among user, materials supplier, and designer to ensure proper testing of materials. Basic materials data should be made available in handbook form to the designer, especially for some nonmetals and coatings. A system also is needed for the orderly and accurate feedback of service experience information. Testing results should be standardized.

### E. Navigation and Communications

Navigation and positioning are prime requisites to safe and successful operations on and beneath the sea. Traditionally, the U.S. Government has supplied geodesy, chartmaking, and navigational aids to its own agencies, industry, commerce, and individuals (Figure 7). While there are many surface navigational aids, they generally lack precision for operations out of sight of land.

Communications systems are essential to intelligence interchange (including telemetry) among submersibles, support platforms or ships, undersea stations, buoys, and associated satellites or aircraft. Safety demands reliable communications equipment. Primary reliable communication links

**Figure 7.** *New Ambrose offshore buoy replacing Ambrose lightship off entrance to New York Harbor, an aid to navigation long provided by U.S. Government. (Coast Guard photo)*

must be provided for command and control and for emergencies. Acoustic frequency and power level allocations will be required as undersea activity increases.

### 1. Navigation, Geodesy, and Positioning

**a. Current Situation** Navigation, used here, means the location of one point on the earth's surface in relation to another. Geodesy is the science of determining the three dimensional coordinates of locations (geodetic control points) on the earth's surface. Positioning is locating oneself relative to a local reference not necessarily established geodetically.

Marine surveys normally are positioned by shore based electronic systems. Multiple methods are sometimes used, including shore based, inertial, satellite, bathymetric, and acoustic systems. Selection depends upon availability, repeatability or accuracy, distance of operations from shore, and purpose.

Distance from shore of commercial developments in the ocean regions is increasing, with no compensating decrease in the need for accuracy. If anything, improved accuracy will be required because of increased operating and exploration costs at greater distances and in deeper water.

Geodetic satellite programs on land are under way to establish a worldwide control point system to an accuracy of ± 10 meters in an earth-centered coordinate system. Applications of satellite methods to marine geodesy are under study. Satellites offer unique capabilities because they are independent of distance from shore and provide a singular reference datum. Current navigation by polar orbiting satellites requires supplementary methods for continuous positioning in the intervals between satellite fixes. Uncertainties in ship velocity and satellite orbit plus sensitivity to azimuth and elevation of the satellite from a ship are current sources of error in satellite navigation. Inertial navigation systems can be used to keep position between satellite fixes. Developments in navigation by geostationary satellites promise marked improvement through taking simultaneous bearings on two or more synchronous satellites continuously on station.

**b. Future Needs** The U.S. Government may have to provide underwater navigation aids as it has such surface aids as LORAN and satellite navigation (Figure 8).

**Figure 8.** *Coast Guard LORAN station at Nantucket, Massachusetts. Both LORAN-A and LORAN-C signals are transmitted from this station. (Coast Guard photo)*

Lack of long range, straightline communications or sensing below the ocean surface severely limits subsurface navigation. The addition of acoustic and optical navigation aids, such as coded transponders, would permit periodic check of position. Networks of such devices would permit sea lanes comparable to air lanes for navigation and traffic control. Both surface- and bottom-mounted units could be used. Inertial guidance systems, if reduced in cost and complexity, could be used to extrapolate between navigation marker locations.

Navigation is basic to most surface and underwater missions; it must be emphasized, however, that position determination is a fundamental technology that justifies advancement independently of mission requirements.

Evaluation of mission requirements for navigation support reveals that current capabilities are inadequate for general nonmilitary purposes. It further indicates that advancement of basic navigation technology, at least in part, should be separated from immediate mission requirements in order that (1) potentially useful systems not be shelved in favor of expediency and (2) a broader spectrum of instruments and information systems incorporating navigation input be made available.

Broad future navigational needs range from precise sophisticated systems for comprehensive ocean surveying to simple, short range, but not necessarily inaccurate systems for the occasional boating enthusiast.

The Department of Transportation presently is developing a national plan for navigation through the U.S. Coast Guard and Federal Aviation Administration. The plan will consider the development and operation of navigation aids for current and future aviation and maritime commerce. It will identify areas of U.S. Government responsibility for navigation services and the current and projected technology to carry out these responsibilities.

## 2. Communications

**a. Current Status** The primary communication link between submersibles, support ships, and bottom habitats is the acoustic underwater telephone. Communication is slow and difficult, particularly when multipaths and reverberation are present. For short range communication links optical systems may be practicable.

Transmission of submersible and station status and operating data by telemetry is preferable to voice transmission. No satisfactory equipment currently exists for this underwater acoustic need. Development of higher data rates is greatly desired.

**b. Future Needs** Needed will be a long-range acoustic communication system requiring investigations into the feasibility of new types of communication links perhaps through the benthic layer or solid earth. In the immediate future, an acoustic link must be developed to test and improve underwater communications and to support advancement of other fundamental ocean technology. For later developments, it will be required as a primary communication link for facilities where cable and radio communications are not feasible, as in remote locations.

Specific developments required for communications:

—High and low frequency sound (infrasound and ultrasound) sources and receivers with narrow beam and directional characteristics.

—Acoustic frequency and time conversion methods to permit direct usage of a larger portion of the acoustic frequency spectrum.

—Use of refraction layers in the ocean to enhance long-range communication and minimize interference from components.

—Development of acoustic and electronic concepts to improve signal-to-noise ratio through signal manipulation.

—Exploitation of other possible communication media and such advanced technology as lasers.

Radio frequency communications among ships, buoys, surface platforms, aircraft, satellites, and shore stations will require adaptation of equipment to the special requirements of the ocean environment (Figure 9). Problems must be solved with respect to allocation of frequencies and bandwidths necessary to support ocean activities.

### 3. Conclusions

Navigation is basic to most underwater missions. Ocean surveying requires the same types of basic reference systems and accuracies as on land. Satellite navigation improves accuracy on the

**Figure 9.** *Communications central aboard USC&GSS* Oceanographer, *one of the most completely equipped centrals aboard non-military U.S. flag vessels. (ESSA photo)*

ocean surface. However, for surveys below the surface, for undersea construction, and for geological evaluation, the improved surface accuracy may be nullified by the underwater navigation method used.

Undersea exploitation is limited by the lack of three-dimensional navigation systems, a combination of navigation and bathymetry. The ocean environment places severe demands upon subsurface navigation. To the extent that subsurface transponders or transmitters exist, accuracy is limited by original position determination plus the inaccuracies of acoustic ranging and direction-fixing.

Acoustic communications are hampered by several basic deficiencies which prevent reliable, high speed, wide band, accurate, short and long range information exchange. Development of underwater acoustic link equipment is required for habitat-to-surface communications.

Increasing surface traffic, wider utilization of submersibles, and future undersea stations and operations will require networks of communications-navigation aids.

Long range acoustic communications are difficult to achieve. As alternatives, seismic and earth-field communications offer interesting possibilities.

Radio frequency equipment must be adapted to ocean needs, and frequencies and bandwidths must be allocated.

Recommendations:

A formal program applying geodetic methods and principles at sea should be initiated to achieve the following:

—Establishment of marine geodetic ranges to validate and calibrate new systems.

—Development of improved positioning systems for shelf surveys and future extensions seaward.

—Expansion of geodetic satellite methods to marine applications for singular reference datums and establishment of geodetic control points.

—Establishment of a system of navigation aids permitting navigation accurate to 150 feet at a distance of 200 miles from shore.

In addition, a comprehensive broad based development program should be undertaken to:

—Improve subsurface navigation instrumentation accuracy and reliability.

—Reduce navigation instrumentation size, complexity, and cost.

—Seek new media and methods.

—Develop equipment to establish a local vertical reference.

—Pursue research and development of acoustic communications and underwater acoustic links.

—Develop a network of communication-navigation aids.

—Perform research on communications through the benthic layers or the solid earth to determine their feasibility for employment in undersea operations.

## F. Tools

Those who work in the oceans agree that most existing tools are seriously deficient in reliability, ease of maintenance, ruggedness, and simplicity of operation. Poor underwater visibility intensifies the problem. The need to resolve the tool problem has resulted largely in using or modifying off-the-shelf equipment, but such equipment is not satisfactory for the more sophisticated underwater tasks. Thus, tools built specifically for underwater work should be designed.

## 1. Current Situation

Land tools are designed for an environment of low viscosity, high visibility, and negligible buoyancy. The diver depends upon a vast number of these land tools modified for water use, including:

—Tools for cutting, hammering, torquing, and welding.

—Air tools to provide selected application of buoyancy forces.

—Water jet tools for clearing muds and digging trenches.

—Knives, scrapers, and pry bars.

The effectiveness of underwater operations is vitally dependent upon the adequacy of such hardware.

The basic characteristics—reliability, ease of maintenance, ruggedness, endurance, and simplicity of operation—are more critical for underwater hardware than for equipment on land. The petroleum industry has modified land equipment skillfully for offshore use. Government agencies, oceanographic institutions, and marine equipment firms have developed hardware for many underwater tasks. However, most existing ocean hardware items are seriously deficient in the basic characteristics.

Human underwater activity is greatly restricted by extremely reduced light transmission in water compared to air. Under ideal conditions, vision is little more than 100 feet; by comparison, very small objects can be distinguished at 2,000 feet in clear air. Typically, vision on the continental shelves of the world ranges from 5 to 50 feet. Where currents keep mud and organic material in suspension, vision may be no more than a few inches.

In order to alleviate these problems, some basic studies are being made in tool development; a few examples are discussed below.

The hammer undoubtedly would have developed along very different lines had the human race evolved in a medium relatively as heavy and viscous as water. Considerable energy is wasted under water during the travel of the hammerhead and shaft prior to impact. An efficient manual underwater striking tool could employ a heavy streamlined weight traveling a relatively short distance along a straight guide. Pneumatic hammers accomplish the same effect with shorter strokes.

Explosive studs fired from a hand gun to penetrate the hull plates of sunken vessels have been known since before World War II. Such tools still are somewhat crude, but the possible variants warrant further development. By clustering six or eight stud guns around the periphery of a circular plate with a lifting eye in the center, a very solid lifting pad can be attached quickly to almost any sunken metal structure. When injecting breathing gas or air into a compartment for buoyancy, a hollow stud driven through the compartment wall can serve as the through-hull penetrator.

Underwater welding techniques must consider the chilling effect of the surrounding water. The problem is especially evident with some high-yield-strength steels. Methods currently are under development to weld in a gas-filled compartment erected around the work area.

Steel can be cut by an electric oxygen torch with a hollow electrode. After an arc has been struck, oxygen is forced through the center of the electrode to burn the hot steel.

Sonic search devices may be carried by divers in poor visibility. A system presently undergoing test employs a continuous transmission, frequency modulated (CTFM) signal. A hand-held device emits an acoustic signal; echoes from obstructions modulate the return signal's pitch conducted to the diver's earphones. A high pitch indicates an obstruction at close range.

Because of high cost, the device is not used extensively. Greater effectiveness and lower price should result from volume production and competition. For many underwater search tasks, a wrist-mounted magnetic compass is adequate, but not reliable near a wreck or other large ferrous structure.

The Naval Underwater Warfare Center has been working on a hydrodynamic winch, a salvage lift padeye using explosive bolts, a buoyancy transport device which can carry objects weighing up to 1,000 pounds, a position and locating system for diver use, and a diver's underwater homing system.

## 2. Future Needs

There is an urgent need for tools designed especially for underwater work. In addition, we must consider the scientist's tasks that will necessitate good tools.

Future tool needs include:

—All-purpose pneumatic wrenches.

—Self-contained power tools or tools with power supplies small enough to be placed in the diving bell and that will function for hours on the bottom.

—Tools adapted for scientific work, such as coring tools with self-contained power supply, bottom samplers with power supplies at or near the diver, and marine life sampling tools which do not disturb the bottom.

In summary, the needs are for safer, more reliable tools for the commercial diver and specialized tools for the scientific diver.

## 3. Conclusions

Recommendations:

New, more sophisticated tools are needed for deeper diving commercial and scientific divers. (An artist's concept of a futuristic diver working at great depths is shown in Figure 10.) To that end, a more concerted basic and applied research program must be implemented. Some industrial tool companies already are making preparations for such work, but Federal assistance would expedite progress. A Federally sponsored, long-range research and development program to provide improved tools and tool procedures would help, but a strong interim capability is needed now to support present programs in the commercial, military, and scientific community.

**Figure 10.** *Artist's concept of future diver-operated jackhammer.*

## G. Mooring Systems, Buoys, and Surface Support Platforms

In any undersea activity, surface support usually is necessary to monitor and control, provide logistic support, render safety and rescue assistance, and serve as a local terminus of operations. In the future submerged support will become more frequent. Small moored systems classified as buoys have a long history as navigation aids. Use of stationary large surface vessels, barges, and platforms for commercial, scientific, and defense purposes is increasing.

Moored buoys also have collected and transmitted environmental information from selected ocean areas. Study of the feasibility of ocean data buoys has lead to formation of a Coast Guard project office to develop a National Data Buoy System. Unmanned moored data buoy networks may be deployed over deep ocean and continental shelf areas to measure automatically environmental parameters under, on, and above the water surface and to transmit the information ashore for

timely use in understanding and predicting the marine environment.

Highly stable ocean platforms like FLIP and SPAR have been designed and constructed by the U.S. Navy in conjunction with oceanographic institutions to collect environmental data.

Requirements for improved mooring and positioning of floating installations will continue to increase. Larger surface vessels and platforms, offshore airports, harbor facilities, mobile breakwaters, and multipurpose floating island concepts depend largely on improved mooring and positioning systems.

### 1. Mooring Systems and Buoys

**a. Current Situation** Open water mooring of vessels and platforms is the traditional method for stationing at sea. Anchor and cable systems are used to moor buoys, dredges, pipelaying barges, semi-submersible oil rigs, and drilling vessels. Brute force mooring techniques have evolved for shallow water locations, exemplified by the heavy sinkers and chain moorings used by the Coast Guard for navigational buoys (Figure 11). Excessive weights

**Figure 11.** *Typical massive anchor and chain for mooring navigational buoys in shallow water. (Coast Guard photo)*

prevent brute force techniques from being employed in deeper waters.

In recent years, dynamic systems have been developed to position surface platforms in deep water. Water depth, positioning accuracy requirements, operational conditions, and platform size economically justify a dynamic positioning system for some applications. For most deep water floating platforms, however, direct attachment to the bottom is necessary.

New materials are replacing the traditional steel cables and chains. Nylon, dacron, and polypropylene reduce weight and minimize corrosion problems of deep moors. New developments in fiber glass cables and chains also promise corrosion-free, high-strength moorings. Connecting devices of commensurate performance are required.

The stable surface platform, or specialized buoy, must perform a variety of tasks peculiar to the ocean environment. Special equipment is required to meet these needs. Surface platforms and buoys have particular requirements for position accuracy which vary widely. The required position accuracy usually is stated with respect to geographic location. Horizontal accuracy is defined as its *watch circle* (the area to which the platform's horizontal movement is restrained).

A system for maintaining buoy or surface platform position with respect to geographic location or bottom reference for extended periods is a primary requirement, except for intentionally-free buoys. Fixed moors require techniques to predict and counteract forces in the mooring cables. If embedment in rock is necessary, explosive anchors or equivalent techniques must be used.

Dynamic positioning systems incorporating various thrust control techniques (cycloidal propellers, directable propulsion units, or bow and stern thrusters) must undergo further evaluation at sea. Automatic control systems must be developed to signal corrective action depending upon inputs, surface conditions, and navigational data; an experimental system should be built and tested at sea. Finally, options between fixed mooring and dynamic positioning must be studied.

The horizontal watch circle in which a moored platform may move is influenced by design provisions. As the watch circle is decreased, greater demands are imposed on the anchor, which must resist both the horizontal drag of the buoy or platform and the vertical pull of the taut mooring line.

Vertical stability can be achieved through appropriate hull shapes like that of FLIP (Figure 12). The platform's design characteristics result in a hull with minimum response to the forces imposed by passing waves.

**Figure 12.** *Floating Instrument Platform (FLIP). Draft is 300 feet in vertical position. (Navy photo)*

**b. Future Needs** Technology leading to more stable and durable buoys and platforms is interrelated with many disciplines. It begins with a better understanding and definition of the winds, sea state, and currents over long periods and their dynamic interaction with floating vessels and platforms. The following specific improvements are needed:

—Methods to survey bottom conditions and predict anchoring characteristics of bottom sediments.

—New types of anchors with greater holding power in different bottoms at greater depths.

—Increased fatigue life of cables and connectors to reduce this most common cause of failure in mooring lines.

—Development of materials for higher strength chains and cables.

—More reliable, longer-life shackles, thimbles, swivels, and other fittings.

—Improved line tension measuring equipment for monitoring and limiting loads imposed by floating platforms on mooring cables.

—Analyses of the coupling of the motions between the platform and mooring cable under the excitation of wind and sea.

—More sophisticated sensing and control systems for dynamic positioning of large drilling ships and barges. Dynamic positioning is relatively new, and continual advancement will be required to establish its economic feasibility under all conditions at sea.

—Low cost (high production) expendable buoy technology including deployment concepts applicable to large-scale buoy systems for use on a global or quasiglobal basis.

Improved technology is expected to allow buoys to be positioned in remote areas to report synoptically observations via synchronous satellites using VHF or higher UHF frequencies. Particular emphasis should be placed on improved reliability so the service interval can be extended.

## 2. Surface Support Platforms

**a. Current Situation** Human underseas activity, except for military submarine operations, has required surface support. Development of submerged support systems will not negate this requirement.

Today the primary operating cost of deep submersibles results from the ships and systems to support them. Except for high pressure associated with great depths, the greatest and most dangerous ocean forces are at the surface with its attendant weather and wave system. Great hazards exist for the small submersible even in moderate seas during launching, retrieval, and transfer of cargo and personnel. A few wave lengths below the surface, wave effects disappear.

Avoiding surface effects by using submarines is ideal. Long endurance submersibles using nuclear, thermodynamic, or other power sources could minimize the need for support ships.

Current surface support systems development by the Navy include a new class of ASRs (Figure 13). These ships, with catamaran hulls, are designed to support rescue submersibles as well as other Navy missions. The ASR is a greatly improved support platform, but definitely limited by wave action in more severe seas. A test support ship, the IX-501, will be used for surface support of Sealab III (Figure 14). It depends on moorings and relatively protected waters to support test operations.

**Figure 13.** *Artist's concept of first of new series of submarine rescue ships (ASR). Catamaran hull configuration provides stable platform and large working area necessary for launching, retrieving, and supporting Deep Submergence Rescue Vehicle (DSRV) and advanced diving systems. (Navy photo)*

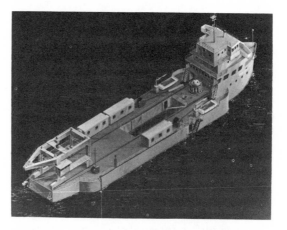

**Figure 14.** U.S.S. Elk River *(IX-501), special purpose range support ship first used in Sealab III operations, has center well, 65-ton traveling gantry crane, deck decompression chambers, and two personnel capsules. (Navy photo)*

The Navy is modifying nuclear submarines and one diesel sub to test carrying the DSRV piggy-back—a promising beginning of an all-weather and under-ice submersible support system divorced from the hazards of the ocean surface.

Through its own laboratories and in association with academic institutions, the Navy built FLIP and SPAR, two deep draft, surface stable platform vessels for oceanographic and acoustic research. They have proved very successful as stable platforms; FLIP is reported to have experienced vertical motion of only three inches in the presence of 35 foot waves.

The following are important operations performed by stable surface platforms:

—Vehicle handling. Launching and retrieving manned and unmanned vehicles involves handling heavy masses through a very rarely calm, ocean-atmosphere interface. Equipment and techniques must be improved before launch and retrieval can be accomplished safely and routinely. Submerged retrieval (involving underwater docking) is a possibility being developed for the Navy's Deep Submergence Rescue Vehicle.

—De-ballasting. Mining, construction, and salvage operations at continental shelf depths may require large quantities of high and low pressure air for de-ballasting operations. Routine provision of air supplies at depth has not been accomplished.

—Diver support. A satisfactory surface system is required to continuously support extended saturated diving operations at sea.

—Logistics. Surface platforms must be supplied with materials and personnel while on station. At-sea transfer techniques during severe weather must be developed; vertical replenishment with helicopters offers a possible solution. Platforms may be required to provide potable water, electric power, high pressure air, heat, supplies, quarters, subsistence, and medical care to personnel working at the site below.

b. **Future Needs** In the past there has been a strong inclination to adapt off-the-shelf equipment to needs of surface support vessels and platforms, resulting in repeated failure of equipment to function in an environment for which it was not designed. A specially designed stable surface support system could provide reliability, relative freedom from weather and sea state conditions, safer and less costly support, and availability.

The trend is toward improved support capability. Development of new platforms designed specially for all-weather submersible support whether by submarine or by deep-draft surface stable vessel, is strongly encouraged. By 1980, a more subsurface Navy and a proliferation of commercial submersibles will dictate improved support systems capability. Work at continental shelf depths and deeper will require surface support ships where surface conditions are favorable and where the underwater task is such that a surface supported system can be deployed more rapidly or economically. For many shelf operations large submersibles may perform tasks without surface support.

For underwater tasks requiring surface support, a variety of ships will be used. It is unlikely that a single multipurpose platform could perform all support functions. A need exists to investigate platform requirements including selected model studies and ancillary equipment development.

Various stabilization systems are already in use (e.g., stabilizers, tuned ballast, hull shaping) to decrease motion of ships under way. However, little has been accomplished for stationary platforms other than for FLIP and SPAR. Such stabilization techniques as mass traps should be considered. The traps are formed by two long plates held apart at intervals; water inside is trapped, providing an apparent mass that dampens the motion of the platform.

A system to maintain a surface platform's position for extended periods with respect to geographic location or bottom reference will be required. Project Mohole did much for dynamic positioning.

A variety of lifting and emplacement requirements will be put upon future platforms. Available equipment or technology provides for lifts up to 200 tons. Winches stabilized to counteract ship's motions during a lift operation have been thoroughly studied. For heavy lift or emplacement in excess of 200 tons, a large floating crane or similar device must be evaluated.

3. **Conclusions**

Mooring and anchoring techniques and hardware are inadequate for the heavy load and long exposure demands of present and future deep ocean platforms and buoys. Present mooring systems employing wire rope encounter problems of excessive weight, corrosion, kinking, low elasticity, torsional unbalance, and massiveness of handling equipment. Systems employing nonmetallic nylon or dacron ropes encounter problems of fishbite, lack of electrical cables for underwater instrumentation, and mechanical attachment.

The National Data Buoy System project under the Coast Guard will demand substantial development and improvement in deep ocean mooring and buoy technology, from which engineering in many other areas will benefit.

Present support for undersea activities is chiefly by surface ships. Experience with FLIP and SPAR demonstrates that specially designed hulls can maintain remarkable stability under conditions of severe sea and weather. Specially designed surface stable platforms are necessary to support deep ocean vehicles, stations, and activities. The dynamics of various types of floating platforms are sufficiently different that each must be treated independently in establishing a satisfactory mooring system.

In the future, large stable surface platforms may evolve into mid-ocean storage depots, transportation centers, power stations, etc. (Figure 15).

**Figure 15.** *Artist's concept of future large stable surface platform. (North American Rockwell photo)*

They will serve as an upper terminus, power source, supply depot, and safety monitor to deep ocean construction work and undersea station maintenance. These platforms will evolve from FLIP, SPAR, and other systems which can maintain remarkable stability even in adverse weather conditions.

Recommendations:

**Research and development should be performed in mooring technology and equipment to support deep ocean operations at 2,000 feet in 5 years and at 20,000 feet in 10 years.**

**Several types of buoys and platforms should be investigated to determine effects of size, configurations at the air-sea interface, underwater-shape drag, draft, metacentric and pendulum stability, platform directional control, mooring attachment location on different mooring systems, and the system best suited for each type of platform.**

**A National Project for a Pilot Buoy Network in support of the National Data Buoy System project of the Coast Guard should be implemented.**

**The more promising cable materials should be evaluated under operational conditions.**

**Surface stable platforms capable of supporting underseas vehicles, stations, and construction and salvage activities to 2,000 feet in 5 years and to 20,000 feet in 10 years should be developed. The platform must provide a surface terminal for logistic support, vehicle handling, compressed air, diver support, heavy lift, electric power, and other services as needed by the undersea activity.**

## H. Biomedicine and Diving Equipment

Biomedical technology must go hand in hand with equipment development to (1) improve human capability to withstand variations in pressure and temperature, (2) enhance vision, hearing, and tactile perception, (3) provide mobility and orientation, and (4) make tool use effective while in a virtually weightless condition.

The most effective diver is one who operates freely, carrying his own life support system. Thus, technology must be applied to resolve diver problems through biomedical research and development and design of proper suits and breathing rigs.

## 1. Biomedicine

**a. Current Situation** Fundamental man-in-the-sea technology is bio-engineering oriented and is particularly concerned with human functions and performance undersea. Devices, equipment, and materials must be provided which (1) enable man to withstand changes in pressure and temperature associated with increasing depth for extended and repeated periods, (2) accommodate his sensory requirements to maintain adequate visibility, orientation, feel, and hearing, and (3) provide him with directional and locator capability, mobility, and tools.

Although experimental dives have been made to depths in excess of 1,000 feet, current technology restricts operation to approximately 600 feet for relatively short intervals.

Scuba (untethered diving wherein the diver carries his life support system, maintains near neutral buoyancy, and enjoys nearly complete dexterity) currently is most useful for shallow short-duration dives.

Normally in commercial operations, divers are tethered to the surface. The diver receives gas from the surface and maintains communication with topside personnel who calculate his decompression time. Diver bottom time is increased over scuba. Deep diving systems often are employed when operations require dives in excess of 300 feet for several hours.

The nucleus of the deep diving system is a pressure vessel that serves as an elevator transporting divers to the underwater site. Many such systems provide for mating the personnel transfer capsule with a deck decompression chamber so divers can decompress in relative comfort. Deep diving systems eliminate in-water decompression and provide backup life support to enhance safety.

If a man is to work for a long period at a particular depth he must adapt physiologically. Prolonged living under increased pressures has been demonstrated in such saturated diving experiments as the U.S. Navy's Sealab and the Cousteau Conshelf. Using this technique, after about 24 hours a diver has absorbed all the gas his system will at that depth, and the time he must spend in decompression remains the same. Therefore, the longer the diver stays, the greater his productive time compared to decompression time.

Saturation diving has been employed in the open sea to about 650 feet and probably will be extended beyond 1,200 feet in the near future. Saturation diving, however, requires expensive special life support equipment and instrumentation and so is not economical for most current operations.

Special breathing mixtures pose a host of physiological and bio-engineering problems.

*(1.) Physiological* Toxicity of breathing gases, individually and combined, for greater depths is not established firmly—particularly for extended periods of continuous exposure.

The total effect upon respiration and metabolism of operating at greater depths imposes severe restrictions on such basic operational parameters as rate of ascent, diving depth, duration, and work accomplished. For example, the breathing apparatus must precisely measure and control partial pressure of oxygen when the concentration is well below one per cent.

Gas density and sound velocity change with gas composition and distort the voice, making communication difficult.

*(2.) Bio-engineering* Essentially all engineering designs must be revised to accommodate variations in density, viscosity, thermal conductivity, and other properties of gas mixtures employed. Materials, equipment, and instrumentation are subject to serious malfunction because of these variations. It is a specialized engineering problem, and discretion must be exercised in employing off-the-shelf hardware.

The Navy's Biomedical Engineering Program is conducted as a coordinated effort of several groups. The Deep Submergence Systems Project and the Office of the Supervisor of Salvage are involved principally with hardware development for near-term application.

The Underwater Bio-Sciences Research Program of the Bureau of Medicine and Surgery is a comprehensive five-year plan for basic research in support of Navy underwater operational requirements. Concurrent human factors research is directed by the Office of Naval Research. The overall plan was issued by the Chief of Naval Development, who enlisted the aid of several organizations and the academic community.

**b. Future Needs** The following Navy programs in underwater biomedical research and development are designed to meet future biomedical needs.

(1) General physiology
    (a) Cardio-pulmonary physiology.
        (i) Pulmonary ventilation, work of breathing, and related studies.
        (ii) Thermal and gaseous effects on circulation.
    (b) Heat loss and caloric requirements of underwater swimmers.
    (c) Nutritional requirements in hyperbaric environments.
    (d) Physiological effects and indications of stress resulting from prolonged exposure to environments.

(2) Decompression studies
    (a) Study of deep and prolonged dives using various mixtures to depths of human tolerance.
    (b) Feasibility studies of computer use for decompression computations.
    (c) Studies of basic physical-physiological factors in bubble formation.
    (d) Development of advanced therapeutic procedures for decompression sickness.
    (e) Studies of the effects of chronic exposures to hyperbaric environments.

(3) Studies of inert gases and artificial atmospheres
    (a) Studies of new gas mixtures and effects to depths of tolerance or to 2,000 feet.
    (b) Basic and clinical research in oxygen toxicity.
    (c) Effects of gases under pressure on cellular metabolism and neuromuscular function.
    (d) Solubility and distribution of inert gases in body tissues.

(4) Pharmacology
    (a) Evaluation of drugs in hyperbaric environments.
    (b) Pharmacological agents to combat stress and fatigue in underwater environments.
    (c) Pharmacologic adjuncts for hyperbaric oxygen therapy.
    (d) Prophylaxis and therapy of illness and injury from marine life.

(5) Atmosphere studies: isobaric and hyperbaric
    (a) Trace contaminants toxicity.
    (b) Toxicological appraisal of undersea construction materials.

(c) Psycho-physiological effects of air ions.
(d) General atmosphere studies in isobaric closed environments.

(6) Psychology
    (a) Selection and training.
    (b) Sensory and motor adjustments.
    (c) Psycho-physiological adjustments.
    (d) Group functioning.

## 2. Diving Equipment

**a. Current Situation** *(1.) Breathing Rigs* Semiclosed rigs predominate when diving is supported by a submersible chamber. They also are used extensively by free swimming military divers (Figure 16). The system requires less than one-tenth the gas supply of completely open-circuit breathing rigs. The diver's exhalation passes

**Figure 16.** *Diver testing a tethered, semiclosed breathing rig. (Westinghouse photo)*

through a baralyme or sodalime canister which absorbs the carbon dioxide, recycling most of the exhaled gas for rebreathing. Semiclosed rigs are simpler than closed-circuit, mixed-gas rigs, but the improved gas economy (duration) of the closed-circuit rig compels its consideration in the future.

Closed-circuit pure oxygen rigs are very simple; however, human physiological reaction to oxygen restricts their use generally to depths of 25 feet for one hour. Unless there is a basic breakthrough in diving medicine, closed-circuit pure oxygen rigs will find little application.

The closed-circuit, mixed-gas rig offers the same gas economy as the closed-circuit, pure-oxygen rig (Figures 17 and 18). However, the consumption of oxygen in the mixture varies with work rate and depth, and addition of oxygen must reflect such changes. This requires precise sensors and control devices that increase cost and complexity while degrading reliability.

Some of the most advanced rigs employ either polarographic or fuel cell oxygen sensors. Control of partial pressure of oxygen through cryogenic technology has been demonstrated.

Because of the narcotic properties of nitrogen in compressed air and the very high air consumption rates, open-circuit sport scuba rigs and the

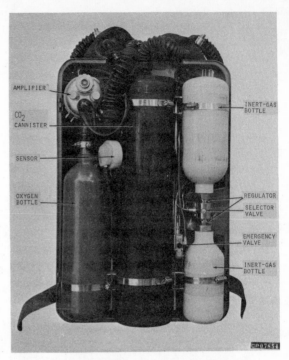

**Figure 18.** *Closed-circuit, mixed-gas breathing rig (back view). (Westinghouse photo)*

standard hard hat air rigs have little place in saturation diving.

*(2.) Protective Clothing* Diving often involves exposure to cold water, making protective clothing essential. Even water that feels warm can result in important heat loss if an exposure suit is not worn. Notwithstanding the many advances in diving technology, much commercial diving still is done with the heavy rubber and canvas dress associated with hard hat diving invented by Augustus Beebe in 1837 (Figure 19).

A recent notable departure has been the metal suits having rigid subsections with movable joints. These are one-atmosphere suits; whereas, the hard hat suits expose the diver to ambient pressure. The latest is a development from a space suit. Because of the complex geometry of the human anatomy, the joints are very difficult to make. To be useful, the joints must be flexed easily while an effective seal at pressures of several hundred pounds per square inch is maintained.

In the last 25 years, close-fitting, pliable rubber and neoprene suits have been developed for free swimming divers. These fall into two main cate-

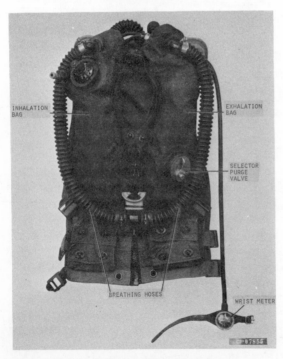

**Figure 17.** *Closed-circuit, mixed-gas breathing rig (front view). (Westinghouse photo)*

The wet suit is made of closed cell neoprene sheets, and consists of a close fitting jacket, trousers, hood, gloves, and socks. The layer of tiny gas bubbles entrapped in the closed cell neoprene between the cold water and the diver's body provides insulation. The thin film of water inside the suit is virtually stagnant and rises very quickly to skin temperature. Because the flexible suit material contains gas in closed cells, the increasing pressure of depth compresses the material, diminishing its insulating value and the diver's buoyancy.

Heated suits are among the most recent developments; they contain electric heating elements or tubes for hot water circulation (Figure 20). One

Figure 19. *Hard hat diver. (Westinghouse photo)*

gories: dry suits, intended to keep the wearer dry, and wet suits, which have a thin, relatively stagnant layer of water between the swimmer's skin and the suit.

The dry suit still is preferred for extremely cold water. It usually is made of rubber, relying on seals at waist, neck, wrist, and ankles to keep water out. Woolen underclothing may be worn inside. A major disadvantage is that a tear admitting water practically destroys the suit's insulating effect. More sophisticated dry suits (constant volume suits) now are available; a regulated gas supply keeps the inside of the suit slightly above ambient pressure and prevents squeeze as the diver changes depth.

Figure 20. *Model of hot water circulation suit. (Westinghouse photo)*

new water heated garment consists of a modified neoprene wet suit supplied with hot water by a hose from the surface or from a diving chamber. The hot water enters a simple hose distribution system from a control block at the waist and flows to the hands and feet. From the extremities, water flows back over the diver's skin and exits from the suit to the ocean at the face and neck openings.

Another diver undergarment contains tubes stitched to the fabric, an adaptation from a cooling garment used in outer space. Water enters at the waist, is piped back again to the waist, and returns thence to the heating unit. The tubes extend to hands, feet, and fingers.

The bulk of a suit relying only on the insulating value of its material limits diver mobility and dexterity. In water below 45°F., insulation will not protect fingers inside a glove. When manual dexterity is required, mission duration is limited to about one hour. However, a diver can be sustained indefinitely in near-freezing water by hot water or electrical energy readily supplied. Present technology would require about 500 pounds of silver-zinc batteries for the energy necessary for a six-hour mission. For this reason, such advanced concepts as isotope heat sources are being investigated.

**b. Future Needs** The most critical problem with exposure suits is development of a light, compact, selfcontained energy pack for a free swimming diver. The most promising systems rely on silver-zinc batteries to supply electrical energy, a pyrotechnic cartridge to supply heat, or an isotopic power source to supply both. Suits produced for the astronauts may be adaptable for underwater use. Because of the high cost of development, the initial versions are likely to be tailored for military needs.

Diving with a selfcontained underwater breathing apparatus is restricted by the compressibility, solubility, and narcotic effects of gases. Increased volumes of gases can be made available by cryogenic technology. Another solution would be to use breathing mixtures that are not compressible. Liquids such as physiologic saline solution are likely to behave as biologically inert respiratory gas dilutants at great depths, in contrast to compressed inert gases.

No excessive amounts of inert gas can dissolve in the blood and tissues of a diver with liquid filled lungs regardless of depth. Hence, the diver could

return to the surface regardless of the time spent underwater and as rapidly as desired.

Medical technology has produced artificial kidneys and artificial lungs. It may be possible that suitable extracorporeal gas exchangers modeled after the gills of fish could be constructed. An artificial gill, enabling a diver to obtain oxygen by diffusion from the sea rather than from stores carried in cylinders, would have obvious logistic advantages. Even more important, a diver equipped with an artificial gill, extracting oxygen like a fish from the water, could never be exposed to toxic oxygen partial pressures (Figure 21).

**Figure 21.** *Artist's concept of future diver wearing gill-pack.*

The possibility of man exchanging respiratory gases directly with an aquatic environment have not been explored seriously until the present decade, and it is difficult to predict the outcome of such research.

Underwater breathing systems during the next few decades will be dictated by the need for breathing support related to man existing under high pressure. More people will spend appreciable time in wet environments operating untethered from a habitat or diving system. Therefore, they will need compact, reliable systems and the ability to eliminate or reduce manyfold the present decompression time penalties. The technique of liquid breathing, anticipated as a revolutionary departure from mixed gas breathing, opens the possibility of greatly shortened decompression periods.

Needs in breathing gas technology include:

—New breathing mixture components that provide chemical inertness and nontoxicity without undesirable changes in density and thermal conductivity.

—Better understanding of the toxic reactions of oxygen, carbon dioxide, nitrogen, and hydrogen.

—Better understanding of the effects of various gas mixtures—one component on another.

—Data on the physical aspects of respiration under water during various levels of physical activity.

—Better understanding of the aeroembolism processes (blood and tissue gas dynamics) and subsequent establishment of more precise decompression procedures.

—Toxicity of oxygen at high pressure and prolonged exposures.

—Central nervous system narcosis by nitrogen and other inert gases.

Closely related is the need for bio-engineering development to solve the problems of:

—Equipment and materials to maintain body heat balance and to preserve tactile sense and manual dexterity.

—Increased resistance to breathing under increased pressures.

—Long, slow decompression.

—Loss of body heat during prolonged submergence.

—Impairment of speech by artificial atmospheres.

—Action of drugs and medical procedures for man in the sea.

Effective, compact, and compatible swimmer doppler navigation and sonar systems are needed. Today's support equipment is too heavy, bulky, and difficult to integrate into the total diver system.

There is an urgent demand for breathing apparatus using available breathing gases most efficiently and for a system to heat diving suits under deep sea pressures and temperatures.

## 3. Conclusions

Current diving technology permits operations in protected or relatively shallow waters to a depth of approximately 600 feet; however, free diving in excess of 1,200 feet will probably soon be realized. With proper emphasis, this capability probably can be increased to 2,000 feet or more, but there are extremely difficult physiological hurdles to be overcome in diving at much greater depths.

Progress of free diving at greater depths is retarded by such numerous problems as safety, breathing gases, body heat retention, diver speech, and decompression. Research and development is in progress on these matters. Liquid breathing research, if successful, may provide a means of attaining depths in excess of 2,000 feet.

Oxygen toxicities and hypoxia have been extensively studied, but long-term exposure to such inert gas mixtures as helium-oxygen, nitrogen-oxygen, or hydrogen-oxygen mixtures at pressure has not been studied sufficiently to establish appropriate diver exposure limits. Reduction in decompression time for saturation divers is expected to become a critical economic factor in utilization of free divers.

In engineering designs of diver support equipment, specialized problems are involved and off-the-shelf techniques should be used with discrimination.

The number of deep ocean divers is multiplying on all coasts, and saturation diving will become common practice in the near future. There is a shortage of sustained funding for personnel and facilities engaged in advanced diving research and medical treatment.

Recommendations:

**Research should be pursued to make possible effective free diving at depths of 2,000 feet in 10 years or less, seeking to attain increased depth capabilities in 20 years by perfection of liquid breathing.**

**Research and development should be accelerated to improve and simplify diving techniques,**

diver safety, breathing gas technology, body heat retention, diver speech, diver nutrition, and decompression technology.

Experiments should be conducted exposing lower animals to inert gases and mixtures up to one month at various pressures, temperatures, humidities, and activity levels to determine guidelines and limitation of diver exposure.

A national program to train medical personnel and expand facilities for diver medical treatment and research should be established.

## I. Environmental Considerations

The major features of the geophysical environment—air, sea, and the land beneath the sea—must be understood to further ocean technology. The systems and techniques to study these features encompass ships, aircraft, satellites, buoy systems, undersea fixed platforms, and maneuverable submersibles. Much basic technology of marine science is at hand to make great progress, but efforts are fragmented and information is scattered.

A thorough understanding of the following factors is necessary for operations in and under the sea.

—Submarine topography, stability of slopes, microbathymetry, bottom composition, engineering and chemical properties, and bottom currents (including turbidity flow).

—Temperature, salinity, density, dissolved gases, pH, Eh, and nutrients.

—Fouling, bioluminescence, dangerous animals, and false-target and sound-scattering organisms.

—Currents, waves, breakers, surf, internal waves, sea level, and tides.

—Distribution, concentration, and thickness of sea ice.

—Spatial and temporal variation, deflection of vertical anomalies of gravity and magnetism.

It should not be inferred that knowledge is completely lacking in the above factors, but improvements in environmental measurement and prediction are essential for success in increasing national capabilities in the ocean.

The near-surface environment of the oceans varies greatly from place to place and time to time. However, near-surface current velocity, sea state, visibility, background noise, and sound propagation are probably less variable and influential on undersea systems than ocean floor and sub-bottom environmental differences like bathymetry, sediment distribution, and acoustic characteristics. The sea floor is much less well known than the nearsurface environment.

Improved techniques for undersea surveys are needed for economical and timely completion of such needed ocean information as the following:

—Gross bathymetry, slope, and roughness.

—Small scale bottom roughness.

—Sediment shear strength.

—Liquid-solid interaction and bearing strength.

—Geological patterns, salt domes, and examination of outcrops.

—Gravity and magnetic readings and false magnetic targets.

—Small scale reflection profiles and seismic characteristics.

—Temperature and heat conductance.

—Circulation and tidal currents, including turbidity currents.

—Internal waves.

—Behavior of visible light and water clarity.

—Sound propagation, background noise, and false acoustic targets.

Data collection techniques now utilized (mainly analog) require lengthy processing and analysis procedures. Use of digital techniques, including realtime data collection and processing at sea, is increasing, but much still must be done to meet basic needs (Figure 22).

### 1. Sea Floor and Bottom Strata

**a. Current Situation** Submarine topography and microbathymetry operations include (1) preparation of bathymetric (bottom topographic) charts

**Figure 22.** *Computer aboard USC&GSS* Oceanographer *is used for data collection and processing.* *(ESSA photo)*

of the oceans prepared to various scales and various contour intervals and (2) studies of the sea floor to determine provinces of similar structures such as basins, ridges, and rises and to determine direction and degree of slopes.

Location and description of submarine physiographic features are indispensable to:

—Determining areas of potential mineral or petroleum deposits.

—Site selection for bottom installations.

—Surface or subsurface navigation.

—Developing sonar techniques for finding new fisheries.

**b. Future Needs** There have been few major developments in bathymetric survey techniques and systems since invention of the sonic echo sounder and graphic recorder, although progress has been made in precision depth recorders and side-looking sonars.

One major step, digital recording of soundings as a supplement to graphic recording, has cut drastically the time required to produce bathymetric charts. This development can be improved even further. Faster and more detailed bathymetric surveying methods based on advances in acoustic, photographic, recording, and other types of instrumentation are needed.

Research into the seafloor's changing topography and structure also is necessary for both military and nonmilitary use. Development of free, self-propelled, unmanned undersea probes as well as manned exploration submersibles will enhance survey capabilities. Such systems must operate to depths of 20,000 feet.

The Navy Shipboard Survey Development Program includes capabilities to take narrow beam and wide beam bathymetric data from a cable towed instrument package operable to 20,000 feet. The system includes devices to display essential data on a ship's bridge. The Navy plans such capability for 11 vessels, 2 of which are now in operation, *U.S.N.S. Silas Bent* and *U.S.N.S. Elisha Kane.*

### 2. Bottom Composition and Engineering Properties

**a. Current Situation** Knowledge of the composition, properties, and mechanical behavior of seafloor sediments is essential for designing foundations, recovering minerals, predicting the behavior of vehicles and equipment on or in the ocean floor, tunneling, pipeline and cable laying, controlling pollution, disposing of waste, salvaging and recovering objects, and interpreting geophysical records. In underwater work, soil mechanics must be applied in drilling, coring, pile driving, dredging, mining, and operations involving penetration into seafloor sediments.

Soil mechanics is established reasonably well for engineering tasks on land. With very few exceptions, theoretical and applied ocean soil mechanics (away from coastal areas) is no more than 15 years old. The studies and measurements made in this relatively short time are few. High pressures, dynamic conditions, and inaccessibility contribute to the complexity of the problem.

The reliability of underwater soil engineering data must be better than for land applications. Failures of land structures due to erroneous soils data can be remedied and normally are not catastrophic. Submerged installations, however, are not susceptible to convenient repairs; failures can be costly and hazardous.

Remote sediment sampling from surface ships by snappers, dredges, and corers is unsuitable to obtain the relatively undisturbed samples needed for engineering purposes. *In situ* sediment sampling has been accomplished in shallow waters by scuba divers and in deeper water by submersibles. Submersibles permit direct observation of the sampling process and can acquire samples with thin wall devices in the upper six feet of sediment.

Laboratory experiments on seafloor sediments have been conducted using samples recovered by coring devices, submersibles, or other means. Meaningful engineering measurements can be made in the laboratory and related to *in situ* measurements. Selective sampling of large areas should yield reconnaissance information of wide applicability such as in preliminary site studies.

**b. Future Needs** Prediction of foundation stability should be facilitated by determining such sediment properties as permeability and dynamics of water movement, depth-dependent strength gradients, compressibility characteristics, and elastic and plastic equilibrium to predict foundation stability. Mass sediment stability characteristics include bearing capacity, settlement, slope stability, penetrability, and breakout forces.

These properties are important to such applications as operation of mining machinery on the ocean floor, reflection and refraction of sound energy striking the ocean floor, geophysical exploration, and foundation site selection and preparation.

To determine slope stability and layer thicknesses, sediment properties must be known to considerable depths. Properties cannot be determined now below the uppermost few feet. Also, there is a need to determine the probability of occurrence, the properties, and possible effects of turbidity currents on installations. Instrumentation systems able to remain submerged for long periods must be developed.

Chemical additives or mechanical conditioning may be able to increase sediment strength or prevent stirring fine particles which reduce visibility. However, in some places the need for artificially improving visibility is eliminated since strong currents carry suspended sediments away.

Comparative analytical studies of all common sediment types are needed to relieve the need for detailed *in situ* sampling. Instrumentation systems lowered to the ocean floor could transmit or record data on density, sound velocity, shear strength, and sediment bearing capacity to quickly characterize an area.

Research and development needed to advance undersea soil mechanics capabilities include:

—Samplers for use by divers, submersibles, and surface ships.

—Instruments for on-site measurements like vane shear at several depths within a sediment body.

—Equipment to take long borings in deep water, including techniques to re-enter bore holes.

—Instrument packages for narrow beam echo sounding and high resolution profiling devices to be towed at cruising speeds.

—Instruments to record properties of turbidity currents.

Foundation engineering criteria must be established and transformed into pertinent seafloor data requirements. Because underwater foundations will be constructed on the basis of information acquired under adverse conditions, methods are needed to inspect them and surrounding soil and to effect repairs.

Interaction between underwater foundations and bottom soil can result in the creation of complex moments and forces. Techniques are needed whereby lateral, uplift, twisting, and overturning forces and moments can be applied and measured singly and in combination. Sensors to detect changes in pressures, deflections, or displacements would be useful in surveying the ocean floor locally prior to and following construction.

### 3. Physical and Chemical Properties of Seawater

**a. Current Situation** The three properties that most affect underwater design are pressure, temperature, and salinity. They influence the basic physical properties of seawater—density, specific volume, electrical conductivity, compressibility, sound velocity, viscosity, and surface tension. Osmotic pressure, freezing point, and boiling point are determined by salinity only.

*(1.) Density* On the average one cubic foot of seawater weighs 64 pounds; one cubic foot of ice weighs 56 pounds, and one cubic meter (35 cubic feet) of seawater weighs one long ton or 2,240 pounds. However, these values vary with tempera-

ture, salinity, and pressure. The water column consists of multiple density layers rather than a steadily increasing density with depth. A direct method to measure density is needed.

*(2.) Acoustic Properties* Sound is the principal means of communication and detection in the sea. For locating objects, positions, and terrain features or for probing the nature of sediments, sound is essential. Unfortunately, temperature changes with depth bend sound waves, and the changes vary with time and space.

For these reasons, water temperature is the ocean property most widely measured. The Navy alone makes more than 5,000 temperature soundings per month. Such data are essential for the Naval Weather Service to derive daily maps of near-surface sonar propagation conditions.

Sound from a source in the ocean's near-surface region follows many diverse paths generally classified as:

—Surface duct. Sound travelling in the near-surface region.

—Bottom bounce. Sound reflected off the ocean floor.

—Convergence zone. Refracted sound travelling along a deep path and sometimes reinforced with energy from the bottom.

The development of operations in the latter two categories requires geophysical data. New technology for measuring temperature, salinity, and pressure includes:

—Salinity-temperature-depth system (Figure 23) which records water salinity and temperature at various depths.

—Expendable salinity-temperature-depth system.

—Airborne radiation thermometer which measures sea surface temperature by infrared radiation, enabling an aircraft or a satellite to quickly amass data over a large area.

—Buoy temperature sensor cables.

—Expendable bathythermographs for measuring temperatures at various depths by surface vessels and aircraft.

**Figure 23.** *STD sensor for measuring water salinity, temperature, and depth being lowered from USC&GSS* Oceanographer. *(ESSA photo)*

*(3.) Electromagnetic Properties* Seawater rapidly absorbs almost every wave length in the electromagnetic spectrum. Radio waves (except extremely long high-energy waves) are attenuated immediately in water. Infrared waves are absorbed by water molecules. Ultraviolet, X-ray, and gamma rays are absorbed by electrons or atomic nuclei. However, water is relatively transparent to visible and near-ultraviolet light.

*(4.) Salinity* Salinity is defined in terms of dissolved solid material in seawater. The salts of sodium and chlorine are the most important, accounting for approximately 85 per cent. Of the various constituents, only calcium is present in a state of saturation; seawater is far from saturated with the others. Seawater's ability to dissolve large amounts of solids and gases without reacting chemically with them is one of its most important properties.

Salinity varies in different ocean areas; however, approximately 90 per cent of seawater falls within 34 to 35 parts per thousand. New discoveries have been made in hot spots where salinities are as high as 240 parts per thousand. In some areas gold concentrations are over 600 times the ocean average. (Such discoveries could be important in ocean mining.)

The Nansen bottle, developed in the 1890's, still is used to take samples for analyzing seawater salinity. Improved instruments are needed to sample and measure very deep waters quickly and easily.

The mutual exchange of energy and material between ocean and atmosphere at the ocean surface depends largely on the chemistry of the topmost layer of water. The importance of diffusion processes near the deep ocean bottom is just beginning to be appreciated. In some cases these may be studied by such natural tracers as the upward diffusion of radium from the sediments into the bottom waters. Mixing mechanisms and rates between upper, intermediate, and deep ocean layers can be studied by artificial radioactive tracers as well as natural chemical tracers.

*(5.) Dissolved Gases*  Gases constitute about 0.25 per cent by weight of ocean water, their solubility decreasing with increasing temperature or salinity. The most important and abundant gases in the ocean are oxygen, nitrogen, and carbon dioxide. Dissolved oxygen is of special interest to undersea systems because of its corrosive effect on materials. Surface waters are usually saturated with dissolved oxygen.

The amount of dissolved oxygen decreases with depth until an oxygen-minimum layer is reached at a depth of 2,000 to 3,000 feet. Below this oxygen content gradually increases until the bottom is reached. Very deep bottom waters frequently have an oxygen content approaching that of surface water.

Dissolved oxygen indicates the age of deep cold currents entering from surface polar regions. This free oxygen is consumed by deep water marine life. In waters within the sediments, the oxygen content drops radically because of the activity of bacteria and bottom dwelling organisms.

Nitrogen in seawater, occurring as free dissolved gas or in such compounds as nitrates, nitrites, and ammonia, is essential for living matter and determines the growth rate of ocean plants. Sediments on the bottom often have only a small amount of organic nitrogen, correlating with the concentration of organic matter in the sediments and in the overlying waters. Carbon dioxide occurs in relatively large amounts in seawater as carbonates and bicarbonates.

Some ocean areas produce abundant gas bubbles that greatly impede sound waves. In the Southern California Bight and in the Red Sea virtual curtains of gas continuously are rising from the ocean floor. In some areas of high productivity or of stagnation (like the Black Sea) deep waters produce hydrogen sulfide bubbles and contain little or no oxygen.

*(6) Hydrogen Ion Concentration (pH)*  Values of pH, a measure of hydrogen ion concentration range from zero (highly acid) through 7.0 (neutral) to 14 (highly alkaline). The carbon dioxide content mainly determines the pH value of seawater. In the deep ocean it generally decreases from about 8.3 at the surface to 7.7 at depths between 1,200 and about 3,000 feet, below which it rises to about 7.8. Values as low as 7.5 are found in areas of high biological activity because of carbon dioxide liberation. Near the shore, the pH may drop sharply due to introduction of fresh water streams highly charged with decaying vegetation and organic matter from the land. Sometimes a sharp drop in pH is found immediately above the ocean bottom because of carbon dioxide produced by such bottom organisms as bacteria.

*(7.) Oxidation-Reduction Potential (Eh)*  Organic matter also has a great effect on the Eh of water. (Eh, or oxidation-reduction potential, is a measure of the ability to accept or donate electrons, thus a measure of corrosiveness.) Seawater approximately six feet above sediment sometimes has Eh values of zero; below this level and into the sediment, Eh may drop as low as -300 millivolts. At the sea surface Eh usually is about +300 millivolts. Bottom topography strongly influences whether zero Eh occurs six feet above the bottom or below the sediment surface. Thus, site selection surveys for bottom habitats and installations are necessary to anticipate corrosion problems.

*(8.) Radioactivity*  Disposal of low-activity solid radioactive wastes in specified areas of not less than 6,000-foot depth is permitted. These wastes are sealed in containers and should cause no problems to underwater operations.

The natural occurrence of radioactive elements in seawater is very small, the principal element being potassium-40. Man-made radioactive material enters the ocean by fallout. Although seawater greatly dilutes these wastes, some radioactive elements are concentrated by biological organisms. Ionization chambers, Geiger counters, photomultiplier scintillometers, and similar instruments can be suspended from ships to measure radioactivity.

**b. Future Needs** New techniques to measure directly temperature, salinity, and sound velocity to greater depths are needed to provide direct digital and analog output required for realtime data processing.

Airborne and shipborne deep expendable recording bathythermographs for direct digital measurements of temperature versus depth to 20,000 feet from a moving platform are needed. Direct measurement of sound velocity to great depths is required for reliable sonar operation.

New techniques are required to permit rapid, continuous *in situ* analyses of the important chemical properties of seawater and bottom sediments, particularly at sites considered for undersea installations.

## 4. Dynamic Factors

Ocean energy decreases with depth; therefore, practically all the ocean's environmental energy is contained in gravity waves, tides, and currents. Yet other factors are important because of their potential hazards.

**a. Gravity Waves** Predicting the exchange of energy and material across the air-sea interface is largely concerned with the growth and decay of gravity (wind generated) waves. This aspect has progressed well, making available refined forecasting techniques. Much data on average wave heights exist, although data still are lacking on wave lengths. Current research is directed primarily at the fundamentals of energy exchange, seeking to diminish the heavy reliance on observation and experimentation.

Early wave observations consisted primarily of random visual observations from ships. Of questionable accuracy, these data provide little knowledge of more sophisticated wave characteristics like spectral components, period of maximum energy, and directional behavior.

Older instruments to measure sea state include ship's wave recorders, photo wave recorders, wave poles, and stereo photogrammetry. New instruments take continuous measurements of the sea surface from ships, satellites, and aircraft, providing accurate and more complete observations.

These include (1) the airborne wave meter utilizing a radar altimeter device to acquire wave structure profiles, (2) a sonic echoing device mounted on a ship's bow to measure waves continuously and to compensate automatically for ship motions, and (3) cameras on satellites (especially in synchronous orbit) to produce photographs analyzed for information on sea surface conditions. Wave sensors on fixed ocean platforms like the *Argus Island* permit study of storm waves not normally measured by ships.

Subsurface wave motion, surf conditions (important derivatives of surface waves), and such wave processes as generation, propagation, refraction, decay, filtering, and subsurface pressure fluctuations are little understood.

Mathematical models for computer use are being developed to reduce complex wave motion data to understandable information. The Environmental Science Services Administration is developing mathematical models of ocean-atmosphere interactions and of the conveyance of heat and water. A more sophisticated model of total world hydrology, including sea ice, ground water, and other factors, has been developed, but its application is limited by lack of experimental data. Instrumentation to obtain pertinent data is vitally needed, and the technology to develop it appears available.

Future wave measuring sensors must measure not only height but the entire directional spectrum. Knowledge of waves for engineering design criteria is lacking. Some numerical analysis techniques have been developed for design criteria of the Polaris ballistic missile and other systems. These techniques have been amplified and improved, but the basic problem of obtaining proper measurements has not been solved.

**b. Internal Waves** Internal waves are not well understood but are known to have an effect on underwater sound transmission. Internal waves usually are measured by observing short-term temperature fluctuations at given points in the water column; however, motion of the ship or buoy from which the instruments are suspended could bias results. The very stable FLIP platform has been used for internal wave measurements with good results. To predict motions in the environment adequately, technology is needed to measure three dimensional internal wave spectra by digital data collection techniques.

### c. Unusual Waves—Tsunamis and Hurricane Waves

Tsunamis (tidal waves) are formed by earthquakes or by slides that dislocate the ocean floor. They are of 200 to 300 miles in length but only two or three feet high in deep water. Moving at great speeds, they usually are not detectable to the eye until they increase to as much as 20 or 30 feet in height when approaching coastlines.

Hurricane waves are difficult to predict because the circular motion of hurricane winds causes the waves to move at various angles from the path of the storm. Hurricane waves generally accompany storm surges or storm tides that can run 4 to 15 feet above normal high water as they move toward land. Little effect from surface wave action is felt 200 to 300 feet below the surface.

Hurricane research is active, although a storm's course cannot yet be predicted, nor its fury controlled. Technology is needed to slow the process of evaporation of water from the sea in a hurricane and to disrupt the convection process that adds the extra energy to convert a rain storm into a hurricane. Technology is needed also to develop improved mathematical models of storms.

### d. Thermodynamics

The exchange of thermal energy affects the thermal structure in the upper ocean layers, generation of ocean weather, maintenance of global atmospheric circulation, and propagation of perturbations in climate. Unfortunately, the process is little understood, and progress has been slow mainly because technology is not developed sufficiently for the refined observations needed to establish more effective theory.

Ocean heat comes primarily from the sun. For undersea operations, however, heat flowing from the earth's crust also is important (Figure 24). It is practically uniform on the shelf and in the basins but is significantly higher in areas of midocean ridges and trenches. Deep drilling into the crust is required to improve knowledge of these phenom-

ena. The deep ocean depths are the coldest parts of the seas (3.8°C average).

**Figure 24.** *Heat probe for measuring ocean bottom heat flows and taking core sample being lowered from oceanographic survey ship. (ESSA photo)*

### e. Currents

Surface currents are horizontal movements and include both tidal currents (produced by tidal movements of water in ocean basins) and circulation currents. Navy interest in currents traditionally has centered on their navigational effects. New developments in surface and submerged current measurements include the automatically recording deep moored telemetering buoy.

Subsurface currents, important to undersea operations, include deep-layer vertical movements (upwelling or sinking) and movements caused by tides or large-scale turbulence. Shifts of sound signals is one way of measuring subsurface currents. Long-range sonar is affected by dynamic changes in location and characteristics of ocean water masses, thus requiring extensive data on currents to be effective.

However, obtaining that information in deep water is so expensive and time consuming that few measurements have been made. A few moored current meter arrays have been installed at the Navy's Atlantic Undersea Test and Evaluation Center and elsewhere. Variations in current are computed from data taken from these arrays and compared with concurrent temperature and salinity data.

Although deep ocean currents are generally of low velocity, some evidence exists that these currents coupled with the presence of a structure could create turbulence, erode the bottom, produce a wake of turbid water, and affect foundation stability. These effects could make a bottom installation more detectable by acoustic means and could upset or bury the structure; therefore, further investigation of near-bottom currents is a necessity.

**f. Hydrospace Handbook**  At present the ocean engineer has no single source of information summarizing data on environmental factors and their effects on materials and components considered in designing ocean systems. The U.S. Air Force prepared the *Handbook of Geophysics* and *Aerospace Materials Handbooks* to provide information for design of aircraft, missiles, and spacecraft. A hydrospace handbook containing information on environmental factors affecting ocean engineering design could be invaluable. One such handbook is expected to be released in the near future.

An important function of both industry and government will be to assure that such handbooks are continuously updated and technical memoranda, failure analyses, and engineering data to help advance ocean capability are published. Another responsibility is in preparing ocean engineering texts for teaching and technical reference.

A possible *Hydrospace Handbook* outline:

## HYDROSPACE HANDBOOK

**Chapters**

I. *The Marine Environment*
    a.   Properties of Salt Water
    b.   Properties of Soil, Silt, and Sand
    c.   Hydrostatic Pressure vs. Depth
    d.   Sound Propagation
    e.   Light Transmission
    f.   Wave Motion and Forces
    g.   Sea Temperature, Salinity, Density vs. Depth (worldwide)
    h.   Wave Heights, Storms, Meteorological Data, Currents
    i.   Navigation Data

II. *Materials*
    a.   Physical Properties
        (1)  Density
        (2)  Strength
        (3)  Corrosion and Fouling
        (4)  Galvanic Table
        (5)  Welding Characteristics
    b.   Corrosion Protection
    c.   Buoyancy Materials
        (1)  Efficiency Curve for Cylinder/-Sphere vs. Depth
        (2)  Syntactic Foam
        (3)  Buoyant Outer Hull
    d.   Pressure Hull Penetrators

III. *Structural Data*
    a.   Pressure Hulls
        (1)  Shapes and Volumetric Efficiencies
        (2)  Design Data (Equations for transition areas, viewports, hatches, buckling)
    b.   Wetted Hulls
        (1)  Design Data (Unstiffened, ring stiffened, ring and stringer)
    c.   Simple-Beam Equations for Moment, Shear, Deflection

IV. *Fluid Mechanics*
    a.   Fluid Statics
    b.   Real/Ideal Fluid Flow
    c.   Fluid Measurements
    d.   Flow About Immersed Objects
    e.   Drag, Lift, and Cavitation

V. *Thermodynamics*
    a.   Liquids and Gases
    b.   Gas Laws
    c.   Refrigeration and Heating
    d.   Humidity
    e.   Air Conditioning
    f.   Modeling Theory

VI. *Hydrodynamics*
    a.   Basic Relation to Gas Dynamics
    b.   Propulsion
    c.   Steady/Unsteady Flow
    d.   Skin Friction
    e.   Shape/Drag Curves

VII. *Electrical*
    a.   Direct Current Circuits and Power Sources

        (1)    Batteries
        (2)    Fuel Cells
        (3)    Nuclear
    b.    Alternating Current Circuits
    c.    Electrokinematics and Magnetic Circuits
    d.    Electrostatics and Dielectric Circuits
    e.    Electrical Connectors and Cables
    f.    Electromagnetic Interference Reduction
    g.    Connectors, Conductors, and Cable Properties

VIII. *Bio-Engineering*
    a.    Human Factors
    b.    Diver Decompression Tables
    c.    Diver Gas Mixtures vs. Depth Tables
    d.    Life Support Systems

  IX. *Communications*

  X. *Safety and Certification*

*APPENDIX A*–Table of Definitions
*APPENDIX B*–Milestones in Undersea History

**g. Conclusions**    A great need exists to map synoptically the physical and dynamic ocean and ocean bottom processes. The expendable bathythermograph has provided a revolutionary tool to map temperatures. Similar systems are needed to measure sound velocity, waves, and currents.

Knowledge of probable extremes in the ocean environment is insufficient to establish engineering design criteria. Variations within the sea and the sea floor are little known or understood relative to land variations. Exploitation of the deep sea and the continental shelf will require detailed information on the interrelationships of temperature, pressure, salinity, and currents and on the effects of fouling and corrosion on materials, bottom mounted structures, cables, buoy moorings, and systems.

Underwater soil mechanics affects all missions involving objects attached to or in contact with the ocean floor. Soils information is important to (1) preparation of foundations for structures and installations, (2) bottom sitting or crawling submersibles, (3) drilling, coring, dredging, pile driving, mining, and production, (4) waste disposal, and (5) salvage, rescue, and recovery. Soil mechanics state-of-the-art is not adequate for effective

sampling, let alone prediction. Yet these data must be more reliable for ocean than for land application.

For military applications (especially in antisubmarine warfare) the advent of new detection systems utilizing bottom bounce and convergence zone modes has emphasized the need to measure ocean floor acoustic characteristics.

Bottom loss characteristics are little known, because present systems and techniques are inadequate to measure detailed topography, acoustic properties of sediments at all frequency ranges and grazing angles, and bottom losses. The marine geophysical surveys sponsored by the Naval Oceanographic Office have provided new and valuable information, but more is needed.

**Recommendations:**

**New and improved instruments and instrument suits must be developed for oceanographic sampling and measurement including means of:**

**—Improving underwater optical visibility.**

**—Viewing and recording bottom features without using the visible spectrum.**

**—Making rapid,** *in situ* **measurements of the mass physical properties of both water and marine sediments, and of other properties to provide engineering data for seafloor construction.**

**—Making rapid, continuous** *in situ* **analysis of chemical properties, Eh, and pH of sea-water and bottom sediments.**

**—Making rapid, continuous surveys of bottom topography.**

**A vigorous program should be pursued to examine, understand, and determine subsea physical, biological, and geological environmental conditions as they affect engineering design. The data critical to engineering design should be accumulated and published in handbooks, technical memoranda, and engineering data sheets and updated continuously as knowledge permits.**

**Effective surface, diver, or submersible-emplaced, engineering-oriented,** *in situ* **sampling and measuring devices must be developed to characterize the ocean floor and sub-bottom and to study turbidity currents over long periods, if**

seafloor soil mechanics is to be understood. The information derived should be made available in engineering design handbooks. Operational techniques that minimize soil disturbance and ways of increasing subsurface sediment structural strength must be sought.

## J. Data Handling

Problems of handling large quantities of diverse environmental data will continue to increase rapidly. The technology of fast, high-capacity automatic data handling systems has increased markedly in recent years with third generation high-speed digital computers now in general use.

Storage and retrieval systems can provide random access to large masses of data, permitting reduction of data storage in the computer itself. This advanced technology has not been applied to the marine program to any important degree as yet.[4] Shipboard computer use was begun fairly recently and is increasing. However, most of these computers are being employed primarily as data storage mechanisms, not as realtime data processing systems.

### 1. Current Situation

**a. Data Gathering**  Many new instruments for collecting oceanographic data have been designed for direct digital data collection. Examples are sound velocimeters, salinometers, and expendable bathythermographs. To date, however, these generally have had their own shipboard digital recorders.

**b. Data Display and Recording**  Both digital and analog displays are being used now in marine data collection, permitting immediate, rapid data evaluation and checks on collection quality. However, many techniques still are primitive. Strip chart records, for example, require laborious manual processing and analysis. Digital magnetic types are in use but in lengthy experimental programs large volumes of tape can be generated, creating a storage problem. Therefore, techniques to com-

press digital outputs will be necessary to optimize information content, especially with buoy systems.

**c. Data Processing**  With shipboard computers in oceanographic measurement programs, speed of data collection and processing has increased significantly. Much processing is routine as in the reduction of Nansen cast data and correction of reversing thermometers. Shipboard employment of the computer as a realtime data processor has been limited. Some use has been made of realtime collection and processing systems for acoustic studies, especially for and by the Navy.

**d. Data Relay Developments**  Systems are being developed to telemeter data required at sea in realtime directly or via relays (ships, buoys, satellites, or shore stations) to central data processing activities (Figure 25). Here the data can be immediately interpreted and new instructions sent back to the survey vehicle. This offers improved accuracy and speed while making possible use of simpler, less costly equipment aboard the survey vehicle.

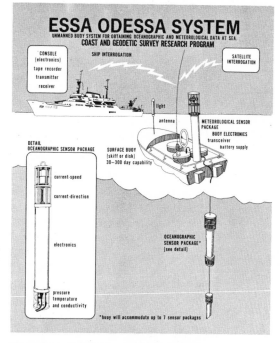

**Figure 25.**  *ODESSA system telemeters environmental data from unmanned buoys to ship or satellite for subsequent transfer to central data processing facilities. (ESSA photo)*

---

[4] The problem of data handling is under intensive study by the National Council on Marine Resources and Engineering Development.

**e. Data Storage and Retrieval** The data storage and retrieval systems now handling marine data are antiquated and require either duplicate storage or very slow sorting and retrieval procedures. For example, the National Oceanographic Data Center (NODC) does not possess any random access capability.

The National Oceanographic Data Center handles primarily ocean station and bathythermograph data, plus limited geological and biological data. NODC does not handle engineering (such as fouling, corrosion, and strength of materials), bathymetric, magnetic, gravimetric, photographic, or many other types of important marine data. These data exist at widely scattered locations throughout the Nation but could be much more useful if in compatible formats and located centrally.

## 2. Future Needs

Integrated realtime data processing systems are needed to handle multiple uses of new, diverse instrumentation developed with digital recording capability. Thus, computer interfacing is required to permit immediate processing of data from these instruments in a compatible manner. Progress to date must be extended and rapidly accelerated, especially in view of anticipated buoy developments.

Random access capability is needed in data retrieval from all marine data bases to ensure rapid access by users. Random access disks and magnetic drums are available but have not been used extensively in the marine field, except for selected mission-oriented Navy programs.

## 3. Conclusions

A need exists for much greater realtime data reduction and analysis at sea by computer or through relay to central data processing facilities ashore. Computers offer the advantage of reducing large quantities of data rapidly into comprehendable format for prompt review and analysis. Data from several ships can be correlated simultaneously. The resulting on-site knowledge would permit more efficient use of sea time for critical measurements and control of data acquisition. The technology of operating instrumentation systems at sea under adverse environmental and platform stability conditions, however, effects the reliability of automatic data facilities.

Currently, the National Oceanographic Data Center is developing data bases for physical, chemical, geological, and biological data. No data bases for important engineering criteria (fouling, corrosion, and strength of materials), bathymetric, magnetic, gravimetric, bottom photography, and sea ice exist. These data are contained in widely scattered generating activities and generally are not available to meet user requirements.

**Recommendations:**

**Standardized computer hardware and software systems should be developed for oceanographic tasks. Such systems should include data plotting and navigational control and should become an integral part of all government funded research vessels. Since automatic computation equipment presently is available for use at sea, future large-scale government sponsored and conducted environmental data missions should not be undertaken unless onboard automatic realtime data collection and processing capabilities are utilized to assure the efficient employment of scarce scientific talent.**

**NODC should be equipped with random access capability to increase the speed and efficiency of data retrieval under various categories such as cruise or institution. Branch data centers should be established throughout the nation, the location depending upon technical competence and user interests.**

**To be most effective, NODC should be supported entirely as a line item in a single agency's budget. This could be achieved best as an adjunct to an expanded Navy ocean mission to support national objectives (see Chapters 2 and 4), especially since much NODC-held data will be from classified Navy missions.**

## K. Life Support

Life support in small submersibles, cargo and support submarines, and ocean bottom stations is complex and challenging. Fortunately, considerable knowledge and experience exist, a large part contributed recently by the National Aeronautics and Space Administration, by nuclear defense shelter development, by Navy's nuclear fleet submarine operations, and by the Navy Sealab experiments.

## 1. Current Situation

Life support activities may be divided into seven functions:

—Atmosphere control (breathing mixture and contaminant control).

—Climate control (temperature and relative humidity).

—Water supply (potable, wash, and machinery makeup).

—Food supply (preparation, refrigeration, freezing, and storage).

—Waste removal (solid and liquid waste products).

—Habitability (human factors design consideration).

—Personnel (crew's psychological wellbeing).

**a. Atmosphere Control** Atmosphere control, although the most difficult of life support functions, is not a new problem. Submarine and, more recently, space vehicle designers have devoted considerable time and effort to its solution. However, only recently have human beings been subjected to a completely closed environment for extended periods without frequent rotation. Miners, although exposed for many hours, have daily recuperative periods before re-entry into the mine, as do diesel submariners during surfacing or snorkeling. Polaris submariners regularly spend 60 or more consecutive days submerged with no opportunity for their bodies to recuperate.

Since relatively little is known about the cumulative effects of long-duration exposure, it is extremely important to keep the atmosphere of manned underwater structures as pure as possible. Once the desired atmosphere has been defined, various methods to maintain it can be analyzed.

The simplest method is a ducted supply and exhaust system with filters using the earth's atmosphere to provide air. This method is applicable to land-linked mining operations having tunnels extending under the ocean floor or to shallow underwater habitats.

A second method is to bleed fresh air from storage tanks, to filter the habitat atmosphere, and to pump contaminants overboard. Considerable power and frequent resupply are necessary; the method has proved to be extremely inefficient in providing a uniform clean atmosphere.

The third and most feasible method is to provide a sealed habitat with oxygen supplied either from storage or from an oxygen generator. Oxygen storage can be either high pressure or cryogenic; the advantages and disadvantages of each must be analyzed for a particular application.

Oxygen generators have been improved over the early years of nuclear submarine operation. The current units provide good service but require assiduous care in operation and maintenance; improvements are necessary to enhance reliability and safety. Currently, a very promising oxygen generator module (a byproduct of fuel cell research) is under evaluation for the Navy.

Chlorate candles and chlorate candle furnaces have been used on nuclear submarines. However, control is presently impossible, because once ignited the whole candle is consumed; hence, an automatic system appears impractical. Other methods combining oxygen generation with carbon dioxide removal are in preliminary stages. Some appear promising but only for limited compartments and small crews.

Filters, catalytic burners, and carbon dioxide scrubbers may be used to purify habitat atmosphere. Activated charcoal filters, electrostatic precipitators, and mechanical means may be considered also. Catalytic burners (as carbon monoxide-hydrogen burners) perform well with little maintenance or adjustment. Carbon dioxide removal can be accomplished by liquid scrubbers or dry chemical plates. To date only monoethanolamine scrubbers have proved efficient and reliable for large volume purification. Smaller volumes may be cleaned by lithium hydroxide plates or crystals.

The problems of sealed atmosphere control in submerged structures can be solved with present technology, but the system selected will depend upon the structure's volume, crew number, mission duration, and to some extent power source chosen.

Another problem is monitoring habitat atmosphere for contamination from materials and consumables. Hardware in the market for both automatic and manual monitoring of atmospheric contaminents must be considered. For most compounds, commercial detection units are available; however, each has certain shortcomings. Manual sniffers are extremely reliable and should be used for backup and checking automatic units. Many types of hardware have been employed in existing diving systems and submersibles.

Components and materials must be screened as soon as preliminary designs are begun. Paints and adhesives must be selected with care, for many evolve toxic gases during deterioration. Consumables brought into the structure must be controlled, including lubricating oils, halogenated hydrocarbon solvents, and aerosol packaged products. When passed through the catalytic burner, many create such chemical derivatives as hydrochloric and hydrofluoric acid vapors, even more dangerous than the original products. Similarly corrosion, fire, and explosion hazards must be eliminated through constant surveillance.

Emergency breathing stations should be installed in numbers to support the occupants while rescuing them from the station or raising it to the surface. Such a system would have to be closed-circuit to preclude excessive internal pressure build-up within the vehicle or station, unless anticipated rescue time is very short.

Additionally, backpack breathing sets may be furnished for use in contaminated areas. These must be untethered to allow wearer to pass through a lock. When personnel return from a contaminated space, some of that atmosphere will be brought into the general living compartments; provision must be made to control such contamination.

**b. Climate Control** The function of an air conditioning system is to remove heat and humidity from air used as a heat sink by personnel, electronic equipment, and various auxiliary equipment. Within certain limits, control of compartment temperature and relative humidity is necessary for personnel comfort and proper operation of internal equipment.

Design of the air conditioning system will be influenced by:

—Outside water temperature.

—The need to minimize the number and size of pressure hull penetrations.

Three methods of air conditioning are available:

—Vapor compression.

—Absorption.

—Thermoelectric.

Vapor compression systems currently employed in submarines are subject to leakage of refrigerant vapors at seals, valves, pipe joints, and control connections. Absorption systems, such as the lithium bromide type generally used, are extremely heavy and bulky and have a low coefficient of performance. Both the vapor compression unit and the absorption system use refrigerants hazardous to personnel.

For example, Freon becomes a personnel hazard at concentrations of 250 parts per million or higher. If not removed by the atmospheric control system, these vapors can contaminate the atmosphere during long periods of submergence. Further, Freon also can break down into more harmful compounds in the presence of such high temperature sources as cigarettes, galley ranges, and pyrolytic burners.

Various internal systems convert energy to heat, which is ejected into the internal hull atmosphere. The heat must be passed overboard to the sea, and since many heat sources may be localized, the associated heat removal devices may be localized.

The magnitude of heat rejection associated with fixed and variable heat loads must be determined. Fixed heat loads are generated by internal systems which are required for performance of mission functions but are essentially independent of crew life support requirements. Included are radiation, convection, and conduction from hot piping, machinery, and electrical and electronic equipment.

Variable heat loads are generated principally by life support functions. These include heat from the waste and water system, galley, food storage refrigeration, laundry and showers, metabolic water condensation, body heat, carbon dioxide absorbing equipment, and the oxygen recovery and supply equipment.

One approach to designing the heat rejection system is to eject all waste heat to the sea through a single heat exchanger. An intermediate coolant can be used to collect waste heat from the various systems. Alternatively, several heat exchangers inside and outside the pressure hull can be used. Both approaches must be evaluated to determine system layout, cost, and safety.

Another approach employs thermoelectric devices adjacent to a particular heat source. This eliminates movement of large volumes of air but requires electrical hull penetrations to a hot plate outside. Thermoelectric air conditioning can also be used as a heater by the reversal of the power supply voltage.

**c. Water Supply** Water is required at different degrees of purity: potable water for drinking and food preparation; fresh water for personal hygiene, and rinse water in sanitation, laundry, and dish washing.

Fresh water can be supplied from storage tanks or extracted from sea water. For long missions and large crews, storage may be impractical. Several types of fresh water machines are available. For very large installations, combination nuclear power generation and fresh water evaporation plants are possibilities.

Vapor compression units have been used successfully on submarines and small surface ships for years; for steam driven ships, several firms offer reliable compact units.

As part of water management, measures must be taken to minimize water discharge. For example, a system must be considered (similar to that used in commercial airlines) whereby toilets are flushed with water pumped at high velocity from a drain collecting tank. The tank will accumulate effluent from showers and other sources.

In general, two basic water management concepts can be considered. The first is essentially a closed system incorporating various forms of regenerating waste water while storing on board waste products. It involves various filter processes. Little or no makeup water will be required in an efficiently operating closed system.

The second system is the conventional open system that rejects unprocessed all waste water overboard and utilizes sea water distillation as a fresh water source. This is presently used aboard submarines. Fresh water from distillation is stored in central tanks. Additional unprocessed water may be used for flushing toilets. However, the differential between the normal internal atmosphere and the ambient pressure of the depths

argues for a closed system, especially as depth is increased.

**d. Food Supply** The food supply can range from the prepared variety used by astronauts to the kitchen-cooked meals served aboard nuclear submarines. The latter require space, equipment, and additional atmosphere control equipment. Frozen meals with wide menu selection and well balanced diet could be furnished. Preparation would be minimal. Mission duration, crew size and composition, power source, and logistic procedures will determine the most suitable system.

**e. Waste Disposal** Solution of waste disposal must consider power and men available, mission duration, depth, and location of the habitat (or operating depth of submersibles). Freezing or chemical systems supported by between-mission replenishment would be most desirable for small to medium size crews (15 to 25 men) and less than 120 days.

However, for long missions and large crews some mechanical means must be utilized. Blowing sanitary tanks with compressed air (as in conventional submarines) requires greater amounts of energy with increased depth; this method becomes impractical at great operating depths. In addition, sewage must be removed from a habitat's vicinity to avoid contamination of intake water and to prevent disturbing the scientific environment.

A closed system could store all liquid wastes in a waste receptacle containing a chemical disinfectant to arrest bacterial activity. Garbage and fecal waste could be compressed, treated chemically, sealed in drums, and packed in freezer storage space as food supplies are consumed. Trash could be baled and stored. It is conceivable that little additional space and facilities would be required for a closed system.

**f. Habitability** Much work is being done in human factors from a design viewpoint. In early design of habitats, little attention was paid to comfort, because major emphasis was on safety; however, that phase has passed. Because of concentration on long periods of underwater habitability, attention has been focused on the human factors.

Habitability has become a major factor in designing for sustained system effectiveness. Certain factors like ventilation and lighting may be equated directly to performance errors during operation. However, design of living quarters, recreation areas, and other nonoperational facilities also can affect ultimate performance through impact on morale, fatigue, and other factors.

Other design factors less directly related also are important. A significant consideration in the crew's adjustment to isolation and confinement is the availability of a safe, reliable escape method.

**g. Personnel**  More than any research project, nuclear submarines have shown that men can live together in close confines for long periods. Personnel selection, mobility, pleasant surroundings, activity to increase mental stimuli (school, music, movies, machinery operation and repair, watch standing), sanitary conditions, food preparation, atmosphere, sleeping facilities, and crew size must be considered in design of a manned underwater structure.

Good communications keep up interest in the outside world and offset isolation. This has been experienced during Polaris patrols when emphasis has been placed on information from families ashore, although security regulations permit no reply.

The effects of isolation and confinement upon human performance have been considered in recent manned space flight programs. Dramatic changes have been observed in single individuals isolated for several days or weeks. In small groups (two to five individuals) some subjects developed regressive behavior and feelings of hostility, although anger seldom was expressed directly. Both regression and hostility may, of course, be extremely detrimental to performance. The passage of time usually increases the effects of other stressful conditions like boredom, lack of communication, sexual deprivation, and machinery noise.

To combat the negative effects described above, the habitability of both living and working spaces should be enhanced. Several features in the current Polaris system, for example, reflect that privacy is important to those living in a confined space.

## 2. Future Needs

Life support functions now can be performed by any of several methods and equipments. The best choice will hinge on engineering analysis considering vehicle or station characteristics, mission, and cost. Adaptation and improvement will be necessary as vehicles and stations become larger, operate deeper, and cruise longer, and as higher standards or more difficult goals are introduced. Reliability, maintainability, and endurance must keep pace.

Problems remain with new hardware where no prior experience exists upon which to draw—for example, the overboard discharge of liquid and solid waste and the intake of sea water in sufficient volume at depths to 20,000 feet.

## 3. Conclusions

At depths greater than 2,000 feet, transfer of sea water in and waste water out of a pressure hull demands large energy consumption, a hazardous hull penetration, and hardware of special capabilities. Atmosphere control is by far the most difficult life support function.

In air conditioning, factors influencing design are outside water temperature and number and size of pressure hull penetrations.

Utilization of energy by various internal systems results in heat which is rejected to the internal hull atmosphere. This ultimately must be ejected to the sea.

Operating depths greater than 2,000 feet have a major impact on design of internal systems. Because of the danger inherent in taking aboard large quantities of sea water and the difficulty of discharging waste water at this great depth, a carefully planned system of water inventory management will be necessary.

The solution to waste disposal must consider power and men available, mission definition, depth, and location of habitat or operating depth of submersible.

**Recommendations:**

A research and development program is needed to provide safe, effective, economical pumps, valves and piping to transfer fluids and solids in and out of pressure hulls at depths to 20,000 feet. As an alternate, a completely closed-cycle water and waste system should be perfected.

Other research and development work on life support methods and equipment should be done to support the national projects recommended in

Chapter 7 of this report and in particular the undersea laboratories, stations, and vehicles.

## II. TEST FACILITIES

The conquest of three strange environments in the last 30 years demonstrated the need for complete and adequate testing. In striving for high altitude operation of military aircraft in the late 1930's and early 1940's engineers quickly discovered that operating conditions in the rarified atmosphere above 10,000 feet were completely different.

They were compelled to design and build entirely new environmental simulation facilities to test, evaluate, and qualify aircraft engines, electrical systems, and mechanical systems. Development of the B-29 aircraft was delayed at least two years, and the jet engine was delayed for an indeterminate time beyond initial conceptual stages because facilities did not exist.

After the first supersonic flight in October 1947, the aircraft industry encountered problems of adiabatic temperature rise in mechanical and electrical components due to ram air compression. Entirely new concepts of test equipment were essential to simulate high altitude, high temperature operation.

The first Sputnik in October 1957 launched the world into the third new environment, the vacuum of space. Recent construction programs on large and expensive space simulation facilities again forcefully demonstrated that test facilities must be provided to conquer a new hostile environment.

### A. Simulation Facilities

### 1. Current Situation

Developing and utilizing the undersea frontier may face a completely unnecessary barrier—lack of test capability to qualify, certify, and ascertain operational readiness and effectiveness of future deep operating equipment. Without this capability, undersea development will be faced with failures, frustrations, wasted effort, and possible loss of life.

Within government and industry there are only 17 large pressure test facilities capable of simulating pressure to 2,270 feet (1,000 pounds per square inch) and five large tanks capable of simulating pressures to 22,700 feet (10,000 psi). Figure 26 presents a summary of these facilities.

**Figure 26**
**LARGE U.S. PRESSURE TEST FACILITIES**

| Maximum Static Pressure (PSI) | Diameter Feet | Length Feet | Location[1] |
|---|---|---|---|
| 20,000 | 4.0 | 8.0 | IITR |
| 15,000 | 5.0 | 8.3 | Southwest Res. |
| 15,000 | 4.0 | 20.0 | NSRDC |
| 10,000 | 10.0 Sphere | | NSRDC |
| 10,000 | 5.0 | 10.0 | NCCCLC |
| 6,000 | 6.0 | 21.0 | NSRDC |
| 5,500 | 6.0 | 10.0 | NCEL |
| 4,000 | 7.5 | 19.0 | Southwest Res. |
| 3,750 | 4.0 | 8.5 | Southwest Res. |
| 3,000 | 6.0 | 10.0 | NASL |
| 1,300 | 8.0 | 28.0 | Perry |
| 1,200 | 8.3 | 36.0 | NOL |
| 1,200 | 11.5 | 33.0 | NSRDC |
| 1,200 | 7.5 Sphere | | Southwest Res. |
| 1,000 | 8.3 | 26.0 | NRL |
| 1,000 | 7.0 | 14.0 | Electric Boat |
| 1,000 | 7.5 | 19.0 | Electric Boat |

[1] IITR - Illinois Institute of Technical Research, Chicago

Southwest Res. - Southwest Research Institute, San Antonio, Texas

NSRDC - Naval Ship Research and Development Center, Carderock and Annapolis, Maryland

NCCCLC - Naval Command, Control, and Communications Laboratory Center, San Diego, California

NCEL - Naval Civil Engineering Laboratory, Port Hueneme, California

NASL - Naval Applied Science Laboratory, Brooklyn, New York

Perry - Perry Submarine Builders, Riviera Beach, Florida

NOL - Naval Ordnance Laboratory, White Oak, Maryland

NRL - Naval Research Laboratory, Washington, D. C.

Electric Boat - General Dynamics, Electric Boat Division, Groton, Connecticut

Few environmental tests have been conducted on structures, external machinery systems, or other deep submersible components. As structures and components are designed for lighter weight, greater strength, and increasingly improved performance, it becomes necessary to utilize more advanced materials, which may affect the performance and fatigue life of the systems.

Navy data indicate that the fatigue life of HY-140 steel may be only one-tenth that of HY-80 steel, and fiber reinforced plastic pressure housings may have a very short life measured in only tens of cycles. Simple crush tests will not demonstrate expected performance. It will be necessary to subject structures and components to temperature and pressure low cycle fatigue tests, requiring extensive test time.

Once gross integrity of the hardware system and safety of man have been assured, it is important to determine mission effectiveness of complex manned systems operating in a challenging environment. Experience has indicated many occasions where complex interaction of vehicle, sensors, auxiliary systems, and man require prior analysis and simulation to determine overall effectiveness for mission goals. No simulation facilities exist where relevant parameters including pressure, temperature, and salinity can be reproduced and manipulated to assess their combined effects.

Navy data indicate a tremendous deficiency in simulation test facilities, particularly for great depths.[5] A deficiency of 430 test years in tank sizes up to 20 cubic feet at pressures over 15,000 psi was noted, without including the need for low-cycle fatigue testing. This deficiency was calculated on currently defined five-year funding plans and did not provide for an increased national effort in the deep sea.

Equipment testing to less than the full submerged operating pressures has been necessary due to lack of adequate test facilities. For example, available facilities restricted testing the pressure hull for the first Deep Submergence Rescue Vehicle to only 2,700 feet rather than the potential 5,000 foot performance capability. The first Deep Submergence Search Vehicle (DSSV) capsule will be only static tested to its operating depth of 20,000 feet because no tank will be available for cyclic testing until at least two years after delivery. No chamber capable of cycling the DSSV or similar capsule to operating depth is planned.

Over the next five years, deep submergence programs will pinpoint operational problems encountered in sustained operations at 2,000 and 20,000 feet. As feasibility of a new generation of operational systems is demonstrated, new deep diving systems will be developed with markedly increased capabilities.

Military systems could include deeper operating attack submarines, new strategic missile submarines, and bottom-sitting or bottom-mobile systems. If these vehicles were approved for production, they would require Navy simulation facility expenditures exceeding $1 billion over the next 10 years.

If deep ocean programs merely doubled over the next 10 years, existing and planned test facilities would accommodate no more than 20 per cent of the required development work, only 10 per cent of required equipment testing, and no testing to certify the fully assembled vehicle.

Attempted use of off-the-shelf equipment on essentially all existing vehicles forced *in situ* testing and resulted in a long list of equipment failures. The NR-1 is an exception; all subsystems will be tested thoroughly before installation. Nevertheless, no facility exists to test the entire vehicle before launch. Initial at-sea operation without any equipment malfunction is the exception rather than the rule. Because deep diving submersibles must have much equipment external to the pressure hull, many new structural and external machinery problems are encountered.

## 2. Future Needs

Progress in undersea systems will necessitate testing and evaluating equipment prior to selection and installation on vehicles. Testing, evaluation, and certification of whole vehicle systems are needed to minimize failures during at-sea operations.

In the decade 1970-1980, a proliferation of deep ocean simulation facilities will be needed. When economical and feasible, test facilities should have multiple capabilities. For example, a vehicle test facility might be built to accommodate diver tests as well. Requirements include:

—Certification and test facilities for small submersibles to 20,000 feet.

—Certification and test facilities for full size deep operating submarines and undersea stations.

—Anechoic test chambers for sonar equipment and quiet operating machinery.

—Coastal engineering facilities.

—Test facilities for pressure capsules and housings to 20,000 feet.

—Facilities for testing external machinery and power systems.

---

[5] Navy Ship Research and Development Center, *Deep Sea Simulation Facilities Navy-Wide,* Part I, Report C 2515-1, (NSRDC, Annapolis, Maryland, 1967).

—Facilities for deep operating weapons and explosives testing.

—Hyperbaric seawater aquaria to handle organisms which live only at the deepest depths.

—Small hyperbaric tanks for capture, transfer, and examination of specimens inhabiting the depths.

—Facilities for calibrating, testing, and evaluating oceanographic instrumentation systems.

## B. Hyperbaric Facilities

### 1. Current Situation

The term *hyperbaric facility* generally is applied to a man-rated pressure chamber complex intended primarily for experimental studies of human behavior and physiology under increased ambient pressures. Such facilities have been used for therapy and for commercial and military diver training. Categories of man-rated chamber uses include:

—*Medical and Experimental*
(1) Human physiological research
(2) Clinical medicine
(3) Medical therapy
(4) Biology, especially marine biology

—*Swimmer and Diver Development*
(1) Physiology, including decompression table development
(2) Equipment development, test, and evaluation
(3) Mission training and development

—*Saturation Diver Work Systems Support*
(1) Oil and mineral
(2) Salvage and construction
(3) Rescue and medical treatment
(4) Military

The Navy currently has hyperbaric chambers at the Naval Medical Research Institute, Bethesda, Maryland, and at the Washington, D.C., Navy Yard Annex. The latter houses both the Experimental Diving Unit (EDU) and the Naval School for Deep Sea Divers, each having hyperbaric complexes consisting of four connected pressure chambers. An outer lock, an inner lock, and an igloo are on one level, a diving tank below. Depth simulation

capability is approximately 1,000 feet. A sectional view of the arrangement is shown in Figure 27.

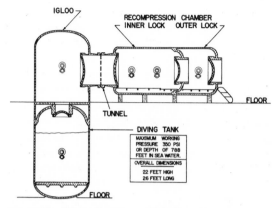

**Figure 27.** *Diving facilities at U.S. Navy Experimental Diving Unit and Naval School for Deep Sea Divers. (Navy drawing)*

The diving tank can be filled to a depth of approximately eight feet. A similar facility is planned for the Naval Submarine Medical Center, New London, Connecticut. The complex at the Medical Research Institute, being uprated to a 1,000-foot capability, has a wet tank depth capability of only three feet.

The 2,000-foot hyperbaric facility being designed for the Navy Mine Defense Laboratory, Panama City, Florida (Figure 28), when completed will be the largest, deepest, and most complete facility of its kind in the world. One end of the

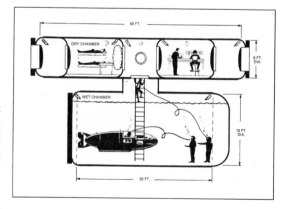

**Figure 28.** *Proposed multipurpose pressure facility at Navy Mine Defense Laboratory. (Navy drawing)*

wet chamber has a full-diameter door providing access for small submersibles. Support systems planned include comprehensive data gathering, evaluating, and monitoring devices and a computer system to allow simulation of a large open ocean area. Preprogramming of entire experimental runs and automatic gas control will be possible. Use of the chambers will concentrate on diver equipment development, evaluation, and training.

One industrial high pressure simulation facility, a three chamber complex, will go into operation in early 1969 at Annapolis, Maryland. It is a 1,500-foot facility with one water filled chamber. Support systems include a gas storage and distribution system which makes possible charging any selected chamber with air or other gas mixtures. Decompression may be accomplished manually or automatically along a selected decompression curve.

The largest currently operational hyperbaric facility is at Duke University, Durham, North Carolina. Its five interconnected vessels have more than 9,000 cubic feet of volume. The largest, a 20-foot sphere containing an operating theater, is rated to 225 feet of seawater equivalent pressure. Three of the vessels, one a wet chamber, are rated to 1,000 feet.

The University of Maryland and Ohio State University are building hyperbaric facilities with 1,000-foot capacity. A facility with a 1,600-foot seawater rating is nearing completion at the University of Pennsylvania in Philadelphia.

Although there is widespread interest among the academic and industrial communities in ocean related research and hyperbaric medicine, the substantial first cost and operating expense deter many. Also, because the field is relatively new, hyperbaric projects tend to be uncertain investments. More experience is required before the pattern for using these facilities is established with confidence.

## 2. Future Needs

Research will be needed to better understand physiological phenomena, especially with the anticipated increase in depth of routine operations. In determining the limits of human endurance, experiments under closely controlled conditions are essential so immediate corrective action can be taken. *In situ* testing to determine human limits is

unacceptable. In addition, much work remains to determine optimum decompression schedules. This is especially important since deep diving operations require several days of decompression.

Military activities also will be expanding human capability limits. Most marked needs will be in training and equipment evaluation. Industry is building additional hyperbaric facilities, but the main emphasis probably will be on exploiting and consolidating diving capabilities to depths around 1,000 feet. Test facilities with wet and dry chambers will be needed to permit experimental diving to 2,000 feet.

## C. Ocean Test Ranges

### 1. Current Situation

Simulation facilities cannot reproduce certain parameters of the ocean environment as the long-term fouling effects of marine life and the acoustic effects of size. Test and evaluation of systems effectiveness during missions requiring mobility, search, and use of acoustics generally must be performed in ocean test ranges. Noise quieting projects require anechoic characteristics, not yet satisfactorily simulated in a chamber.

Many pieces of equipment which work well in a laboratory pressure tank fail in the hostile, unknown undersea environment. Part of the simulation problem lies in insufficient understanding of which parameters must be reproduced. In addition, simply providing temperature and salinity control increases costs greatly. Thus, it is often desirable to use the sea environment for equipment development.

The Navy owns all but two of the operational ocean engineering ranges (Makai Range in Hawaii and the University of Southern California range on Santa Catalina Island, California). Industry assists the Navy in much of its range operations.

The Navy's Atlantic Undersea Test and Evaluation Center (AUTEC), with principal facilities at Andros Island, Bahamas, and St. Croix, Virgin Islands, is conducting limited testing.

When fully completed in 1970, the center will have a wide range of capabilities to test undersea vehicles, weapons, and weapon systems. Range functions will include operational evaluation of advanced weapon systems and components, measurement of submarine noise and other target parameters, evaluation of antisubmarine warfare exercises, calibration of low frequency sonar transducers, testing of sonobuoys, and test and evaluation of oceanographic instrumentation and ocean engineering developments. Like the model basin facilities at the Naval Ship Research and Development Center, AUTEC can be made available for commercial and scientific use. Becuase of its location, facilities may be valuable in biological, chemical, fishery, and other studies.

An important undersea engineering range is the Ocean Engineering Test Range operated by the Naval Undersea Warfare Center at San Clemente Island, California. This facility can be made available to civilian users on a cost reimbursement basis. The primary test area is a four by five mile tract on the northeastern side of the island, featuring graduated plateaus to 4,000 foot depths and a two dimensional underwater positioning system.

The site was first developed for full scale Polaris underwater launch tests and was also used for Poseidon missile tests. The Navy's Sealab III operation will be conducted at this location. Planned additions include a marine railway, extensive pier and breakwater facilities, and a distressed submarine simulator to train crews of the Deep Submergence Rescue Vehicle.

The range has a special purpose surface support ship, the *U.S.S. Elk River* (IX-501), converted from a World War II landing ship and initially used to support Sealab III operations. It has a center well, a traveling 65-ton gantry crane, and two deck decompression chambers. The *U.S.S. Elk River* can support diver and submersible operations in relatively quiet waters.

The Naval Civil Engineering Laboratory, Port Hueneme, California, has developed techniques for *in situ* testing to 6,000 feet in the open ocean. Their devices include recoverable submersible test units, which have carried materials samples for periods exceeding one year, and a deep ocean instrument placement and observation system for *in situ* measurement of such parameters as shear and bearing strength of sediments.

The Makai Undersea Test Range is being developed at Makupuu Point, Hawaii, and will include capabilities to 18,000 feet within 80 miles of shore. The range is being developed for man-in-sea, deep vehicle, and ocean instrumentation test and evaluation. The man-in-sea facilities are nearest to completion, scheduled for operational readiness in

1969 upon installation of a portable seafloor habitat complex (maximum depth 580 feet), diving equipment, decompression facilities, and an operations control center.

To test mobile systems, especially weapons, ranges require detailed oceanographic surveys dependent on precise navigational control and observational techniques. Coordinated, closely spaced bottom samples, underwater photographs, and depth records provide information for cable routing and bottom samples, structure design and emplacement. Data collection and emplacement techniques will be augmented greatly by use of deep submersibles on the AUTEC ranges (Figure 29). When the need for immediate, continuous data are critical, permanent buoy arrays have been employed.

**Figure 29.** *Artist's concept of Navy's new AUTEC research submarine as it works on ocean bottom obtaining scientific data by use of instruments emplaced by its remotely controlled mechanical arms. (Navy photo)*

## 2. Future Needs

*In situ* test ranges and facilities will continue to be important in measuring complete system effectiveness, instrument calibration, and long-term phenomena studies when pressure cycling is not important. In such cases, range testing may well be less expensive than simulation.

Ranges must be fully developed and instrumented and contain the proper facilities, including in some cases habitable undersea installations and submersibles. For testing systems sensitive to the environment, more abundant and accurate oceanographic data will be required, probably through greater use of submersible and advanced buoy technology.

Active participation by industry in establishing and operating ranges benefits all marine activities. For example, detailed bottom survey measurements apply directly to ocean mining and to search and recovery. Equipment developed for range monitoring can be applied in large scale environmental monitoring and prediction. The wealth of experience accruing from installation, operation, and maintenance of various undersea systems will become part of the industrial base needed to achieve the recommended national goals in the oceans.

## D. Conclusions

The necessity of complete and adequate testing to conquer a strange environment has been vividly demonstrated by aviation advancing into high altitude, supersonic, and space flight. The ocean environment is difficult and will require a vast array of test facilities to permit safe, orderly, and rapid progress. Prior operational experience has borne this out. Test facilities are a national resource as important as any other single factor in the advancement of marine technology. Insufficient facilities already have and will continue to hamper the national ocean program.

Equipment, instrumentation, and systems development are impeded seriously by a lack of environmental simulation facilities. Test tanks of two general types are needed to: (1) advance fundamental technology and prototype subsystem and component evaluation and (2) evaluate vehicle and system certification and effectiveness including man-machine interrelationships. The former category requires test tanks to simulate temperature, salinity, and pressure cycles to great depths. The latter requires larger, integrated facilities permitting dynamic duplication of relevant parameters.

The forces of economic development, recreation, and national security already have moved man into the sea; these forces will grow at an increasing rate. Manrated hyperbaric facilities are needed for medical and physiological research, swimmer and diver equipment research and development, training, operational work, and rescue.

Facilities for physiological research, medical training, equipment development, and saturation diver operational training are grossly inadequate. The limits of human diving endurance cannot be determined safely *in situ;* closely controlled laboratory simulation is required. There exists a major need for hyperbaric trained medical doctors. Further, amateur divers often preempt government facilities for emergency decompression, further intensifying the facility shortage.

Extensively surveyed and instrumented *in situ* facilities and ranges are being developed. These facilities have special advantages because of their size and total environment reproduction. Much work remains, however, to complete range instrumentation and provide such facilities with real operational capabilities. Although in theory the Navy's ranges are available to civilian interests, they quite appropriately must serve Navy needs first, thereby intensifying the shortage of range facilities.

**Recommendations:**

**A national facilities program should be established to (1) determine present and future needs, (2) develop and construct new facilities, (3) improve test scheduling, (4) maintain an inventory of national capabilities, (5) provide criteria to choose between *in situ* and simulation testing, and (6) establish a center of excellence in the technology of test tank and range design. The program's responsibility should include conventional and hyperbaric test tanks and *in situ* facilities. Coast Guard efforts to develop diver rescue decompression tanks (including chambers capable of being airlifted) should be related to the program.**

**Major efforts should be pursued to seek new and economical methods of simulation, including such possibilities as concrete and fiberglas tanks. Deep (2,000 to 20,000 foot) anechoic simulation technology does not exist and should receive special emphasis. If a breakthrough occurs, acoustic and noise suppression efforts will be greatly enhanced through laboratory testing.**

**A significant increase in tank and range test capabilities is basic to the U.S. undersea program. The importance of test facilities as a national resource cannot be overstated.**

## III. DEEP OCEAN ACTIVITIES

Most nations border on and are affected by the sea; their people appreciate its power and hostility. An expression of determination by the United States to go forward with a significant marine technology program and to establish leadership in the understanding and development of earth's last frontier cannot go unnoticed. U.S. prestige surely would be enhanced if it pursued the undersea frontier on its own initiative; the United States would enter international deliberations on the utilization of the sea in a position of strength based upon knowledge and prior achievement.

Achieving exploration and assessment of the ocean bottom within 10 years and the capability to carry out useful operations in the depths within three decades requires new technology.

The oceans are the operating medium of America's foremost deterrent in maintaining the balance of world power. The United States cannot take the risk that a potential antagonist might gain knowledge the United States does not possess, thereby seizing an undersea capability advantage.

In this report, the deep ocean is defined as open ocean areas from the surface to 20,000 feet beyond the 2,000-foot depth contour. The 2,000-foot contour was selected because it is beyond the edge of the continental shelf and because 2,000 feet is the presently projected limit for advanced ambient pressure diving. The 20,000-foot goal is important because it encompasses all but two percent of the ocean floor and approximately 99 per cent of ocean volume. A few operations at intermediate depths, such as on seamounts and midocean ridges, might justify exceptions to the goal.

The step beyond 2,000 feet represents a technological challenge, not so much against a potential adversary (although this cannot be certain), but against a new frontier. The frontier exists primarily because there has not been a national commitment to explore, understand, and master this promising expanse.

It should not be implied that the problems are not difficult. Experience indicates that operations below 2,000 feet are limited by equipment and materials capabilities. Existing systems can perform only small amounts of useful work. Technical problems exist in developing high strength, low cost materials, compact long endurance power sources, and machinery and equipment that will operate reliably in the cold, corrosive, high pressure seawater environment. Successful operations below 2,000 feet require new approaches expected to be valid all the way to 20,000-foot depths.

Although initial investment may be a little higher, no important improvements in early program schedule or nearterm costs would occur if the deep ocean technology goal were set incrementally at depths of less than 20,000 feet. The same problems must be solved, and use of the best materials on hand would be economically justified. In fact, overall costs most likely would be higher for a program having depth goals set in progressive increments.

The sections following contain a review of the kinds of systems available and likely to evolve in performing useful missions in the undersea frontier. An assessment of the state-of-the-art is made with specific recommendations for the future. Expected benefits range from military and scientific to political, social, and economic.

### A. Undersea Systems

Although nearly 10 years ago the *Trieste* went to the deepest part of the ocean, nearly 36,000 feet below sea level, submersible technology is still in its infancy. The deepest dive known for a maneuverable nonbathyscaph was to 8,310 feet in early 1968. Yet this craft is but a primitive forerunner of future submersible systems.

It is known that all the way to the bottom there is marine life and that high grade minerals exist on the seafloor. At the foot of continental slopes sedimentary deposits are likely to contain petroleum. Exploration and development of resources will be enhanced by manned vehicles and remote systems that can operate anywhere in the water column.

It is a great advantage to the scientist to observe firsthand the environment he is studying. Advanced marine technology can and must give him basic tools to extend his senses into the undersea frontier to unravel its great mysteries.

Surveys are needed not only to understand and measure environmental conditions but also to determine areas worth exploring—what resources, where, and in what concentrations?—not only on the shelf but also in the deep sea. At the same time national security demands the ability to inspect, examine, or survey any area of interest in the deep ocean or ocean bottom.

Search, survey, and recovery systems to examine the bottom, much as one views land from a helicopter, are needed. Desirable capabilities include hovering, close station keeping, precise navigation, and the ability to return to a given spot. The system should be able to take biological, geological, and chemical samples (including cores) and to map, make bathymetric charts, photograph, listen, and touch. The floor must be explored to discover exploitable resources, to find hiding places, and to study seamounts, volcanoes, and mud slides. A 20,000-foot depth capability will permit these operations in almost 99 per cent of the world's ocean volume, covering 98 per cent of the ocean's floor, excepting only the deep trenches.

New vehicles and equipment will be needed to support and maintain more fixed, portable, and mobile undersea systems. As Dr. John P. Craven, Chief Scientist of the Navy's Deep Submergence Systems Project has said, "In the long run, underwater transfer is the key to effective use of the ocean depths." Therefore, a key secondary mission for rescue vehicles will be underwater transfer to supply habitats, stations, and submarines not in distress. Such vehicles would provide deployed underwater installations freedom from surface support.

Inherent to practicability of these vehicles is substantial payload capacity. For example, the Navy's Deep Submergence Rescue Vehicle will be able to carry internally only 4,300 pounds of personnel or cargo. Ambient pressure, wet cargo carriers will be necessary to transport thousands of tons, especially for mining, construction, salvage, and the deployment of instruments and equipment.

The Navy has been pursuing actively its Deep Submergence Rescue Vehicle (DSRV) and Deep Submergence Search Vehicle (DSSV) projects and is conducting preliminary studies on a Deep Ocean Survey Vehicle (DOSV) and a Deep Ocean Technology (DOT) test bed vehicle. These projects are of the utmost importance to extend U.S. capability and knowledge of the undersea frontier. Search and rescue projects certainly should receive high priority, since the world has lost an average of two submarines per year in peacetime. Recently a one-half million dollar isotope power source was recovered off the Pacific Missile Range after a long, extensive search.

Submersible vehicles of all types—tethered and untethered, manned and unmanned—will be useful in ocean activities. Once each is developed to its full capability, normal comparative studies will establish the range of conditions and operations for which each is most effective.

## 1. Submersible Vehicles

Submersibles have many operational advantages. They function in an environment free of wave forces and the potential damage and limitations imposed by adverse weather. They provide an ultraquiet platform for acoustic studies. They can take advantage of the force of buoyancy to emplace or recover objects and, perhaps most important, they can bring man into the oceans for observation and work.

**a. Current Situation** Operational submersibles have demonstrated limited usefulness in several exploration and inspection tasks. Many special purpose oceanographic submersibles exist in a wide variety of configurations, hull materials, and depth capabilities. Of the 82 proposed or existing vehicles for which operating depths are known, 24 (29 per cent) are planned for operations to at least 6,000 feet and only 12 (15 per cent) for operations to 20,000 feet. The operating 20,000-foot submersibles can be classified as unmaneuverable bathyscaphs. Additional technological advances are necessary to develop capability for work at great depths.

Typical submersibles (Figure 30) now in operation have pressure hulls generally of ring-stiffened cylinders or spheres made of high strength steel. Maximum speeds vary from two to five knots, mission endurance from 4 to 30 hours, and range from several miles to about 100 miles.

Submersibles usually are powered from batteries located external to the pressure hull, and have external propulsion motors. Ballast systems typically involve both soft or free-flooding tanks blown for additional freeboard and surface stability and tanks or dropable weights to change buoyancy at great depths.

A number of technological deficiencies have reduced the efficiency and potential usefulness of submersibles. Most are highlighted here; more detailed discussions may be found in the appropriate subsections of this chapter, pages 29-77.

**Figure 30.** *Typical commercial submersible vehicles currently operational to depths of 1,000 feet or more*

Aluminaut. *(Reynolds Aluminum photo)*

Roughneck. *(North American Rockwell photo)*

Ben Franklin. *(Grumman photo)*

Deep Quest. *(Lockheed photo)*

Deepstar-4000. *(Westinghouse photo)*

DOWB. *(General Motors photo)*

Shelf Diver. *(Perry Submarine Builders photo)*   Star III. *(General Dynamics photo)*

Electrical cable failures have resulted from tearing by bubbles forming and expanding internally upon ascent. Connectors with adequate insulation and reliable disconnect properties are not available. Essentially no switches, relays, or fuses have been designed for ambient operation. Usually standard equipment designed for use in air at atmospheric pressure has been modified for undersea use by emersing it in oil, which has led to some failures attributed to carbon deposits. Performance of AC and DC electric motors generally has been poor because of bearing and insulation failures.

Small submersibles have been severely limited by heavy, bulky, inadequate battery power sources which require time-consuming recharging. Manipuiators have proved unreliable primarily because of electrical distribution and motor difficulties, water intrusion, and poor control systems.

Hydraulic systems operated at very high differential pressures have failed becasue of water intrusion and incompatibility with certain materials. Lubricants operating in high pressure have caused bearing failures and efficiency losses due to increased viscosity. Pressure compensating oil and gasoline used for buoyancy have serious drawbacks of combustibility and bulk modulus.

Underwater communications, navigation, and positioning systems and equipments for nonmilitary submersibles are too limited in range and accuracy. Materials are deficient in strength-to-weight ratios, toughness, corrosion resistance, and fatigue strength. Critical limitations exist in advanced materials fabrication techniques and testing methods.

**b. Future Needs**  Vigorous pursuit of ocean activities will require continuing development, not only of fundamental technology but also of submersible systems. Submersible use can be forseen in many ocean activities:

—Fish behavior and location studies and undersea fish harvesting.

—Undersea core drilling, site surveying for pipelines and structures, and operations to complete, inspect, maintain, and repair bottom petroleum production installations.

—Mineral surveys, evaluations, and observation of seafloor mining operations.

—Search, identification, and recovery of lost objects.

—Cargo and personnel transfer to undersea installations. Saturated diver delivery to work sites.

—Support of scientific studies of coastal and oceanic processes including observation, measurement, and sampling.

—Ocean surveillance and mapping.

—Support of underwater equipment.

To effect operations, submersibles must be designed to fulfill performance criteria for depth, endurance, speed, payload, instrumentation, and working tools. The vehicles themselves are only one part of a total system which includes shore bases, support platforms, transportation to work sites, maintenance equipment, supply logistics, supporting instrumentation and tools, and personnel. Integrated design of the entire system is necessary for optimum performance.

Exploration submersibles will be needed to support studies directed toward utilizing and exploiting the oceans. The functions of personnel and light cargo transfer and of search and rescue should be included in their capabilities wherever practicable. Based on the state-of-the-art of manned and unmanned deep submergence vehicles and an examination of anticipated requirements, submersible characteristics can be determined for many anticipated technological development tasks with a minimum number of vehicle configurations. Characteristics should not be constrained by the current technology; rather, they should anticipate subsystems and components compatible with future scientific, government, and industrial requirements in the deep ocean.

Submersible requirements for both shelf (to 2,000 feet) and deep ocean (to 20,000 feet) depths include:

—Power sources.

—Propulsion machinery and control, variable ballast, and electrical distribution.

—Pressure hull, outer hull, and buoyancy materials.

—Navigation and positioning equipment, obstacle avoidance and search sonar.

—Improved manipulators and controls.

—Magnetic and seafloor anchoring.

—Underwater communications and viewing.

—Emergency escape.

## 2. Unmanned and Tethered Vehicles

**a. Current Situation** Tethered submersibles historically were typified by diving bells or chambers.

One of the best known one-atmosphere diving chambers is the *bathysphere* in which William Beebe descended to a record depth of 3,028 feet in 1934. Submersible work chambers used in diver operations are another type of manned, tethered system. Some have dual compartments, one at one-atmosphere pressure and the other at ambient sea pressure with provision for diver entry and exit.

Probably the best known unmanned tethered submersible is the Navy's Cable-Controlled Underwater Recovery Vehicle (CURV), operated from a surface ship and carrying equipment for photography, television observation, limited search, and retrieval of small objects (Figure 31). Such a vehicle has unlimited endurance, low initial cost, and a capability for round-the-clock operation. The Navy has under construction a CURV type vehicle capable of operation to 7,000 feet.

**Figure 31.** *Navy's cable-controlled underwater recovery vehicle, CURV II. (Navy photo)*

Bottom crawling or rolling submersibles may be tethered or untethered, manned or unmanned. Several have been built for special purposes. In many cases, obscured vision from disturbed sediments limited mission effectiveness. However, a bottom crawler would be suitable on hard sediments or when turbid water viewing systems (like acoustic imaging) become available. Recently a research submersible operated very successfully along the bottom by ballasting slightly heavy and riding on wheels.

In recent years, several successful tethered unmanned vehicles equipped with special instrument suits have been built. Cable controlled or selfpropelled, they have been used for deep ocean search, survey, and research. Examples include the Naval Research Laboratory's towed search system used to locate and identify much of the wreckage of the submarines *Thresher* and *Scorpion* at about 8,500 feet and the commercial ocean bottom side-scanning sonar platforms.

A self-propelled, torpedo-like instrument package with a preset internal guidance system has been developed with 14,000-foot depth capability for the Navy. The probe, 122 inches long and 20 inches in diameter, is launched from and tracked acoustically by a surface ship. The system has been used for oceanographic and acoustic research—gathering data on sound velocity, thermal properties, and other physical properties on magnetic tape. Sinking instrument packages, launched from a ship and later recovered when ballast or an anchor is released, are another example of a successful unmanned submersible platform.

**b. Future Needs** As more efficient underwater observational equipment and tools for underwater cutting, welding, grappling, hooking, drilling, and controlled lifting become available, a vastly expanded era of undersea construction, salvage, mining, and recovery will evolve through use of unmanned and tethered vehicles and platforms. The state-of-the-art has progressed well, making possible design and construction of a wide variety of equipment for special application. Further development is needed to improve endurance, accuracy, control, reliability, compactness, manipulation, and depth capabilities.

Gross bottom reconnaissance for site selection, geological searches, geodetic surveys, and biological sampling will require a variety of unmanned instrument platforms. In some cases, multipurpose systems may be a less expensive, quickly available interim substitute for manned submersibles.

An advanced sea elevator, derivative of the diving bell, may effect transfer of man and materials from surface support ships and platforms to deep ocean installations on or in the sea floor. It might carry as many as a score of men and supplies to depths as great as 20,000 feet. Eventually, its function may be assumed by transport submersibles, free from severe waves and weather and saving a step in materials handling. The sea elevator also may be displaced or supplemented by pipelines, air lifts, conveyors, and other mechanical equipment.

Undersea construction and salvage will require heavy duty work systems—the counterparts of dredges, power shovels, bulldozers, tractors, pavement layers, trucks, pile drivers, plows, drills, and cranes. Cable controlled or cable towed devices will be hampered and endangered by obstructions, nearby traffic, and concentration of similar devices at a given work site. The hazards of cables suggest wireless control links from the control station to the device. An alternate approach might be small manned submersibles to serve as control cabs from which operators direct and monitor large work devices.

The competitive marketplace or comparative studies for military systems will determine which devices—manned or unmanned—will best serve particular needs.

### 3. Transport and Support Submarines

**a. Current Situation** Transport submarines have been considered seriously for commercial use from time to time. In contrast to surface vessels having speed, safety, scheduling, and passenger comfort governed to a large extent by weather, submersibles can operate in an environment essentially quiet and predictable.

With the advent of nuclear power, advanced structural materials and fabrication techniques, and development of submersibles for military applications, the technical and economic feasibility of transport submarines continues to improve. For transoceanic voyages, the transport submarine has been suggested seriously as a carrier of bulk liquids weighing less than water.

A market will exist for recreational submersibles with large viewing ports if costs are not too high. A submersible recently was a top tourist attraction in Lake Geneva even though the bottom there is quite unspectacular.

**b. Future Needs** Whereas some products recovered from the sea will be transported via pipelines, conveyors, and surface vessels, submarine cargo carriers probably will be needed between offshore production sites and such intermediate points as undersea processing stations, storage tanks, and surface platforms. A strong need will exist for submersible support submarines as high endurance motherships for deep operating manned or unmanned submersibles engaged in search and rescue, wide-area ocean surveys, site selection, communication-navigation aid emplacement and maintenance, and salvage—especially in regions where ice and severe weather predominate.

The mother submarine could be the forerunner of an undersea logistic vessel supporting a submerged Navy and a variety of manned bottom installations. Further, it could be a mobile undersea support laboratory. Significant performance parameters of this mobile support submersible, recommended as a National project, would include:

—Depth capability of at least 1,000 feet. A 2,000-foot depth capability is desirable if the primary technology to be developed (submerged support) is not compromised.

—Submerged endurance of at least 30 days, but modest speeds of five to 10 knots. Nuclear power would be desirable.

—Transport, launch, recovery, logistic support, and command control capabilities for small submersibles.

—Saturated diver lockout, support, and decompression to at least 1,000 feet, preferably 2,000 feet as recommended above. Bottom sitting capability required.

—Retrieval and transportation of objects beyond the lift capacity of small submersibles.

—Oceanographic data collection and survey capability.

—Internal and external servicing of submersibles while submerged. This servicing would largely be performed by saturated divers either in the water or in an ambient pressure compartment.

In addition, designs for transport and submersible support submarines and for special terminals, including modification of existing ports and development of underwater ports, will be needed.

## 4. Military Submarines

a. **Current Situation** Many factors are focusing upon one unassailable conclusion—the importance of the military submersible in modern warfare. The advantage gained by concealment under the surface is of great importance. The historic success of submarine warfare emphasizes the necessity for preeminence in this field of military readiness. The submarine in the past has developed two of the principles of warfare to a fine quality—those of surprise and offensive.

Since World War II a development has taken place which has revolutionized the art of submarine operations and made possible the true submersible. No longer is the submarine forced to depend on the atmosphere for battery charging and human habitation. This development, the adaptation of nuclear power to naval propulsion, has enabled radically new concepts to be attempted.

Many factors, some military and others civilian, should be considered in the development and construction of military submarines. Russia and China are placing increased emphasis on the undersea area and are building submarines at an increasing rate. Commercial offshore technology development and resource recovery activities (particularly oil and gas) are accelerating. The capability to protect domestic ocean industry is a Navy responsibility that must enlarge as offshore activity expands. Even if international regulation and registration are established for deep sea areas, this capability is vital to national interests.

All of these activities influence Navy programs. In addition to well-established roles of antisubmarine warfare (ASW) and missile launching, requirements for such missions as surveillance, intelligence gathering, inspection, and logistics support forecast an expanded military subsurface role.

The U.S.S.R. has not remained unimpressed by the advantages of submarine warfare systems; that strong nation maintains a huge submarine fleet and is rapidly converting its fleet to nuclear propulsion without sacrificing numbers. It is important that the nation as a whole be apprised of this and hence lend support to future oceanic plans and programs.

Wartime ASW includes detection, classification, localization, attack, and destruction of enemy submarines. U.S. submarines have benefited from an extensive quieting program, and it would be a mistake to assume that the Soviets cannot accomplish a similar objective. Long term reliance on present sonar detection, classification, and localization systems cannot be an acceptable alternative. Research and development on ASW implications of additional depth capability to the sound channel and beyond are extremely important and should be emphasized.

The concept of depth has not been neglected in the postwar era. The advent of HY-80 steel has made possible the deeper employment of military submarines. In addition, other materials have been utilized for special Navy and civilian submarines, generally smaller in size than the military type. While much progress has been made in this field, new construction materials and fabrication techniques must be emphasized as they will be needed to satisfy future requirements.

The *U.S.S. Albacore* has made many contributions to submarine technology. The nuclear-powered oceanographic submersible, the NR-1, has great promise as an instrument both for oceanic investigation to serve national needs and for experimenting with possible future military needs.

The recently commissioned *U.S.S. Dolphin* will investigate the tactical advantage of deeper depths and is a triumph for imaginative planners. The Deep Submergence Rescue Vehicle, soon to be completed, will provide a capability for personnel rescue from any military submersible either in being or planned. The *Alvin,* a Navy-sponsored development, was a key recovery vehicle in the Palomares (Spain) operation where an aircraft-carried nuclear weapon was located and recovered in 2,600 feet of water.

The importance of deep oceans has not diminished since the House Committee on Science and Astronautics in July 1960 reported:

*This phenomenon [deep sound channel] may serve to introduce to contention by those interested in the sea that the most urgent reason for penetrating the full depths is military. The sea conceals its contents. This gives the submarine its enormous advantage of concealment and the concomitant property of surprise. Even with exceedingly sensitive devices to measure the sub's disturbance of the earth's magnetic field, detection from the surface becomes more and more difficult as the craft dives deeper. It may take a deep-diving sub to catch a deep-diving sub [emphasis added]. Military strategists may thus consider how much more difficult the problem of detection would be if the entire sea were a military arena, that submarines were extremely quiet requiring the use of active sonar for discovery and searching were necessary throughout the entire volume of the*

*ocean, not simply at the limited depth near the surface in which submarines now operate. They may also choose to consider the far more challenging problem of being able to identify a submarine or even bottom crawler that has secreted itself amongst the hills and valleys of an irregular bottom or is simply sitting on a seamount. Just as higher altitude performance for aircraft has paid off whether it be for combat or for surveillance, the extended depth capability of the submarine suggests the same potential benefits.*

Submarine-based strategic missiles are vital to U.S. deterrent capability. It has been postulated that in the future substantially more U.S. strategic missiles may be sea-based, not only because of reduced vulnerability but also because of the special advantage of separating military targets from large populations.

Leadership in understanding the oceans becomes more important when it is realized that America's key strategic deterrent is contingent on concealment, mobility, dispersion, and very long patrol time. Greater depth capability would provide a much vaster operating volume and in some areas, a bottom sitting capability, thereby attaining improved concealment.

**b. Future Needs** Man's projected sea activities will demand even more accent on new ideas and concepts for underwater effort. Where man goes, his problems go, and this extrapolates into possible new areas for conflict. The fledgling deep sea industry will grow in importance and demand sophisticated protection systems.

The seas suggest that they are the ideal locale for locating strategic deterrence systems. Away from populations centers, the missile-carrying submarine is provided with a cloak of concealment which defies countering systems. Indeed, the Polaris submarine is a triumph of modern science and technology and provides an option of an assured response. The modern attack submarine is a key factor in anti-submarine warfare and undoubtedly will play an ever-increasing role in this regard.

The Navy should accelerate its efforts to attain a limited ability in the oceans' third dimension and operate effectively to 20,000 feet within two decades. To facilitate going deeper, studies should be accelerated to determine the feasibility and effectiveness of carrying weapons external to submarines. In addition, many technological efforts discussed in this section on undersea systems and in earlier sections on fundamental technology will directly benefit deeper operating military systems.

Considered from a different perspective, technology developed by 1975 might permit construction of a combatant submarine by 1980 (very possibly of radically different design) capable of operating at 4,000 to 8,000 foot depths. Materials, welding techniques, penetrations, controls and displays, and other advanced technology being developed for the Navy's DSRV, DSSV, and Nuclear Research Vehicle (NR-1) should be considered for incorporation. The construction of some submersible military systems capable of 20,000-foot operations should be considered. Coupled with an extensive research and development program, such systems might provide future operational flexibility and an understanding of the tactical value of depth.

## 5. Conclusions

Small submersibles capable of descending well beyond 2,000-foot depths already exist. As fixed, portable, and mobile habitats are established in deeper waters, improved submersibles will be required for site selection and elementary construction. Underwater transfer by high payload vehicles will be a key to deep ocean use. A useful challenge is foreseen in providing 20,000-foot, long-endurance exploration submersibles to help explore and assess the deep ocean within 10 years; 20,000-foot work vehicles will follow on a schedule dictated by needs rather than technology. Survey and work submersible prototypes will evolve from current vehicle technology and will be adapted to meet concurrent needs for rescue, salvage, research, and transport assignments.

In addition, a variety of tethered devices like sea elevators, instrument platforms, remote work platforms, observation platforms, and bottom crawlers will be needed for such operations as bulldozing and mineral recovery. They could be available well within 10 years for 2,000-foot operations and later as needed for servicing undersea habitats at 20,000 feet.

Deep submersible systems may have overlooked some special possibilities. Current designs incorporate a maximum number of subsystems in spite of the premium of space and weight on the vehicle. Some subsystems like navigation, recording, readout, display, and monitoring might be located aboard the support vessel. Support vessels should be designed and procured as an integral part of the submersible system.

In open ocean areas, especially in ice and severe weather regions, submersible support submarines will be needed. They will have the special advantages of all weather availability and covertness.

With the advent of the *Albacore* hull, HY-80 steel, submerged missile launching, and nuclear propulsion in the 1950's, great advancements were made in naval seapower. In recent years the promise indicated by the *Aluminaut*, the *Trieste*, the *NR-1*, titanium, glass, ceramics, HY-180 steel, syntactic foam, fuel cells, free flooded machinery, and advanced sensors and controls suggest yet a new era in naval seapower.

**Recommendations:**

**Development and construction of exploration submersibles should begin immediately with a goal of operations to 20,000 feet in less than 10 years for prime assignments in the forthcoming decade of exploration of earth's last frontier. These vehicles should have maneuvering agility, sample-taking and small object recovery capabilities, and improved sensors. A National Project for an Exploration Submersible with 20,000-foot capability will directly contribute to these developments. The Navy-planned 20,000-foot DSSV should be produced with high priority because of its potential benefits to other national goals.**

**Work vehicles with high payloads should be produced as the next priority. Although to serve undersea installations, they should be developed for adaptation by such commercial interests as fishing, petroleum, and mining. Tethered work vehicles of the sea elevator variety also should be pursued for the transport of men and materials from surface or submerged support platforms, bottom sites, and structures.**

**Unmanned instrument platform and remote operating probe technology should continue to be developed. Cableless control should receive attention so that unmanned systems are not automatically ruled out by cable considerations.**

Support systems should be an integral part of submersible systems development. First priority should be given to a submarine support system that is itself a continental shelf work system and can handle deep submersibles in a totally submerged mode. A National Project for a Mobile Undersea Support Laboratory should be developed within five years. Support systems are needed for a variety of purposes including supply terminal and logistic functions, power, and life support regeneration. A prototype submerged harbor facility compatible with submarine support ships should be constructed within 10 years.

The panel is pleased to note current Navy studies on new combatant submarines and their roles. The panel endorses in concept the programs and funding levels recommended by the Deep Submergence-Ocean Engineering Program Planning Group.

The programs recommended by the study group combined with those recommended by this panel are intended to be responsive to the national need.

Cooperative efforts are imperative between the naval and civilian technology groups to determine how programs of mutual interest are undertaken and to facilitate the very important function of technology transfer.

The panel believes that the national interest is best served by having a strong technological capability in both sectors.

All possible encouragement is given to the Navy to increase its subsurface capabilities to operate anytime, anywhere, and at any depth.

### B. Deep Ocean Installations

Undersea installations, portable and fixed, will have a variety of purposes. Nearterm tasks will include understanding the environment, surveillance, testing, and exploration of living and non-living resources. Future uses may include territorial protection, undersea command and control, missile and submarine basing, industrial processing, and power generating stations. Characteristics of underwater observatories or laboratories will depend on surface, water column, and sea floor conditions.

Plants, stations, and bases must be compatible with operational constraints. For example, petroleum recovery installations will differ from solid mineral extraction, sea food production, and underwater transportation facilities.

However, environmental constraints establish many common technological needs. Of basic importance to site selection, construction, and emplacement operations are underwater soil mechanics, terrain features, and bottom currents. There are common needs to develop power sources, distribution systems, materials, viewing systems, communication equipment, life support systems, and waste management and contaminant control systems. The fabrication, emplacement, assembly, inspection, maintenance, operation, ingress/egress, and repair of undersea installations will place severe demands on the entire spectrum of undersea technology.

Technology for underwater installations will result in part from extended current marine technology on mobile undersea vehicles, terrestrial civil engineering, and classic naval architecture. In addition there will be new design, analysis, and building techniques acquired from studies of prototype installations and component and subsystem experiments conducted in relatively large test facilities.

The capability to utilize the continental shelf and deep ocean areas continuously may assist in preserving future rights of access to ocean depths. The recognized U.S. 3 mile limit of the territorial seas and the disputed 12 mile limit claimed by several nations comprise the only areas that currently can be occupied legally.

It is possible that international law will extend the territorial sea concept seaward and allow areas adjacent to bottom-oriented activities in the deep oceans to be occupied legally. Availability of technology and capability to operate in ocean bottom areas will encourage utilization of undersea resources and will complement mobile capabilities described in the previous section on undersea systems.

Within 10 years, all segments of the economy—industrial, academic, and government—may have undersea installations on the continental shelves, and short-time visiting will occur on the slopes, seamounts, and in deep sea areas. Because of immediate capability and convenience, initial activity will concentrate on the shelves. However, a vigorous decade of technology development will permit use of selected deep ocean areas for commercial or military operations.

## 1. Sea Floor Habitats

**a. Current Situation** The United States has not placed any habitats at depths below limits of saturated diving. Such deep habitats require pressure vessels in which a one-atmosphere environment can be maintained. Vehicles capable of transporting men and materials to a bottom installation will be needed to allow the habitat to remain on the bottom. Power sources, life support, and operational equipment must be contained within the habitat or in a satellite installation, because permanent wire cable contact with the shore or surface is undesirable.

One advanced concept is the Naval Civil Engineering Laboratory's Manned Underwater Station (Figure 32), designed for 6,000-foot depths. The station consists of two main cylinders, one for habitation and one for a nuclear power source, with small access and observation spheres above and below.

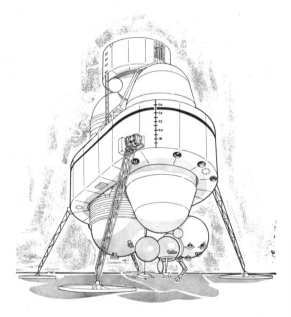

**Figure 32.** *Artist's concept of a manned underwater station. (Navy drawing)*

**b. Future Needs** The first portable bottom laboratories and stations will likely accommodate only small crews of 15 to 25 men. However, if mining, industrial, or major military operations suggest the desirability of bottom installations, they may become substantially larger.

For similar sizes, fixed bottom structures will be cheaper than portable habitats. However, for maximum response to changing situations, and for work at several locations the more extensive development and added construction expense for transportability will be justified.

Such stations and attendant transfer and logistic vehicles could be positioned where military or commercial needs require, such as for recovery of scallops or nodules or for an extended salvage operation. Ocean exploration will disclose new areas for exploitation in which the ability to move manned habitats quickly may be a key to profitable returns.

Underwater inspection, maintenance, and repair will become increasingly important because deterioration usually accelerates with time. New tools, equipment, and nondestructive inspection techniques must be developed; the last, in particular, will be a formidable challenge. Underwater installations must be specially designed for maintenance and repair in a manner compatible with submersible capabilities. Improved materials that resist the sea environment will be another important factor.

## 2. In-Bottom Habitats

**a. Current Situation** Construction of in-bottom habitats will depend on tunneling techniques long used for railroad, subway, automobile, and water tunnels. Over 100 undersea mining complexes exist under many tens of square miles of continental shelf involving thousands of linear miles of openings. As many as 4,100 men work in a single undersea complex (Figure 33). However, all these

**Figure 33.** *Machine shop located in a mine 1,500 feet below sea level off Newfoundland coast. (Navy photo)*

mines have been established by tunneling from land. None opens to the water column. To construct in-bottom habitats or mines far from shore or in seamounts and on midocean ridges, tunnels driven directly from the sea floor will be required.

There are three different tunneling system requirements: in rock, in soft ground, and opencut ditches dredged from the surface. In all cases, thorough preliminary geological investigation and test borings are essential.

In recent years great advances have occurred in boring machines for use in soft rock. Such machines have many cutter bits mounted on a large cutter head with a diameter equal to that of the bore. The largest boring machine in the United States has a cutter head 20 feet in diameter with 43 cutter bits; five 200 hp motors rotate the head at 3.5 rpm. The Soviets have developed a 28-foot diameter borer. A 10-foot bore has been driven as much as 375 feet in one day and 6,713 feet in one month. Advances up to 4,000 feet per week may be achieved within the next decade.

**b. Future Needs**   In-bottom installations will be constructed where large concentrations of men and equipment are to be assembled for extended periods. Sites especially suitable for tunneling are seamounts, mid-ocean ridges, and large rock outcrops on the continental slope.

To date, boring machines have proved economically feasible only in such relatively soft rock as sandstone and shale. Studies are under way to develop machines to bore harder rocks. Future development should be directed at completely mechanized and automated tunneling procedures.

Rapid tunneling at reduced costs depends on perfecting boring machines and on such complementary technology as instrumentation to probe formations for water flows, grouting, guidance and control, lining, and material removal. A need also exists to develop systems for remote unmanned operation at deep ocean sites.

Work vehicles will be needed to perform such functions as foundation preparation, leveling, and drilling. Machines analogous to bulldozers, backhoes, cranes, and emplacement systems will be able to take advantage of the buoyancy provided by water.

Systems for boring and drilling into the bed or side of a seamount and for placing drill pipe or other surface powered devices into an exact location will be required. These tasks imply vehicles with large capacity power sources or availability of a power supply submersible or shore power source. They also imply the need for reliable large-scale external machinery, including motors and drives.

There may be a requirement to establish foundations by such methods as pile driving on the seafloor. More data and prediction methods are needed concerning the bearing capacity of large diameter piles.

## 3. Conclusions

Dr. Carl F. Austin, of the Naval Weapons Center, China Lake, Calif., has said of undersea installations:

*The technology to work and live beneath the sea floor is in hand at the present time for water depths over the entire continental shelves of the world excluding areas of permanent ice cover. Let us learn to use this technology to our economic and national advantage.*[6]

Deep ocean installations will be required for such activities as understanding the environment and its processes, study and exploitation of living and nonliving resources, surveillance, terminals and bases, and underwater power and processing plants. A capability to utilize the slopes, seamounts, and deep ocean basins may be the best and surest way of preserving freedom of access to the land masses under the high seas. Manned stations—beginning with portable or emplaced types and followed by more permanent in-bottom types—can achieve continuous deeply submerged operations.

Prototype ambient pressure habitats have been built for continental shelf depths, and one-atmosphere habitats could be built for limited endurance missions at much greater depths using existing submersible technology. Many technological needs of both habitats and submersibles are similar. On the other hand, certain technology for bottom habitats is in its infancy, such as under-

[6]Carl F. Austin, "Manned Undersea Installation," *Proceedings of the Conference on Civil Engineering in the Oceans,* American Society of Civil Engineers, September 1967, p. 830.

water soil mechanics, foundations, site preparation, and underwater construction equipment.

Commercial mining ventures might be considered forerunners of in-bottom facilities. Undersea mines have been in operation off the coast of England for over 350 years. Tunnels have been built under the continental shelves; however, tunnels have never originated under water. Such operations might be required for seamount laboratories or links between bottom-sitting stations. Precise underwater surveying and positioning, underwater grouting and boring, and heavy equipment technology are all in their infancy in relation to undersea construction.

## Recommendations:

**Underwater working operations will require coordinated development in many basic engineering and component areas. Data are needed on the interaction of waves and currents with an installation. Adequate underwater power sources, equipment, and tools must be developed. Visual observation, television, and viewing equipment will be required as well as command and communications systems. Improved materials will be required for reliable and long-life installations.**

**Technology to support bottom occupancy should be undertaken. This includes construction work systems, underwater precision surveying, soil mechanics, foundation techniques, and submersible boring machines. Developing systems for underwater construction without surface support could be economically rewarding.**

**An isolated station emplaced on a seamount should receive high priority. Within 20 years laboratories should be established in waters as deep as the Mid-Atlantic Ridge, and before the end of the century an ocean bottom station at 20,000 feet should be built.**

## C. Safety, Search and Rescue, and Salvage

To support undersea activities, it will be necessary constantly to examine technological progress and prepare for potential hazards. Loss of life in undersea operations would be not only tragic but could be detrimental to the national effort.

Natural hazards include uncharted obstacles, mudslides, sudden strong shifts of subsurface currents, marine organisms, tsunamis, and such long-term effects as corrosion and fouling.

Sudden storms and fog affect surface support. Other hazards include accidental explosions, especially in areas containing undetonated mines or torpedoes, and operator error resulting from physical or mental ill health.

Deliberate enemy attack could involve forces ranging from conventional depth charges to nuclear explosives. Research is needed to determine characteristics of explosions and other hazards at great depth. Anticipation of hazards is necessary to design, fabrication, installation, certification, and qualification of undersea systems and their crews.

Several hazards directly associated with undersea systems—structural failure, power loss, and fire—perhaps are to be most guarded against. Such dangers should be anticipated and minimized.

### 1. Safety and Certification

**a. Current Situation** Orderly progress into the undersea frontier demands that safety engineering start during the design process, rather than holding safety reviews of completed plans and actions. Certification of manned vehicles, sea elevators, deep diving equipment, and undersea habitats should be the responsibility of a qualified group.

Comparative safety of undersea systems is an important factor in determining marine insurance rates, a substantial addition to the cost of undersea operations. System safety and certification are equally important to assure that an item is safely designed, well built, and adequately tested. Certification is a continuing process that includes concern for safe operation, maintenance, and overhaul.

It is important that fire, one of the worst hazards, be extinguished rapidly. Fire control systems use multipurpose powders, gases, foams, or water delivered by portable extinguishers, fixed pipelines, or manned hoses. Such new agents as high expansion foam have been tested and have possible undersea application. The National Aeronautics and Space Administration, with a similar closed environment problem, has developed information on fire fighting and fire prevention techniques that may be applicable.

Whatever the technique, it must work fast; total combustion of one pound of cellulose-like material in a short period generates smoke, toxic gases, and enough heat to raise the temperature 500 degrees in a 12-foot sphere.

No single agency is assigned responsibility for safety and certification. The Navy has published a certification manual, *Material Certification Procedures and Criteria Manual for Manned Non-Combatant Submersibles* (NAVSHIPS Publication #0900-02802010), which applies to vehicles on which Navy personnel are diving. Legislation proposed to Congress would vest in the Coast Guard responsibility to certify undersea systems. Both the Marine Technology Society (MTS) and the American Bureau of Shipping (ABS) are issuing guidelines for safety and certification of manned submersibles. The guides are similar in many respects. MTS's *Safety and Operational Guidelines for Undersea Vehicles* will serve as an initial standard for the industry, while the ABS guide, willingly or unwillingly, will be followed by those who wish to enjoy the reduced insurance premiums compliance would bring. The Deep Submersible Pilots Association (DSPA) has published *Guidelines for the Selection, Training, and Qualification of Deep Submersible Pilots.* This material was contained in early form in the MTS guidelines and now is available in revised form from DSPA. All these documents will be very useful to the operator and the prospective operator of undersea systems. None, however, to date has the force of law.

**b. Future Needs**  Research programs are needed to determine the likelihood of accidents, the extent of danger, and methods for anticipating the hazards involved. This information should be made available to the designer.

Emergency escape capability is needed. One approach is the detachable buoyant crew capsule, used on *Alvin* and the *Autec* vehicles, operable by the crew or by rescue teams. Another is to develop points for easy attachment of lift cables.

Protection from fire is one of the most severe problems. Technology must be developed to:

—Minimize the presence of combustibles.

—Precipitate or remove smoke particles rapidly.

—Inhibit the spread and duration of fires.

—Extinguish fires without overloading air purification systems.

—Minimize and/or isolate sources of ignition.

Materials to be used internally should be tested for flammability and behavior at high temperature. Methods to suppress fire with powder or inert gas will not be feasible without auxiliary oxygen breathing apparatus. In compartmentalized vehicles the crew must be able to retreat from a fire, seal off the area, and oxygen-starve the fire or extinguish it with built-in systems.

An authority for control of ocean system safety, certification, operation, and maintenance is needed, possibly similar to the combined Federal Aviation Administration/Civil Aeronautics Board control over aircraft. The group could serve as a source of information on system safety and, like Underwriters Laboratories, could develop lists of safe materials, equipments, and methods. It would investigate accidents, report on causes, and make recommendations to prevent recurrence.

The Coast Guard seems the logical agency to exercise this authority. Appropriate legislative action would be required to extend the control now vested in the Coast Guard for surface ship activity to underwater operations. Its authority would extend over the safety of vehicles, diving chambers, underwater power plants, diving systems, on-bottom and in-bottom underwater habitats, and underwater storage facilities. Criteria for review authority would be that a failure could affect human life and safety, seriously disrupt the environment, or damage property of a second party.

**2. Search and Rescue**

**a. Current Situation**  The Navy has a surface fleet of 10 submarine rescue vessels (ASR) which carry McCann chambers. Dependable operation of the chambers requires diver support. As a result of recommendations of the Deep Submergence Systems Review Group (DSSRG) following the loss of the *U.S.S. Thresher,* the Navy (DSSP) has placed contracts for two Deep Submergence Rescue Vehicles (DSRV). The first DSRV will be ready for sea trials in 1969 and will be operational in 1970. Design studies for another DSSRG recommended system, the Deep Submergence Search Vehicle (DSSV) to operate at 20,000 feet, have been completed, and a prototype vehicle contractor has been selected.

Although both vehicles can be used for search purposes, the DSSV has no undersea rescue capability, and the DSRV capability is limited to submarines modified for the purpose. On April 26, 1968, Hon. Paul Ignatius, Secretary of the Navy, in an address to the National Convention of the Navy League, Honolulu, made the following announcement concerning utilization of the DSRV by non-U.S. Navy groups:

*I am pleased to announce at this time that the United States is willing to share with other nations the obvious benefits provided by the Deep Submergence Rescue Vehicle. A document has been prepared giving details and technical specifications of this submarine rescue system which will be available to foreign navies on request through normal diplomatic channels. Nations interested in this rescue system can modify their submarines so that in the event one becomes disabled on the ocean floor, it can be mated with the U.S. rescue vehicle. This is another example of this country's willingness to cooperate in oceanic programs.*

The DSRV mates to the escape hatch of the submarine, and rescue is accomplished by direct transfer of personnel from the stricken submarine to the rescue vehicle (Figure 34). The DSRV, DSSV, and numerous other small submersibles

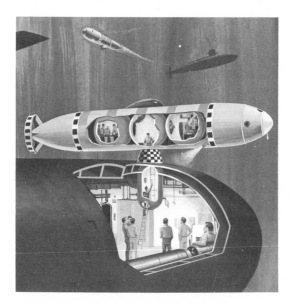

**Figure 34.** *Artist's concept of the DSRV. (Navy photo)*

have manipulators that could be used to a limited extent to free entangled vehicles.

The Coast Guard has the major responsibility for search and rescue at sea. It has joined with industry to develop expertise and tools necessary for effective search and rescue. A Mutual Assistance Rescue and Salvage Plan (MARSAP), now being formulated, will provide the Coast Guard with a limited, interim capability for undersea rescue.

The search phase of at-sea operations depends on the search rate and the search party's navigational accuracy. With aircraft and airborne radar the rate for surface search can be quite high, perhaps 4,000 square miles per hour. Underwater search, however, undertaken by surface ships towing sensors or by submersibles, is extremely slow—about 0.1 square mile per hour—as indicated by the *Scorpion* search.

This underlines the major reason for the high cost of underwater search—the search rate. Better surveillance of surface and underwater traffic can improve locational accuracy, thereby decreasing the time and expense of search operations.

**b. Future Needs** The Coast Guard, working closely with the Navy, should be given responsibility for search and rescue operations in the undersea frontier. It should work closely with safety and certification experts in industry to establish standards to minimize undersea accidents. When determined practical by the Coast Guard, safety and rescue apparatus (such as tracking pingers, lifting eyes, and standard mating hatches) should be required on undersea systems. As the number of undersea vehicles and installations grows, control over vehicle movement will become necessary, especially in congested or restricted areas.

Divers and submersibles will be called on to perform a variety of search, location, and identification tasks. These will be an essential part of most salvage and rescue operations unless a target's position is precisely known and the area is not susceptible to ocean currents or sediment transport. Reliable, high-resolution sensors to locate small objects resting on cluttered bottoms or in sediment will be necessary.

Identification is a real problem. Visual observation is the most reliable technique, yet is slow and difficult without a maneuverable high endurance, manned submersible equipped with observation systems, precise position systems, and digging and scraping tools.

### 3. Salvage and Recovery

**a. Current Situation** Presently there exists a substantial capability to locate, identify, and recover small objects at continental shelf depths and large objects in shallower water. In exceptional efforts, recovery has been achieved at greater depths. The Navy large object salvage program was directed at combining surface ships, lift equipment, and divers to lift submarines and other wreckage from depths of 850 feet. Unfortunately, only limited funds have been available to support development in this area.

The best salvage and recovery system depends on the geometric configuration, condition, proximity to the shoreline, depth, and extent of flooding and burial of target. A small surface vessel with divers and manually controlled equipment may suffice for small objects in clear, shallow waters. In other operations, it could be necessary to employ large, deep-diving work vehicles operating as part of a more complex system.

The surface vessel approach to salvage operations is obviously limited by diver depth capabilities. Hollow structures (like airplanes or cabin cruisers) might be raised from shallow depths by filling with low-density foam (Figure 35). During the Sealab II Project in 205 feet of water, a foam formed of resin, catalyst, and methylene chloride delivered through hoses by a diver-held gun was introduced inside an airplane hulk. It displaced enough water to raise the hulk.

**Figure 35.** *Artist's concept of a sunken aircraft being prepared for salvage by divers. (Navy photo)*

Recovery of small objects from depths below diver capabilities has been accomplished. The Navy's CURV and several commercial systems have recovered numerous torpedoes on test ranges. However, when an object is lost in an uncharted area of rough terrain (as off Palomares, Spain) the search, identification and recovery problems are magnified. Relief maps of the area must be prepared. At Palomares, they were based mostly on observation by television cameras mounted on CURV and extensive extrapolation by graphic arts personnel.

Great depths—2,850 feet at the Palomares recovery point (Figure 36)—further complicate the operation. The lost weapon slipped several times to greater depths. Had it slipped down the next steep slope, recovery by the CURV would have been precluded by the added depth, and recovery by any existing system would have been doubtful.

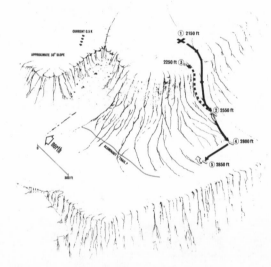

**Figure 36.** *Bottom topography off Palomares, Spain, site of nuclear weapon recovery. Points of interest are: (1) original point of weapon's impact on bottom, (2) position to which it slid, it was first sighted, and first recovery attempts were made, (3) take-off point of CURV unmanned vehicle for first recovery attempt, (4) position of weapon after second slide, (5) final lift-off point for successful recovery. (Navy photo)*

**b. Future Needs** Better underwater observation and terrain mapping equipment, power sources, and tools are needed for recovery operations. Better underwater cutting, welding, grappling, hooking, drilling, and methods to control lift (including constant tension winches and computer solutions of buoyancy and stability problems) are required. Needed are advanced attachment devices to lift large, cumbersome items. A special problem is containing and recovering dangerous liquid cargoes.

Recovery operations at increasing depths will necessitate developing submersible systems with specialized heavy duty external equipment. For certain applications, hovering capability during operations, creation of excess buoyancy for lift, or attachment of a recovery device to an object will be necessary. Under conditions that obviate optical observation, sensors will have to define precisely the position of tools relative to the sunken object. A family of recovery devices will be necessary to accommodate the number of shapes, sizes, and types of objects.

## 4. Conclusions

Undersea systems are vulnerable to damage from earthquakes and other natural events, explosive forces from accident or. enemy action, malfunctions of internal and external subsystems which may prevent surfacing or result in fire.

Loss of life from underwater accidents is unnecessary and could slow exploitation of the undersea frontier. Almost no research and development is being pursued on the cause and forecast of hazards, the prevention of disasters, and emergency procedures other than fire fighting.

Only limited capability exists for deep undersea search and rescue. The Navy's Deep Submergence Rescue Vehicle requires that modifications be made to combatant submarine hatches. The system's usefulness for rescue of small submersibles will be limited to such assistance as attachment of lift lines, observation, and communication, because a small submersible's size precludes incorporation of a mating hatch.

U.S. salvage and recovery capability to present diver depths is good and will improve substantially when saturation diving to 850 feet becomes a Navy fleet operational capability over the next few years. Deeper recovery capability has advanced little since a few scraps of the *U.S.S. Thresher* were obtained following months of effort. Technological development is needed in the areas of:

—Platforms with high-endurance and maneuverability.

—Search, location, and identification systems.

—Lift systems.

—Recovery, attachment, and viewing systems and tools.

Recommendations:

**The Coast Guard should set standards and inspect and certify safety engineering of undersea systems. It should conduct research and development to identify hazard sources, safe materials, equipments, and methods, and document means of coping with emergencies that may occur in undersea vehicles, structures, and operations. A principal objective should be the interchange of information among government and industrial designers, operators, and other agencies concerned with safety and certification. Efforts of the group established to develop a Mutual Assistance Rescue and Salvage Plan (MARSAP) are an example of desired interchange. Another important objective should be administration of rules regarding experimental and test devices, vehicles, and structures. Intelligent regard for safety without hampering useful technological and scientific progress is a necessity.**

**The Coast Guard's search and rescue mission should be extended beneath the seas. Developing an operational capability should be coordinated closely with present Navy efforts. This capability should be commensurate with the rate of industrial and recreational advancement into the sea and should concentrate on developing systems to 2,000 feet within 5 years and 20,000 feet within 10 years. The Navy rescue program should be given sufficient priority to achieve an operational system on the current schedule.**

**Navy salvage development efforts to saturation diving depths should be renewed and should include an effort to extend the capability to 2,000 feet within 5 years. Deep ocean recovery should receive high priority and should be routinely operational to 20,000 feet within 10 years.**

## IV. NEARSHORE ACTIVITIES

The nearshore zone consists of the land immediately adjacent to the sea and the waters over the continental shelf to the 2,000-foot contour. Inshore areas are those in most intimate contact with the shoreline.

Because of expanding industrialization and trade, increased leisure time, and greater disposable incomes of growing populations, the nearshore zone has been under increasing pressures, resulting in serious degradation in many places. Multiple use of this zone must be carefully planned to accommodate the interests of recreation, science, waste disposal, and commercial development.

Pollution, long a growing problem, now has reached proportions requiring not only positive control but active restoration in some nearshore areas. Coastal scientific and engineering efforts are necessary to gain a better understanding of shore processes, to halt harmful erosion of beaches, and to restore selected coastlines to a useful condition.

The Coast Guard role must be broadened and reinforced to provide the necessary services associated with preserving nearshore areas. These services are vital to the nation's utilization of the shelves and the deeper ocean. Initial effort must be concentrated on the nearshore area and much of the technology needed to resolve the problems is at hand.

The ocean transportation industry and the Nation's harbors suffer from many deficiencies. Technical aspects require an overall transportation system approach to research and development programs, ship and cargo handling design, and harbor development and renovation.

## A. Pollution

Much has been stated about inshore pollution control and abatement, waste disposal, and waste reuse. These problems will not be reitereated because investigation reveals that intensive steps already are under way to attack these problems.

The relationship of pollution abatement to water quality restoration is defined in detail in Section V, Great Lakes Restoration. There is a clear need to assure that abatement is positively pursued concurrently with restorative measures. Restoration can be investigated under more controlled conditions in the Great Lakes, a closed system. Hence, it is recommended that initial attempts at water quality restoration be undertaken there. A national commitment is needed to establish and enforce water quality standards and to support technology development necessary to establish the base for water quality improvement.

However, one critical problem is enforcement of existing standards. Research indicates that if strict enforcement were applied to primary treatment, if each industry followed good pollution control practices, and if industry would plan systematically new facilities with adequate incorporated advanced pollution control, pollution would be abated effectively.

This section is addressed only to some advanced pollution monitoring techniques and to sea oil pollution problems. Section V-D discusses restorative measures specifically applicable to fresh water lakes.

## 1. Current Situation

### a. Advanced Pollution Monitoring Techniques

An example of an advanced pollution monitoring method is use of infrared techniques. Research and development of infrared imagery in pollution detection and monitoring has been pursued for several years.

Infrared imagery is the photographic product of remote spectral sensing of infrared radiation emitted by material having temperatures greater than absolute zero. The principal device, the airborne infrared imaging line scanner, is extremely sensitive to small thermal differences. It operates in the invisible portion of the spectrum in either the 3 to 5 or 8 to 15 micron ranges.

Infrared imagery can furnish the oceanographer with valuable basic data unobtainable by any other sensor. It has been used to locate and map the Gulf Stream; it is being used for studies of estuaries. For military intelligence gathering and targeting purposes it has been operational for many years. However, its use in oceanography has been recent and limited.

Current studies indicate the following potential uses of infrared imagery in rivers and estuaries:

—Mapping estuarine surface circulation patterns.

—Mapping tidal variations and circulation patterns (ebb vs. flood).

—Semiquantitative mapping of estuarine surface temperatures.

—Defining main channels of rivers and estuaries by streamlines, turbulence, and thermal patterns.

—Estimating and mapping salinity patterns of estuaries under optimum thermal-salinity relationships.

—Delineating drainage patterns of tributaries having heavy overhanging foilage.

—Identifying well mixed and poorly mixed estuaries.

—Identifying bed and bank sediments.

—Locating offshore bars and breaker regions.

—Monitoring construction of such harbor engineering structures as jetties, docks, groins, etc., and their effect on circulation patterns and sediment dispersal.

—Locating sources of pollution having thermal characteristics.

—Detecting both submarine and terrestrial springs.

—Studying water turbulence.

—Recording wind streaks, hence wind direction.

—Locating shoal areas.

—Locating sea ice and identifying its type, age, and fracture patterns.

Studies using infrared were conducted in 1966 on the Merrimack River Estuary, Massachusetts, by the U.S. Geological Survey. Airborne infrared imagery was obtained in August and September of the estuary from Haverhill to Plum Island at low, flood, high, and ebb tides.

From the imagery, thermal effects of papermill waste, its diffusion in the river at various phases of the tidal cycle, and individual sewage outfalls were detected easily. Estuarine flushing was found to vary widely in different parts of the lower estuary. The surface expression of the freshwater-seawater interface could be seen clearly.

Infrared imagery in the Merrimack study provided a synoptic, integrated, comprehensive, and rapid method to detect pollution sources involving thermal differences. It was useful in determining circulation patterns in the estuary. The imagery provided a synoptic view of the estuary surface's thermal condition at high, low, flood, and ebb tides. It precisely delineated the salt water front at flood and high tides and defined the main channel at low and ebb tides.

The imagery also disclosed that the salt water front during flood tide diverts the polluted river discharge to the southern shore and over the shallow shellfish areas, thereby causing contamination. Data collected on temperature, salinity, tidal fluctuations, etc., provided a standard for semi-quantitiative interpretation of the imagery. Disadvantages of the infrared system are that it is not an all-weather reconnaissance system, it reveals nothing about the type of pollutant, and it determines relative, rather than absolute, temperatures.

Other successful experiments using airborne infrared systems for thermal pollution studies are being conducted in the Columbia River at Richland, Washington. Infrared imagery and radiometric measurements are being collected from aircraft, and the data are being processed by several computer techniques developed to produce qualitative and quantitative displays. One is used for qualitative evaluation of thermal data from a three dimensional color display (Figure 37).

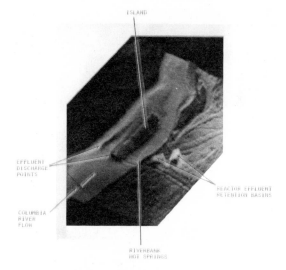

**Figure 37.** *Oblique three-dimensional display of infrared image collected over Columbia River near nuclear reactor site of the Atomic Energy Commission's Hanford Project. (Battelle Northwest photo)*

Turbulence patterns and mixing zones near atomic reactor coolant discharge points in the Columbia River are being determined. Isothermal maps of the river surface are being plotted. The rapid scanning infrared imaging systems obtain measurements that reveal detailed turbulence and mixing zones otherwise extremely difficult, if not impossible, to define. Isothermal plots of the river surface indicate the magnitude and aerial distribution of the heat discharge to the river. Hot spring development along the river bank, due to discharge of reactor coolant into a trench near the river, also has been defined.

### b. Oil Pollution and Other Hazardous Substances[7]

Pollution of the environment by oil and other hazardous materials can occur almost anywhere at any time. Some recent examples in the United States and its possessions are:

—*San Juan, Puerto Rico (1968).* The tanker, *S.S. Ocean Eagle,* carrying 5.7 million gallons of crude oil from Venezuela, ran aground, broke in half, and spilled more than 2 million gallons of oil in the water (Figures 38 and 39).

**Figure 39.** *Pelican caught by great oil slick from tanker S.S. Ocean Eagle. (Coast Guard photo)*

**Figure 38.** *Oil streaks from derelict bow section of oil tanker S.S. Ocean Eagle. (Coast Guard photo)*

—*York River, Virginia (1967).* The Liberian registered tanker, *S.S. Desert Chief,* lost between 500 and 1,200 barrels of crude oil during unloading operations. An estimated 10 miles of the York River and several recreational beaches were fouled, and waterfowl were killed.

—*Cape Cod National Seashore (1967).* Several large slicks of oily material contaminated about 30 miles of coastline, including recreational beaches, and many ducks and other waterfowl were killed. The source of the material was not determined.

—*Long Beach, California (1966).* A levee around an oil company's holding pond broke in a storm, and 200 barrels of crude oil were dumped into the harbor.

—*Missouri River (1966).* A chemical company's storage tanks ruptured, discharging 50,000 gallons of ammonium hydroxide, 100 tons of molasses, and 1,000,000 gallons of liquid fertilizer into the river.

—*Mississippi River (1965).* A hurricane sank a barge loaded with 600 tons of chlorine, necessitating evacuation of area residents in Louisiana during salvage operations.

—*Spring Creek, Missouri (1965).* Railroad tank cars containing 20,000 gallons of cresylic acid and 40,000 gallons of high octane gasoline were derailed, spilling their contents into the creek. Fish were killed, and groundwater supplies were contaminated. Downstream water users were notified, and further damages were averted.

—*Minnesota-Mississippi Rivers (1963).* Storage tanks ruptured, spilling 2,500,000 gallons of crude soybean oil and 500,000 gallons of salad oil. Two thousand ducks were killed, and recreation and wildlife areas were fouled for 130 miles downstream.

---

[7]Most material from here to the end of the discussion on the current situation was taken from: Secretary of the Interior and Secretary of Transportation, *Oil Pollution, A Report to the President,* Washington: Government Printing Office, February 1968.

—*Chattahoochee River, Georgia (1963)*. A burst pipeline spewed 60,000 gallons of kerosene into the river five miles above one of Atlanta's water supply intakes. The river was polluted for three weeks. A treatment plant supplying one-fourth of Atlanta's water was shut down for two days, after which greatly increased chemical treatment of the water was necessary.

—*Coosa River, Alabama (1963)*. A tractor-trailer hit a bridge and spilled 25 tons of barium carbonate. Downstream water supplies were threatened.

—*Minnesota River (1962)*. A storage facility pipeline broke, releasing about 1,400,000 gallons of cutting oil, light mineral oil, and zylene into the river.

—*Illinois River (1961)*. At Peoria, Illinois, a hose ruptured during the unloading of anhydrous ammonia from a barge. Forty-two persons were hospitalized, and 5,000,000 fish were killed.

—*Mississippi River (1960)*. Industry drained several tons of phenol into the river near Baton Rouge. Water supplies for New Orleans and nearby communities were contaminated.

These are only a few of the almost continuous series of similar experiences reported across the nation in lakes, rivers, and territorial waters.

Oil and other hazardous materials constitute a major pollution threat to the Nation's water resources. The danger exists both inland and along the coasts. Whether the spill is large or small, occasional or continuous, each source must be evaluated for (1) the relative hazards involved, (2) the preventive measures that should be instituted, and (3) the damage-control and cleanup capabilities that may be needed.

*(1.) Waterborne Sources of Oil Pollution* With the growth of world and domestic commerce, increasing numbers of vessels of generally larger capacity have been required. Almost exclusively, oil is the fuel of the waterborne commercial fleets, and perhaps one vessel in five is engaged also in transporting oil. Thus, water transport constitutes a great potential pollution threat. The great numbers of these possible pollution sources and the fact that they are mobile over extensive water areas require both government and industry to give careful attention to pollution control measures.

The quantities and varieties of oils and other hazardous materials transported and stored by industry are staggering. For example:

—Four billion barrels of petroleum and natural gas liquids are used annually in the United States, and the figure is expected to reach 6.5 billion barrels by 1980.

—Twenty-five billion pounds of animal and vegetable oils are consumed or exported annually.

—Eighty billion pounds (1964) of synthetic organic chemicals are produced annually by some 12,000 chemical companies. These chemicals, many toxic or with unknown effects on aquatic and even human life, range from everyday food flavorings to pesticides.

No readily available compilation exists of the number, size, and character of facilities for moving and storing these materials. However, the quantities indicate the high probability of pollutants spilling into the Nation's waters from transportation and terminal facilities.

Newspaper headlines seldom announce the flow of 10 or 30 or even 300 gallons of waste oil into a nearby stream or lake. The event is proclaimed only by the trail of grime and damage left behind. These catastrophes might go unnoticed except that they are repeated so often.

*(2.) Pipelines* This country is laced by 200,000 miles of pipelines with pressures to 1,000 pounds per square inch. These lines carried more than one billion tons of oil and other hazardous substances in 1965. Many sections are laid in and across waterways and reservoirs. Lines are heavily concentrated where the demand for petroleum products is great—in the most populous areas along the coasts, rivers, and lakes. Thus, our pipeline system threatens pollution of our waterways, port areas, and sources of drinking water. There are enough leaks from accidental punctures, cracked welds, and corrosion to require alertness and technical improvement.

*(3.) Offshore Petroleum* Offshore oil and gas operations are being conducted in the Gulf of

Mexico, off Southern California, in Cook Inlet, Alaska, in the Great Lakes, and even off the East Coast. For example, in the Gulf of Mexico almost 6,000 wells have been drilled since 1960, and thousands of miles of oil and gas pipelines crisscross the Gulf's floor.

Such operations may pollute offshore waters through well blowouts, dumping oil-saturated drilling muds and oil-soaked cuttings, and oil lost in production, storage, and transportation. Pipelines on the seabed from the offshore platforms to storage facilities also threaten pollution if ruptured by storms or ships' anchors.

## 2. Future Needs

A major effort must be undertaken to curtail oil pollution from ships and oil rigs. A systems approach to preventing pollution spillage at sea, how to monitor it, and how to disperse it is discussed in the following pages.

The shipping and oil industries have some methods to prevent spills and to clean up those occurring. Most are suitable only for small spills; many require bulky equipment or chemicals difficult to carry to the scene. Therefore, one approach to combat oil spills is to make equipment and materials more readily transportable. Another is to adapt present methods to be effective against the largest spills.

In chemical, food, and other industries there are agents, systems, and procedures for the control, dispersal, or conversion of petroleum-like substances. A search of other industries is needed for techniques and equipment adaptable to controlling oil spills.

Finding and applying existing techniques and equipment may offer hope of a rapid solution to the oil pollution problem, but that solution may not be best. Concurrently, research and development efforts should seek completely new solutions.

The problem can be subdivided according to the condition or location of the dangerous cargo and the response time of a remedial system. Figure 40 lists nine combinations of cargo condition and response time, giving each an environmental number. Figure 41 lists some remedies or remedial systems and the environmental number (or alternate) to which they probably would apply best.

### Figure 40
### ENVIRONMENTAL NUMBERS

| Response Time \ Cargo Condition | In Hull | Escaping or Near Hull | Far From Hull |
|---|---|---|---|
| Before Imminent Casualty | 1 | N.A.[1] | N.A.[1] |
| 0-24 Hours After Casualty | 2 | 4 | 6 |
| 1-20 Days After Casualty | 3 | 5 | 7 |

[1] Not applicable.
Source: Trident Engineering Associates, Inc., "A Possible Solution to Pollution of the Sea and Shore by Oil Tankers," unpublished report to the Commission (Annapolis, Maryland, 1968), p. 2.

### Figure 41
### CONTROL TECHNIQUES WITH APPROPRIATE ENVIRONMENTAL NUMBERS

| Control Techniques or Systems[1] | Environmental Number[2] |
|---|---|
| Build foam barriers into cargo tanks (oil-permeable impedance) | 1 |
| Solidify oil | 1 |
| Design safety features into tank | 1 |
| Inject foam sealant into selected tanks | 2 |
| Act to free grounded ship (sacrificial approach) | 2 |
| Gel oil | 2(1) |
| Close tank vents (escape impedance) | 2 |
| Pull light vacuum on selected tanks | 2 |
| Unload tanks to free ship, using stored high-pressure air | 2 |
| Sluice cargo between selected tanks | 2 |
| Install water ballast tanks in critical areas | 2(1) |
| Burn oil above tanker | 2 |
| Solidify oil in selected areas | 2 |
| Build sealing devices into tank | 2(1) |
| Design air-transportable super-foam sealant system | 3 |
| Heat oil ready to pump | 3(2) |
| Bring in emergency high capacity pumping system | 3 |

**Figure 41 (Continued)**

| Control Techniques or Systems[1] | Environmental Number[2] |
|---|---|
| Bring in high capacity fuel transfer system (hose, jets, helicopter-hose system) | 3 |
| Bring in emergency receiving system (corrals, flexible containers, etc.) | 3 |
| Bring in emergency pump power source | 3 |
| Burn combustible liquids | 3 |
| Evaporate oil – high temperature | 3(5) (7) |
| Act to free ship (sacrificial approach with outside system for rapid help) | 3 |
| Corral oil (equipment carried aboard tanker or with helicopter aid) | 4 |
| Corral oil with other outside aids | 4(5) |
| Use foams in other ways | 4(5) |
| Use large-scale corralling | 5 |
| Sink oil | 5(7) |
| Use surface oil evaporation equipment | 5 |
| Corral oil with equipment shipped in | 5(7) |
| Use water surface cleaner, ship- or air-mobile | 5(7) |
| Airdrop light-weight surface cleaning materials | 6(7) |
| Use chemical combustion promoters | 6(7) |
| Use combustion sustainers such as artificial straw | 6(7) |
| Use surface cleaning ships (high speed, high capacity) | 7 |
| Use skimmer | 7 |
| Use corrals | 7 |

[1]Most of the remedial systems of Figure 41 are not existing systems. There are few systems available now, and existing systems either have not been adequately tested or results of their tests have not been published.

[2]Numbers in parentheses are alternate environmental numbers.

Source: Trident Engineering Associates, Inc., "A Possible Solution to Pollution of the Sea and Shore by Oil Tankers," unpublished report to the Commission (Annapolis, Maryland, 1968), pp. 3-5.

The primary development objectives are actually conventional, since they call for the cheapest, lightest, smallest system that will do the job. However, other factors require consideration:

—The system will be in some way handling hundreds of thousands of gallons of crude oil—a substance normally the consistency of lukewarm tar. The objective will be to dispose of the contaminant before it damages nearby shore facilities. Therefore, the rate at which the system works is important.

—Tankers, like any other vessel, are more likely to suffer damage in rough weather. In such weather high winds move escaping contaminants toward shorelines most rapidly. Therefore, any system must have good sea-keeping qualities, functioning well under very unfavorable conditions.

—Even the emergency equipment installed aboard ship to save sailors' lives often receives cursory maintenance. Equipment to preserve beaches, wildlife, and shoreline industry and property probably would receive even less attention. Therefore, the system must withstand being unused for years with little or no preventive maintenance.

### 3. Conclusions

Data collected by infrared imaging systems can be used for quantitative and qualitative water pollution studies. Qualitative evaluations of imagery using oblique three-dimensional displays and stereo coverage will allow the interpreter to sense the true intensity relationships. The potential of color-coding specific radiation levels and developing false color imagery has been demonstrated. These techniques and their variations should make possible more effective systems to monitor pollution.

Oil and other hazardous substances are a continuing major pollution threat to the inland, nearshore and offshore waters of our Nation. Catastrophe can occur anywhere or anytime, especially in areas of high population concentration. Methods to combat major pollution accidents are entirely inadequate.

### Recommendations:

**Detailed research and development programs in infrared imagery use for pollution monitoring should be increased.**

**A major systems program should be implemented to cope effectively with the accidental pollution of the Nation's waters by oil and other hazardous substances, including investigation of**

methods of pollution control and restoration—
even the redesign of ships, if necessary.

## B. Coastal Engineering

The shoreline of any nation is a natural location for industrial and commercial activity, transportation terminals, and transfer facilities. It is where the most prized resorts and residential neighborhoods develop and it is an essential recreational area for a majority of the population. The bays, estuaries, and nearshore waters rank among the most important for food production and harvesting, not to mention hatcheries for many species important to the ocean fisheries. Therefore, the shoreline (coastal zone) must be considered a vital national resource.

Shorelines have been misused and poorly managed for such a long time that major advances in our knowledge and its application to the coastal zone are essential to prevent further degradation and to effect restoration. Greatly increased priority in national planning must be given to protecting existing shoreline and facilities, modifying the shoreline to achieve its most prudent utilization by the many competing demands, and its extension by construction of inlets, peninsulas, and offshore islands.

### 1. Current Situation

The most effective shoreline modification and construction of fixed structures in the coastal zone require knowledge of: (1) coastal zone oceanography, physiography, ecology, and substructure, (2) the properties of sediments both above and below the waterline, and (3) the multitude of natural processes occurring in the coastal environment. Further, such modification and construction must consider that changes in the shoreline or bottom topography, modification of sediments, and introduction of man-made objects will alter natural coastline processes.

Planning and design phases prior to modification and construction require qualitative and quantitative information to provide accurate definition of nearshore properties and processes. Also the engineer must be able to predict the effects of these properties and processes on the modification or structure and, also, to predict the effects of modifications and structures on the environmental and coastal processes.

The lack of such critical information constitutes a technology barrier if (1) the needed criteria require the acquisition of data which cannot be obtained without technological advances, (2) basic understanding is inadequate to permit accurate interpretation of such data, or (3) the acquisition of the information requires long-term observation.

Principal inadequacies of basic engineering criteria exist in environmental design, coastal planning, conservation of sand, construction and modification technology, movement and stabilization of sediment, and environmental protection.

Environmental design criteria to support coastal modification and construction is needed in (1) sub-bottom structure and bottom topography (bathymetry), (2) prevailing and maximum conditions of wind, waves, surface currents, tides, and subsurface currents, and (3) design methods that accurately account for the effects of these environmental factors in planning and design.

For the coastal zone, much technology is in hand. However, such information is not readily available to the coastal engineer at present. The well-recognized need to develop environmental criteria for planning and design (particularly those activities in which coastal zone development is expected to be most rapid and extensive) is being pursued as rapidly as time and present funds permit.

The state of knowledge for translating environmental data into design criteria is not adequate, particularly for wind and wave forces. Model studies of natural processes at the land-sea interface have had only limited success, mainly because scale effects are poorly understood. The major concern and uncertainty are for structures, vessels, or devices which penetrate the air-sea interface and are integral parts of undersea activities.

In undersea activities, principal unknowns are a knowledge of subsurface currents, the effects of surface waves on subsurface structures, the relation between subsurface phenomena and the disturbance of ecology, and the phenomena occuring at the air-sea interface. This information is essential for optimum planning, design, and modification of structures in the coastal zone. Lack of initiative in advancing technology for measuring basic coastal environmental characteristics will have serious negative effects on all future engineering programs in the coastal zone.

A National Project for Coastal Engineering and Ecological Studies, as defined in Chapter 7, will develop the fundamental technology to investigate the unknowns with emphasis on ecological disturbances. Near-shore ecology needs as related to the scientific community are described more fully in the basic science panel's report.

In coastal planning the first requirement is adequate technical knowledge of shore processes, storm frequencies, and storm tide elevations for the area concerned. Especially on the Pacific Coast (including Alaska and Hawaii), the effects of tsunamis (earthquake-generated waves) must be considered. This information, applied to the topography of the coastal area and the adjoining continental shelves, makes possible prediction of flooding and erosion hazards in each area. Such knowledge then may be used to establish zoning and building regulations and the needs, types, and dimensions of works to prevent flooding or erosion.

In highly developed areas, economic considerations usually will justify the expense of protective construction projects which will insure preservation of land improvements and values once the need is recognized and the type of construction established.

Undeveloped or sparsely developed areas offer great opportunity for advance planning and control, particularly where intensive development is imminent. Appropriate procedures can be adopted to conserve remaining natural protective features. Proper regulation can result in minimizing cost of protective measures and ensure adequate protection. Also, regulation can assure that substantial areas of the coast remain in a natural or near-natural state for general recreation.

Erosion planning should not be considered for every small beach. Instead, a *long reach* of 30 to 50 miles only should be considered. In fact, if a *short reach* is repaired without proper planning, the adjacent beaches may be adversely affected and the problem not solved but magnified.

Sand—dunes, beaches, and nearshore areas—is the principal material protecting our seacoasts. Where sand is available in abundant quantities, protective measures are greatly simplified and reduced in cost. When dunes and broad, gently sloping beaches can no longer form by natural means, it is necessary to resort to massive struc-

tures, and often the recreational appeal of the seashore is lost or greatly diminished.

Sand is a rapidly diminishing natural resource. Sand once was carried to our shores in abundant supply by streams, rivers, and glaciers. Unfortunately, large stretches of our coast receive essentially no replacement sand from these sources. Inland development by man reduces further sand available for erosion abatement of the shore. Thus, to save sand, wasteful practices must be eliminated and losses prevented wherever possible.

Fortunately, nature has provided extensive stores of beach sand in bays, lagoons, and estuaries; these can be used in some areas as beach and dune replenishment. Massive dune deposits also are available at some locations; however, these must be used with caution to avoid exposing the area to flood hazard. Sources of sand are not always located for economic utilization, nor are they inexhaustible. When they are gone, cost of preserving the shorelines will increase rapidly.

Mechanically bypassing sand at coastal inlets is an increasing conservation practice. Removal of beach sand for building purposes is being curtailed as coastal communities recognize the value of good beaches. Modern hopper dredges, used for channel maintenance in coastal inlets, are being equipped with pump-out capability to discharge their loads on the shore instead of dumping sand at sea. It is hoped that dumping at sea ultimately will be eliminated. On the California coast, where large volumes of sand are swept by currents into deep submarine canyons near the shore, facilities are being provided to trap the sand and transport it where it can resume natural beach-building processes. Planting beaches with appropriate grasses and shrubs reduces wind erosion and preserves the dunes. Sand conservation is very important in the preservation of our seacoasts; it must not be neglected in long range planning.

Protection of our seacoasts, not a simple problem, is by no means insurmountable. It has increased tremendously in importance in the past 50 years. While the cost will mount as time passes, it will be possible through careful planning, adequate control, and sound engineering to do the job properly within economic means. Shore protection must be undertaken as a cooperative effort at all levels of government, Federal, regional, State, and municipal.

Currently construction in the coastal zone is accomplished almost entirely by surface methods and equipment. Moreover, most construction techniques have remained static for the past century (excluding development of new power sources). Divers are used for preliminary surveys, inspection, salvage, simple installation, and assembly operations, but the operations are basically dependent upon land or seasurface methods.

It is conceivable that wave energy will be controlled and focused to accomplish work at the land-sea interface. Natural bottom contours guide wave fronts, concentrating wave energy at points along a coastline. If wave refraction and reflection could be controlled by the emplacement of portable undersea barriers, enormous work could be accomplished at a great saving of time and money. Moving sediment along the coast from an oversupplied area to a denuded area is one obvious application; however, no investigations of the feasibility of harnessing wave energy for this purpose have been attempted. Controlled use of wave energy is at present an undeveloped technology.

In some instances, the impetus to improve technology in such coastline engineering as harbor and port development, artificial islands, tunnels, and underwater transportation and distribution systems is coming from other sources. Examples are mineral exploration and exploitation, pipeline installation, petroleum production, etc.

The application of underwater technology to coastal engineering probably will result as spinoffs from other developments with more immediate need.

Coastal design and construction technology must include underwater methods and equipment to a greater degree. Requirements for offshore cities, passenger and freight terminals for ocean or air transportation, or recreational facilities establish a need for application of underwater technology as an integral part of coastal engineering. In the following paragraphs, some activities are considered briefly as a means of identifying potential technological opportunities.

Dredging sediments for navigation channels and barrier island passes, for drainage or diversion of currents and sediment, or for construction of islands, peninsulas, and beaches is a major coastal zone activity. In shallow and protected waters, surface vessels will continue to be the primary means of moving sediments for such projects.

In deeper waters, in waters with adverse surface conditions, and where the bottom is coral, consolidated sediment, rock, etc., subsurface drilling, blasting, hydraulic jetting, and hauling may be necessary. The presence of equipment in the sea will compel the presence of men so means of underwater communication and observation will be essential for supervision and control.

These requirements do not pose insurmountable problems, although considerable development is needed. Primary is heavy machinery operating on the ocean floor to haul or handle material. In coastal areas, such equipment could be powered by cabled electric power or snorkel equipped engines. Work illumination will be a major problem to undersea operations; hence, further development of illumination devices—even electromagnetic or acoustic—will be required.

Sediment stabilization will become a greater problem as offshore installations and coastline modifications create more complex current patterns and traffic. Present methods depend upon mechanical stabilization—the application of such hard mechanical cover as shell, riprap, scrap metal, etc. The feasibility of chemical additives applied under water needs further investigation. Development of a fine-grained artificial material with the aesthetic qualities of natural sand but more practical characteristics for beach stability (i.e., in terms of specific gravity, etc.) is a future possibility.

The difficulty of men and machines working underwater while maintaining adequate communications and lighting is a prime problem. This is especially true in areas of concentrated activity and where current and wave action interface. For some operations working from the surface may pose fewer problems than attempting heavy earthmoving or site preparation with underwater equipment and methods. Extensive tunneling under the bottom starting from shore appears more feasible than an offshore sea bottom entrance with less tunneling required. This entire situation could reverse if a simple method of making a sea bottom entrance could be perfected.

Protection of materials used in coastal modifications and structures will require technology advances. Present protection against corrosion, biological attack, erosion, waves, and currents is inadequate or excessively expensive for many missions. For example, monel metal covering at the water line and sacrificial cathodic protection can usually solve the problem but become prohibitively expensive.

Different activities will dictate levels of expenditure that can be justified economically. Control of biological encroachment and encrustation is both a structural and an operational problem. It requires many solutions for different areas and species. Mechanical protection against environmental forces and erosion is less difficult. Both chemical and biological corrosion are technology barriers requiring improvements in corrosion-resistant materials, protective coatings and devices.

## b. Future Needs

The following observational and measurement capabilities are required to permit meaningful study and definition of coastal zone processes:

—Methods and instrumentation for rapid on-site measurement of the engineering properties of sediments (i.e., static compression and shear strength, stability, bearing characteristics, and dynamic response).

—Methods, equipment, and instrumentation for rapid core sampling of sediments and rapid (preferably automatic) analysis of cores for primary physical, geological, and chemical properties.

—Methods and instrumentation for continuous mapping of bottom sediments by primary geological classification and primary physical properties (e.g., density, sonic attenuation, and shear velocity).

—Effective experimental methods and associated instrumentation and data processing systems for study of primary coastal processes, particularly those controlling sediment transport and deposition.

Special research and development programs are required for:

—Development of improved modeling techniques for the study of coastal processes, including design of such improved model basin equipment as wind, wave, and current generators and controls plus a variety of materials for simulation of water and sediment properties.

—Evaluation of new methods and equipment for major shoreline modification and construction and for island building.

—Development of faster and less costly methods and materials to stabilize sediment.

—Reduction of future costs by stockpiling sand, once a dredge is set up and in operation for another purpose. For example, after a dredge has replaced sand on a denuded beach, large stockpiles of sand can be strategically placed so that wave action automatically replenishes losses over future years.

## 3. Conclusions

Shore erosion is caused by wave action, tide currents, rain, wind action, and severe storms and is affected by offshore depths, slopes, shape of the shoreline, and other factors. In most cases, shore erosion can be controlled by properly planned and executed corrective measures. Shorelines have been misused and inadequately managed; major advances in knowledge must precede preventive and restorative action.

Protection, modification, and extension of shorelines assume greatly increased importance in national planning. Optimum modifications of the shoreline and construction of fixed structures require a knowledge of oceanography, physiography, sediment properties, and natural processes. Planning and design prior to modification and construction require accurate definition of near-shore properties and processes and interrelated effects.

Principal inadequacies of basic engineering criteria exist in environmental design, coastal planning, conservation of sand, construction and modification technology, movement and stabilization of sediment, and environmental protection.

Coastal planning requires technical knowledge of shore processes, storm frequencies, and storm tide elevations for the area concerned. Undeveloped or sparsely developed areas offer great opportunities for proper advance planning and development control.

Sand is a rapidly diminishing natural resource requiring conservation. Protection of our seacoasts is not an insurmountable problem. Construction and modification in the coastal zone is frequently accomplished by antiquated surface methods and equipment. Wave energy can be focused by portable structures to accomplish enormous work.

Dredging is a major coastal zone activity. Sediment stabilization will become a greater problem as more complex current patterns and more traffic result from human activity. Present methods of protecting materials from corrosion, biological attack, erosion, waves, and currents are inadequate or excessively expensive for many missions.

Recommendations:

The following observational and measurement capabilities should be developed:

—Methods and instrumentation for on-site measurement of the engineering properties of sediments.

—Methods, equipment, and instrumentation for rapid core sampling and automatic analysis of samples.

—Methods and instrumentation for continuous mapping of bottom sediments.

—Effective experimental methodology and associated instrumentation and data processing systems.

Research and development programs should be conducted to:

—Improve modeling techniques for the study of coastal processes and controls.

—Evaluate new methods and equipment for major shoreline modification and construction and island building.

—Develop faster and less costly methods and materials to stabilize sediment.

C. Shelf Installations

In order for man to conquer the sea, he must go into the sea. Much has been said about the complexity of advancing technology to exploit, occupy, and manage the U.S. Continental Shelf. However, it is now technically possible to occupy the shelf by applying developments of the past several years. Conquest of the ocean depths must start on the continental shelf, for experience gained there will be the foundation for the thrust into the deep oceans.

Several ambient pressure, continental shelf habitats have been demonstrated in recent years, in the United States and abroad. They have been temporary installations depending upon cables to surface ships or shore for power.

A Fixed Continental Shelf Laboratory as described in Chapter 7 is designed to facilitate development of the technology to occupy and manage the shelf and to minimize logistic support. The laboratory will be available for joint civilian-academic-military use in the accomplishment of subsystem and component development tasks.

1. Current Sitatuion

a. Habitats Widely varying approaches have been suggested and tried for undersea habitats. Some are quite small; others are large, providing working space for six to eight divers. For a single worksite, a relatively immobile shelter may be planted on the bottom. Moving worksites for inspection of communication cables or pipelines may require a mobile habitat integral to a submersible vehicle. All systems have three features in common:

—They can maintain the diver at or near the ambient pressure at the worksite for extended periods.

—The habitat (or an elevator-like chamber interfacing with it) can bring divers to the surface for decompression. When an elevator is used, divers nearly always are transferred to a separate and larger chamber on the surface for decompression.

—The chamber at the underwater worksite has at least one bottom hatch from which divers can enter the water and return.

Functionally, seven habitat types can be identified: (1) continental shelf station, (2) variable depth habitat, (3) composite chamber, (4) decompression staging system, (5) personnel transfer capsule/deck decompression chamber, (6) vehicle with diver lockout, and (7) hybrids.

b. Continental Shelf Station The most elementary configuration provides structural simplicity and relative freedom for divers from the turbulent air-sea interface (Figure 42). If intended only for bottom installation, the hull need be designed for

**Figure 42.** *A movable continental shelf station which completed successful trials in late 1968. (Oceanic Foundation photo)*

**Figure 43.** *Artist's concept of a composite chamber suspended from a shipmounted crane. (Navy photo)*

only small pressure differentials—indeed, it may be made of fabric or rubber. Providing the men in a station with electric power, food, water, sanitation, and supplies can be formidable, especially in foul weather. For a very large work force active over acres of the sea floor, one can envision several stations arranged about the worksite. The equivalent of a fence, fixed lights, storage, implement sheds, and the foreman's office would complete the resemblance to a job site on land.

**c. Variable Depth Habitat** The variable depth habitat is anchored on the ocean floor but can be floated to intermediate depths. The habitat serves as a work station, transport vehicle, and living quarters. If the worksite extends vertically to the level of one or more decompression stages, divers can continue useful work during each decompression stop. This system typically is confined to a small-scale operation, involving two or three divers under rather special site and task conditions.

**d. Composite Chamber** This sytem is virtually a variable depth habitation suspended from a ship-mounted crane (Figure 43). The diving compartment is nearly always a pressure hull, making it possible to decompress divers on the surface. An observation compartment (usually spherical) is mounted atop the diving compartment and connected with it via a pressure-tight hatch; it performs several functions:

—With the hatch closed, it can carry one or two scientists or engineers in a shirt-sleeve environment to view the underwater job site.

—With the hatch open, it can serve as an antechamber to the diving compartment or as a lock to enter or leave the diving compartment when the chamber is on deck.

—If a major fault should make the diving compartment unusable during a dive, the divers can enter the observation compartment under pressure. (Normally, divers would work from the lower compartment, while observers would stay in the observation compartment throughout the dive. The observers, not being subjected to high pressures, can leave the compartment as soon as it is hoisted on deck).

The composite chamber is quite versatile, is relatively easy to transport, and is more suited to the smaller, short-term missions than to major diving projects. Without the ability to mate with a larger chamber, the composite chamber compels divers to remain inside until fully decompressed; this puts a definite limit on the total time under pressure.

**e. Decompression Staging System** This is a series of underwater stations located at principal decompression stop levels. Personnel working at a bottom site may decompress by entering the next higher habitat, spending a night, then swimming to the next (Figure 44). Gradually ascending through several such stations, diving personnel undergo decompression and simultaneously make use of heretofore enforced idle time. This system is attractive only under special conditions of terrain.

Plans to expand one nonmilitary undersea test range include a series of habitats from nearshore to shelf depths, including this use of decompression staging.

**Figure 44.** *Artist's concept of a decompression staging system. (Westinghouse photo)*

**f. Personnel Transfer Capsule/Deck Decompression Chamber** This system, first used for commercial saturation diving, allows divers to live in a deck decompression chamber (DDC) (Figure 45). A single small chamber, the personnel transfer capsule (PTC), transports divers from deck chamber to the worksite. The divers enter when the PTC is mated with the DDC, both being pressurized equally. The PTC is lowered by a crane. The system's pertinent features are:

—Divers live and sleep above water.

—The PTC has horizontal mobility within the range of its surface support platform and full vertical mobility.

—Both chambers can mate at any pressure from atmospheric to maximum rated pressure to transfer divers. The system can be mounted on a dam, drilling platform, barge, or ship.

Possible alternate means of operation include (1) two PTCs mating with adjoining compartments of one DDC or (2) PTC serving two or more DDCs. For safety reasons, a DDC should consist of not less than two self-contained pressure vessels; two main chambers and an entry lock are the most practical.

**g. Vehicle with Diver Lockout** The system is a two-compartment vehicle with one compartment exposed to ambient pressure (Figure 46). The system is valuable for a series of short, widely-spaced dives (e.g., photographing and marking damaged spots on a submarine telephone cable). Such a system could be used where weather restricts deployment of normal surface support methods. Currently, storage batteries are the power source for the vehicle, limiting mission duration to a few hours and restricting speeds to less than five knots.

**Figure 45.** *A personnel transfer capsule/deck decompression chamber system. (Westinghouse photo)*

**Figure 46.** *A submersible vehicle with diver lockout. The diver lockout hatch is located aft on underside of hull where open hatch cover is visible. (Perry Submarine Builders photo)*

If such a system were integral to a full-size nuclear submarine, speed and endurance limitations would be virtually removed. The size of the diving team, supporting sensors, and amount of equipment delivered to a site would extend saturation diving capability beyond anything possible today.

**h. Hybrids** The systems described above are not all-inclusive; variations on any system are possible, and combinations of two or more may be effective for particular missions (Figure 47). For example, a bottom-anchored, variable-depth habitat with a mating trunk used with a DDC would permit divers to eat, sleep, and undergo decompression in a larger surface chamber. A DDC could be combined with a submersible decompression chamber operating from a fixed winch. The submersible chamber could be fitted with a propulsion system to provide limited horizontal positioning capability. The operator could remain in a shirt-sleeve environment inside a spherical observation chamber atop the diving chamber.

The main task of a diving program is to select the best system for a particular job and site and to evolve a safe, economical method of operation.

Thought must be given to problems of logistics, chamber operation, and maintenance; when several men are under pressure for a week or more, plans must be made for food supply, laundry, and personal hygiene. These problems are greatly simplified if the main habitat is located on the surface rather than several hundred feet beneath. Continuous, correct gas supply and carbon dioxide absorption must be well planned before the operation; redundancy of systems is necessary, especially if operations are to be conducted in remote areas.

**i. Availability of Decompression Chambers**
Several small decompression chambers are in use today, approximately as follows: Gulf, 40; California, 20; Florida, 2; and Alaska, 6. During peak seasons, commercial divers in the Gulf number around 1,000 and in California, over 300. There are approximately 25 combination personnel transfer capsule/deck decompression chambers today.

**j. Accidents** The number of divers working offshore in the Gulf is expected to increase markedly in the next few years; an estimate of 3,000

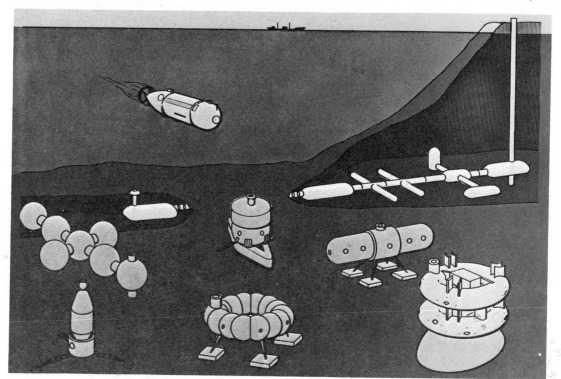

**Figure 47.** *Artist's concept of underwater habitat designs.* *(Navy photo)*

within 10 years is conservative. Presently no medical facilities on the Gulf Coast are available and attuned to the needs of divers. Three to five diver deaths occur each year in the Gulf.

**k. Bottom Activities** Many activities already are taking place in the shallow bottom areas. Tunnels built on the surface in sections can be economical where the conditions are favorable, as in protected waters with unconsolidated sediments on the seafloor. Sections of tunnel several hundred feet in length are fabricated on shore, floated to the site, lowered into a dredged trench with a suitably prepared foundation bed. The sections are joined together with the aid of divers, and the trench is backfilled. The Trans-Bay Tube now under construction for the San Francisco Bay Area Rapid Transit System is an example. It has tunnel sections about 48 feet wide and 22 feet high, located 135 feet below sea level at the deepest point. As advances in procedures for working under water are made, open-cut tunneling may be extended to deeper, less-protected offshore sites.

Tunneling in soft ground follows the same general procedure as tunneling in rock, except drilling and blasting are not required, and critical attention must be given to temporary lining. For very soft and wet ground, especially for undersea sites, shield tunneling methods are used. While the technology of shield-driven tunnels is well along, continued improvements will increase advancement rates and reduce costs.

Site preparation can be accomplished by pile driving and caisson sinking—standard operations in conventional construction work, particularly in the nearshore regions. In the offshore petroleum industry, piles and pipe caissons are being driven from barges in water depths exceeding 300 feet. The most commonly used drivers are pneumatic hammers, sometimes combined with such supplementary means as jetting and drilling. Vibratory and sonic drivers are used occasionally and may have considerable growth potential.

In the nearshore zone, concrete can be placed underwater from the surface using either drop-bottom buckets or tremies.[8] Bags filled with concrete or grout intrusion of emplaced aggregates are sometimes used. Methods for trenching to bury

pipelines and cables include plowing, hydraulic jetting, combined jetting and suction dredging, and use of shaped charges.

Protecting offshore oil and gas pipelines from damage by dragging anchors, soil movement, and underwater currents has required improved deep burying techniques. Large trenching barges can dig ditches 12 feet deep and 5 feet wide in water 200 feet deep, using a special dredging sled pulled along the pipeline. Towed sea plows on sleds are used to bury seafloor cables. A sea plow of sophisticated design was used to bury more than 100 miles of transatlantic cable in waters from 120 to 900 feet deep to safeguard it against damage from fishing vessels.

Dredging, a well-established construction and mining technique in shallow waters, has been used to deepen navigation channels, remove overburden for foundations, excavate open-cut type tunnels and outfalls, mine and place fill materials, and recover placer and seafloor deposits. The dredges, however, are severely limited in capacity and cannot be considered for major seafloor construction or mining in deep water.

Construction and mining require moving large amounts of material. Commercial mining requires production rates of thousands of tons per day to be economically justifiable. Capacities of this magnitude to 2,000-foot depths may be achieved by developing improved hydraulic or airlift dredges.

## 2. Future Needs

Improved cements that will set rapidly in low temperature sea water and concretes more resistant to deterioration in sea water are needed. As demand grows for concrete foundations in waters to 2,000 feet, major improvements will be needed in placing concrete from surface barges. Concrete mixing and emplacement on the seafloor using underwater plants or equipment may be required in the more distant future.

There will be a need to extend trenching and dredging operations to greater depths and deeper cuts. Devices such as mobile breakwaters and pneumatic curtains to shield operations may be needed. The ability to observe and monitor underwater would help greatly to increase operating efficiency, but a major breakthrough in observation techniques in turbid water will be required.

---

[8] Funnel-like devices lowered into the water to deposit concrete.

Assistance by submersibles probably will be needed.

Portable Continental Shelf Laboratories capable of operation at any depth to 2,000 feet should be developed during the coming decade. Each such station should be equipped for submerged transport vehicles to convey crew members or supplies to and from the surface or nearby shores. Crew size will vary greatly and will be dictated by the mission.

Specialized subsea power equipment will be required analogous to drills, cranes, bulldozers, pavement layers and concrete pourers used on land. Their ability to be mounted on a family of standardized, remotely controlled, power-driven chassis would increase their versatility. When an operator is required at the work location, the assembly might well be designed for temporary attachment of a small portable operator's capsule or a small submersible vehicle.

Assembly and fabrication of an underwater complex completely under water may be required when the entire structure is too cumbersome on the surface or the components are of a configuration that can be assembled only in place. Regardless of depth, the operation will require carefully planned evolution of an integrated system including surface vessels, pontoons, submersibles, divers, monitoring equipment, and automatic controls.

All underwater work operations will require coordinated development in many basic engineering and component areas. Soil mechanics and foundation design are clearly essential, as are data on the interaction of waves and currents on the installation. Underwater power sources, equipment, and tools adequate for the tasks must be developed. Accurate means of locating and positioning the installation must be available. Visual observation, television, acoustic imaging equipment, and command and communications systems will be essential. Improved materials are a basic requirement for reliable long-life installations.

It is predicted that within 10 years all segments of the economy—industrial, academic, military, and civil government—will be managing selected portions of the U.S. Continental Shelves and conducting exploration operations in the deep sea. Immediate capability, convenience, cost, and potential productivity dictate that initial activity be concentrated on the continental shelves.

## 3. Conclusions

It is now technologically possible to utilize the continental shelves in view of the progress and development of the past several years. The experience of working on the shelf should provide solutions to subsequent problems of utilizing the deep oceans.

Several ambient pressure, continental shelf habitats have been demonstrated in recent years; however, these have been temporary installations depending on cables to surface ships or shore installations for power. Technical advances during the next 10 years will permit autonomous manned stations on the ocean floor.

Present habitats and concepts for the future have three main features in common:

—They can maintain the diver at or near the ambient pressure at the worksite for extended periods.

—The habitat (or an elevator-like chamber interfacing with it) is capable of bringing divers to the surface for decompression.

—The chamber at the underwater worksite has at least one bottom hatch from which divers can enter the water and return.

Tunneling in soft and hard ground under the water is feasible and can be aided greatly by manned underwater support.

**Recommendations:**

**Pursue the National Projects to develop and construct Fixed and Portable Continental Shelf Laboratories; Seamount, Slope, and Abyssal Stations; and Mobile Undersea Support Laboratories as well as other forms of undersea habitats during the 1970's.**

### D. Transportation and Harbor Development

The present U.S. commercial oceanborne cargo trade ($36 billion annually) will continue to have a major impact on programs to extend ocean uses. This, moreover, should continue as the value of the U.S. world trade should more than double in the next 20 years.

The impact of maritime transportation on U.S. national interests is a product of underlying technologic, economic, and political forces operating on a worldwide scale, as well as of interests and policies within U.S. Government control. These forces affect not only U.S. shipping interests but shipbuilding interests as well. And, finally, programs for offshore harbor development have important interrelation with such Federal and State activities as urban renewal, trade promotion, and transportation development.

Revolutionary changes in merchant ship configuration and integration of ships into multi-mode transport systems for point-to-point cargo delivery will have great influence on developing uses of the oceans. As maritime transportation progress leads to larger, deeper-draft ships and containerization techniques, today's ports will be unable to handle these ships. Programs for progressively deepening these ports now are encountering severe physical obstacles, costly dislocations and ecological disturbances created by channel dredging.

## 1. Current Situation

**a. Shipping and Ports**  Data on past and present volume of waterborne trade by U.S. and foreign flag vessels, compiled by the Bureau of Census, reveal that export and import waterborne trade is increasing. During 1950, ocean shipments totalled 159,389,000 short tons of which 39.3 per cent was carried by U.S. flag vessels. Total tonnage increased to some 405,205,000 short tons by 1964; however, only 9.9 per cent was carried by U.S. flag ships. Tanker cargo carried by U.S. flag vessels dropped from 53 per cent in 1950 to only 5.9 per cent in 1964. This drastic shift from U.S. flag vessels to foreign vessels is a function of myriad factors including shipbuilding costs, wages, age of ships, and automation.

The Atlantic coastal region in 1966 accounted for the major share of imports, whereas the combination of Atlantic and Gulf Coast ports accounted for most of the Nation's exports. Cargo tonnage by all vessels for coastal distribution has remained approximately constant for the last 10 years. During 1964 the principal oceanborne import commodities were crude petroleum, residual fuel oil, gas, iron ore, and aluminum ore. The major export commodities were bituminous coal and wheat.

Many U.S. major ports have a disparity between the amount of cargo imported and exported. New York is a major port for imports; however, Norfolk, Virginia, is the major port for export on the Atlantic. New Orleans is the major Gulf port for export. Import and export trade of the Gulf Coast is distributed primarily among the Louisiana and Texas ports. Similarly, import and export trade on the Pacific Coast is distributed among the California and Washington ports. The competition between these adjacent ports is illustrated by the fact that Long Beach harbor handled 7,582,000 short tons with only 1,447 receipts, whereas the adjacent Los Angeles harbor handled 10,379,000 tons, with more than 4,000 receipts.

It is obvious that Long Beach harbor is shipping a larger percentage of bulk cargo requiring less handling and shorter turn-around times. All factors relating to packaging, equipment, and personnel must be considered in any evaluation of the influence on trade in U.S. ports.

Competition between ports exists where more than one port is in an area. This competition is generally a stimulus to efficient port operation. It requires that users and potential users be convinced constantly of the economy and efficiency of a port.

The erection of modern physical facilities to improve efficiency is only the beginning. Total cost is the dominant consideration in routing freight. Inland transportation, port charges, and water transportation costs combined must equal or better that of a competitive routing.

Technological advances, especially automation and handling, are penetrating the ocean shipping business rapidly. The port authorities must create new port facilities as they are needed—deep water terminals, offshore terminals, and automated handling equipment for new large bulk cargo carriers.

Most other maritime nations are doing more than the United States to keep pace with technological change. Gigantic superports are being planned in Ireland, France, and Japan; expansion is under way in Italy, Belgium, and Holland.

During the next few years as utilization of oceans changes, many problems must be solved; actual construction of the hardware may be the simplest. Expediting paperwork, removing customs bottlenecks, coordinating land and water transport, developing simplified pricing systems, increasing safety, and dislocation of ports and labor will be most difficult. Port and harbor problems will be solved only through systems analysis, research and development, and modern procurement policies. Similar procedures made large defense and communications systems possible.

The broad and complex interrelationship between harbor and waterfront development must include the following Federal programs:

—The civil works program of the Army Corps of Engineers.

—The water pollution and fish and wildlife programs of the Department of the Interior.

—The urban renewal, open space, urban beautification, historic preservation, water and sewers grants, public facility loans, and public works planning programs of the Department of Housing and Urban Development.

—The economic development, trade promotion, technical assistance, business loan, and port planning programs of the Department of Commerce.

—The transportation systems, transportation facilities, urban freeway, and Coast Guard port and maritime programs of the Department of Transportation.

—The surplus facilities disposal programs of the General Services Administration and of the Department of Defense.

Forecasts of port needs, identification of urban renewal opportunities and desirable recreation areas, delineation of pollution problems, and determination of means of financing all need study.

The United States is on the threshold of a revolutionary change in merchant shipping. For economy of operation the trend is to larger sizes, deeper drafts, smaller crews, better cargo handling facilities, and higher speeds. Most of today's ports will be obsolete and unable to handle the more cost-effective ships. Offshore handling and unloading facilities will be needed where it will be impractical to provide for the greatly increased ship drafts. The efficiency of larger, more automated ships will require concentration in a few large, well equipped ports rather than many small ports. Ports should be located away from congested downtown areas providing ample room to exchange cargo rapidly, to return the ships to sea,

and to redistribute the cargo for overland shipment.

In the past, the Corps of Engineers has responded to the demand for deeper harbor facilities by progressively deepening these major ports. However, they are encountering serious obstacles that constrain future dredging: (1) damage to water supplies by salt water intrusion into aquifers, (2) dislocation of private property adjacent to harbors and channels, (3) relocation of major land transportation and communications facilities, (4) replacement of such major navigation structures as locks, (5) encountering bedrock, conduits, vehicular tunnels, etc., (6) disposal of dredged spoil, and (7) disruption of harbor ecology.

The greatest obstacle to harbor development is the cost of relocations and dislocations resulting from channel enlargement. Major harbors have such extensive industrial developments at waters edge that harbor or channel improvement requires relocation of industrial, commercial, and residential structures.

At Oakland, California, harbor deepening would result in very high costs for modifying Army, Navy, and city waterfront facilities. The Chelsea River Channel in Boston Harbor is dredged nearly berth-to-berth in several locations, and dislocations will be required if dredging proceeds to greater depths. In New Orleans, producing oil wells located on and adjacent to the banks along the Calcasieu River, Pass Channel, and the Mississippi River Channel must be moved if the channels are enlarged.

Examples of major land transportation facilities that must be relocated include highway tunnels at Oakland, Baltimore, Norfolk, Mobile, and the mouth of the Chesapeake Bay. The many highway, rail, and subway tunnels crossing New York Harbor constitute an outstanding example.

The problem of removing increasing quantities of rock to accomplish harbor deepening is a problem associated with particular harbors. On the Gulf Coast dredging very long approaches through unconsolidated sediments covering the gently sloping adjacent shelf is a problem.

Deeper dredging creates water conservation problems by permitting the intrusion of the salt water farther up fresh water streams or rivers and by damage to the protective covering of fresh water aquifers. The problem of damage to water supplies appears to be most significant on the Atlantic Coast, particularly in the Delaware River estuary. Potentially serious problems exist at the mouth of the Columbia River and in San Francisco Bay.

Identifiable problems exist in the Great Lakes and the Pacific Coast harbors:

—Disturbance to harbor bottom and lake bed ecology.

—Pollution affecting water quality, fish species, and fish habitats.

—Changes in tidal flow that affect the habitats for fish and shellfish.

—Loss of waterfowl breeding grounds through spoil dumping.

The effect of harbor deepening on the estuarine ecology has resulted in growing concern by naturalists and conservationists throughout the country, emphasizing the need for additional information.

**b. Protection of Life and Property** The U.S. Coast Guard is envisioned as the principal agency for (1) rescue of ships, submersibles, and divers, (2) safety inspection and certification of submersibles, diving equipment, diver training, and small boats, and (3) relevant law enforcement. However, it is necessary to examine the Navy's role in certification of Navy submersibles so that the experience can be transferred to the Coast Guard. The panel endorses the role contemplated for the Coast Guard in future ocean operations.

There is proposed legislation and discussion by the Coast Guard on a U.S. Continental Shelf safety program as an orderly, comprehensive, and coordinated means of protecting life and property on the shelves.[9] This treatment of safety reflects this Continental Shelf Safety Program and has been endorsed by the National Council on Marine Resources and Engineering Development. The program includes the following major areas of endeavor:

---

[9] Has not yet cleared the House Merchant Marine Safety Committee; no bill number assigned as of January 1969.

—Resolution of the conflict in use of U.S. Continental Shelf areas.

—Reduction or elimination of wrecks, debris, pollutants, and litter on the U.S. Continental Shelf.

—Establishment of safety standards for continental shelf structures and devices.

—Continuance of the Nation's lead in continental shelf capabilities and activities.

—Estuarine pollution, conservation, regulation (tentative).

The present functions and activities of the Coast Guard are:

—Provide search and rescue services.

—Develop and administer a merchant marine safety program.

—Maintain a state of readiness for military operation in time of war or national emergency.

—Provide a comprehensive system of aids to navigation for the armed forces and marine commerce.

—Enforce or assist in the enforcement of Federal laws on the high seas or waters subject to the jurisdiction of the United States.

—Conduct an oceanographic program, maintain data on ocean status, provide ice-breaking services and iceberg patrol, and train officer and enlisted reserves.

## 2. Future Needs

Today and for the foreseeable future the marine transportation industry is essential to the well-being of the United States. The viability of the national economy to a large extent is dependent upon a steady growth in world trade. National defense relies heavily on shipping and shipbuilding to ensure adequate military response. Marine transportation and trade help maintain satisfactory political relationships between the United States and most of the maritime powers of the world.

The future of the ocean transportation industry is dependent on faster, more economical ships, possibly nuclear powered, that will allow the

United States to become a leader in world shipping once again.

A program for port and urban waterfront development and redevelopment should be established involving all interested Federal and State agencies. It should embrace a range of activities from creation of entirely new port or waterfront complexes to rehabilitation and conversion of existing port and waterfront lands and facilities. The program should entail: (1) comprehensive surveys of port-transportation requirements, interfacing with community needs, and studies on urban renewal, recreation, and pollution, (2) development of plans for port, harbor, and waterfront area renovation, and (3) integration of port and waterfront planning with programs for conservation of estuarine resources. The Army Corps of Engineers already has begun work related to the first two in cooperation with the Departments of Transportation, Housing and Urban Development, and Interior as follows:

—The Department of Housing and Urban Development and the Corps of Engineers have conducted a preliminary survey of areas engaged in or interested in harbor or urban waterfront renewal. Waterfront renewal activities to be planned involve: (a) eliminating sources of drift and debris, including removal of dilapidated or obsolete structures, (b) clearing lands for housing, open space, or recreation, (c) substituting small boat or marine facilities for abandoned commercial areas, and (d) removing sludge and solid pollutants from urban harbor areas.

—The Corps of Engineers presently is engaged in pilot studies in the New York and Boston areas to determine what new Federal initiatives or authorities are required to execute waterfront renewal plans. The studies will identify the legal, financial, and associated problems of harbor area renovation stemming from abandoned private facilities and sunken or derelict vessels. They will recommend changes in statutory authority to insure optimum use and effective redevelopment of the harbor area resources.

—The Department of Transportation is developing a Port and Harbor Access Program based on planning methods to determine optimum urban roads, terminal points, and intercity roads and rail lines to serve the port area.

To plan properly a program for port and urban waterfronts, alternatives to harbor deepening must be considered if this is not economically feasible. There are basically four technical alternatives to harbor deepening. First, where there is a long approach channel to reach port or harbor facilities, offshore unloading stations within protected waters may be constructed. Corresponding handling and transportation systems ashore must be constructed or modified to deliver the bulk commodities to their final destinations. It is conceivable that the construction or modification would be financed by private or joint enterprise.

Second would be a combination of lightering by barge, followed by transit up the channel to the pier head. Extensive studies reveal that, depending on local conditions, it is economical in some cases to transship cargo and lighter by barge.

Third is to provide more efficient scheduling of the bulk carrier by determining the decrease in the ship's draft due to fuel consumed en route and computing the decrease in the ship's draft due to cargo to be unloaded.

A fourth alternative is a systems design of ship size and port capacity in conjunction with existing channel depth, involving faster ships with improved cargo handling facilities and scheduled control of all ships calling at the port. As the world's fleets increase in number and speed, it is conceivable that *fleet controllers* similar to airway controllers may effect proper and safe traffic flow within the harbor.

If channels are to remain fixed in depth, and ship size and speed are to increase as predicted, installation of offshore cargo handling facilities is necessary. Any extensive harbor and channel deepening must be preceded by an extensive land-use pattern study. Due to consumer and locale requirements, it also may be advantageous to relocate the industry, shortening land routes in the transportation networks.

For bulk cargoes in general, it is conceivable that political and economic conditions at the destination may compel the preprocessing of some bulk cargoes for the recipient countries. This would reduce substantially the backland[10] requirements for bulk cargoes in U.S. ports.

---

[10]Backland is the area of a port city where warehouses, terminals, etc. are located inshore from the waterfront.

However, higher landing and terminal costs may result and the trade-offs must be studied.

Of the various nontechnical alternatives to channel deepening, the legal and regulatory predominate, including restrictions to ship operation, channel regulation, and safety. As ship size increases, directional stability at low speeds becomes more difficult; hence, to avoid high fees for using tugs in channels, many ships maintain speed, creating a substantial wake that damages structures along the channel. As ship size and traffic in the port increase the probability of collisions and channel blockage also increases. Economic loss from total blockage and port shutdown is incalcuable; higher insurance costs and port charges are a distinct possibility.

Large ships may create major economic problems in regional port development. As ship size increases, the tendency is to concentrate cargo capacity at one location to the detriment of neighboring port facilities, causing socioeconomic impact on the region with predictable reaction by labor unions.

The exhaustion of bulk cargo sources threatens ports and their regions with a shift of trade routes and ports of call. If the source of cargo for large ships is depleted and channels have been deepened explicitly for large ships, the huge investment in the channel and perhaps in the handling equipment will be wasted. If channels are not deepened and ship size increases, port authorities and other regulatory bodies may impose a progressive tax on large ships as an economic restraint on super sizes. Since depth is the most expensive variable in channel construction, the tax probably will be a function of ships' length, beam, and draft—with emphasis on draft.

As bulk ships increase in size, so will the inherent dangers of such hazardous cargoes as naptha and nitrates. Port authorities may restrict large hazardous cargo operations to remote areas; or by law they may restrict dangerous cargoes to ships of present sizes.

Regional development of port systems will be influenced by the very nature of large ships coupled with advanced scheduling techniques. Operators of super ships may find it more profitable to change the schedules and use one port system suitably modified for their increased capacity.

The high rate of ship technology development could make a large investment obsolete before its normal economic life. (For example, general economic lives for systems elements are: container—10 years, ship—25 years, terminal—50 years.) Therefore, it would seem advantageous to construct the facilities that have shorter economic lives and are easily maintained or replaced—pipelines, conveyor belts, long finger piers, etc.

Other non-technical considerations would include the decline of the present commodity movements, the increasing volume of new commodities, shifting trade routes, population pressures causing port systems to be reduced in size, safety requirements, air space requirements, pollution, etc.

The Coast Guard, as the Federal maritime law enforcement agency, has the responsibility to enforce Federal laws relating to water pollution. The Coast Guard also is responsible for enforcing the Oil Pollution Act of 1961 which prohibits offshore pollution. These are largely preventive measures only, and it would appear that broader responsibilities should be authorized. Over the U.S. Continental Shelf and in other Federal navigable waters, there is a need for this agency to provide greater assistance in the protection of the natural resources through pollution abatement and control.

## 3. Conclusions

The present U.S. commercial oceanborne cargo trade will continue to have a major impact on any programs designed to extend ocean uses.

The future needs of the transportation industry are dependent on faster, more economical ships, possibly nuclear powered, that will allow the U.S. to become a leader in world shipping once again.

Technological advances, automation, and need for economy of operation are penetrating waterborne shipping business at a very rapid pace. As a result, port authorities must stand ready to create such new port facilities as deep water terminals or offshore unloading terminals with automated handling equipment for new large bulk cargo carriers.

Progress in marine transportation is leading rapidly to larger, deeper draft, bulk carriers and high speed ships with improved cargo handling systems such as containers and lighters. The impact of containerization on the efficiency of cargo handling is revolutionary and will continue to increase.

Port design in addition to ship design will pace future progress. The deepening of harbors to accommodate large bulk carriers is encountering such severe physical barriers as bedrock, man-made tunnels, and long shallow approaches. In general, terminals for containerized shipping must be totally new and located outside downtown metropolitan areas, a trend which can release valuable land for urban development.

Offshore unloading platforms and lightering techniques are being considered as one of the most progressive and economical means of handling larger, deeper draft ships.

The Coast Guard role in protection of life and property must be strengthened; this responsibility for the U.S. Continental Shelf undersea activity must be consolidated under one responsible agency. It is obvious that chaos will result from the advancing use of the U.S. Continental Shelf with its myriad of men and equipment unless one agency concentrates systematically on the tasks of protecting life and property.

Finally, to insure proper protection of life and property, the Coast Guard should pursue research and development programs to strengthen capabilities of traffic control and monitoring, search and rescue (including underwater scuba divers, submersibles, and habitats), pollution abatement and control (oil and other hazardous materials), and fisheries regulation.

Recommendations:

**Port and harbor development should be based on a total systems approach to marine transportation, concentrating on design of offshore and improved methods of intermodal (air-land-sea) transfer to allow more effective use of the coastal land.**

**To ensure proper protection of life and property, the Coast Guard should pursue a research and development program to strengthen capabilities for traffic control and monitoring, search and rescue (including underwater divers, submersibles, and habitats), pollution abatement and control (oil and other hazardous materials), and fisheries regulation.**

## V. GREAT LAKES RESTORATION[11]

Virtually every activity man pursues modifies his environment in some way. While not all these modifications are detrimental, the sum of discrete activities undertaken to achieve specific goals can be detrimental unless efforts are made to balance resource utilization and environmental quality. This balance must be sought with a full understanding of the interactions between resources, benefits, detriments, and long-range costs to society.

The public has become aware of the importance of this balance only very recently; previously, concern for preserving and maintaining our natural resources was subordinated by parochial interests. This shortsightedness now demands measures be taken to cure the sicknesses of our environment; preventive measures alone will pass a legacy of ruin to future generations.

The five Great Lakes demonstrate misuse and abuse of environment by man. One only need compare the rate of population growth in areas immediately surrounding each of the Lakes with the rate of deterioration of water quality (Figure 48). Ranked according to impaired water quality or interference with beneficial uses, Lake Erie exhibits the greatest impairment, followed by Lakes Ontario, Michigan, Huron, and Superior. Total population in the drainage basins around each of the lakes corresponds closely; the rate of population growth reflects the rate of accelerated aging or *eutrophication* processes in the lakes.

The conclusion is inescapable—man is directly responsible for the accelerated deterioration of water quality. If corrective action is not taken, further deterioration will parallel future population growth.

Fortunately, this situation has been recognized by all sectors of our society, and preventive measures to arrest deterioration are being implemented. These measures, however, probably are not enough. Whether the lakes—Lake Erie in particular—can recover from previous environ-

---

[11]Most of the material in this subsection was taken from Battelle Northwest, Research Report, *Great Lakes Restoration—Review of Potentials and Recommendations for Implementation* to the Commission (Unpublished report, Battelle Memorial Institute, Richland, Washington, 1968).

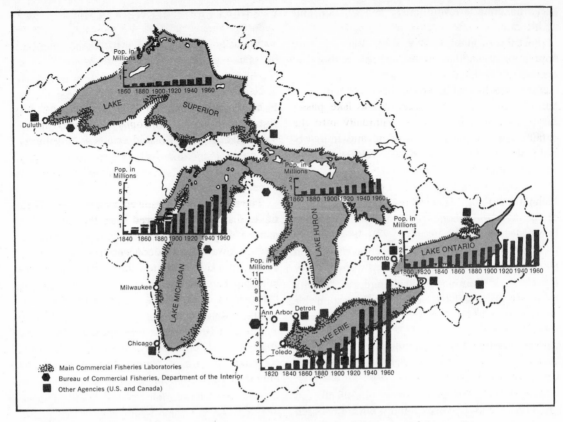

**Figure 48.** *The Great Lakes and their drainage basins, showing population increase in each basin. (Battelle Northwest photo)*

mental damage through implementation of preventive measures alone is debatable. The recovery period probably would be inordinately long and the forfeited benefits considerable. Thus, restorative as well as preventive measures must be considered to achieve resource utilization and environmental quality managed in the best interests of the United States and Canada.

## A. Current Situation

The fact that something has gone awry in Lake Erie is obvious. People cannot enjoy its use in the same ways they could 20 years ago. Southern Lake Michigan and parts of Lake Ontario exhibit some of Lake Erie's symptoms. The common denominator limiting the multiple use of the Great Lakes resources is water pollution.[12] Most authorities agree with this conclusion.

---

[12]Testimony of Dr. David C. Chandler, Director, Great Lakes Research Division, Institute of Science and Technology, University of Michigan.

The Federal Water Pollution Control Administration (FWPCA) Report (1966), *Water Pollution Problems of the Great Lakes Area,* identifies the major physical problems of the Great Lakes area as:

—Over-enrichment of the Lakes.

—Build-up of dissolved solids in the Lakes.

—Bacterial contamination of the Lakes and tributaries.

—Chemical contamination from industrial waste discharges.

—Oxygen depletion of the Lakes and tributaries.

Like all lakes, the Great Lakes are undergoing an aging process leading to extinction. Historically, young lakes are relatively barren of biological life; they are *oligotrophic.* As aging progresses, the material retained by the lake gradually increases in the bottom sediments; the sediments decompose, and the lake waters become richer in nutrients on which minute water plants thrive. As the plant population on which they feed increases, the population of minute water animals and higher animals multiplies.

Increased biological productivity changes both the surface and deeper waters. The lake passes from the *oligotrophic* phase eventually into the *eutrophic* phase in which organic and inorganic materials fill the basin. Rooted aquatic plants become established, gradually converting the area to marshland.

*Eutrophication,* the aging process, is the process of enrichment with nutrients. Accelerated eutrophication of lakes results from the input of nutrient materials, largely nitrogen and phosphorus from man's activities. Natural aging proceeds slowly in the geological time scale; however, acceleration of the process by human activity causes aging that can be observed within a generation.

Accelerated eutrophication is emphasized because it is critically impairing the benefits of the Great Lakes. It is a very difficult problem requiring several remedial measures. Problems of build-up of dissolved solids and oxygen depletion are closely associated with eutrophication.

Accelerated eutrophication of Lake Erie is manifest as follows:

—Blue-green algae, diatoms, and other algal proliferations cause noxious odors and appear as unsightly scums on the water surface.

—These algae impart unpleasant tastes to water supplies.

—Dissolved oxygen levels are depressed in thermally stratified areas.

—Desirable bottom dwelling, clean water animal species are displaced by less desirable species tolerant of pollution and low oxygen concentration.

—Fish populations change from such highly-prized game fish as pike, trout, and whitefish to such coarse, less valuable fish as carp, catfish, and sheepshead.

—Objectionable filamentous algae growing in shallow waters wash up onto the shores and beaches.

—Unsightly, malodorous masses of algae and other pollutants interfere with the recreational use of waters and beaches, clog municipal and industrial water intakes, and depress property values.

Nearly all Lake Erie is eutrophic; Lake Ontario is nearly eutrophic, and Lake Michigan exhibits some symptoms of eutrophy, especially in the southwestern part. Isolated evidence of pollution has been observed in Lakes Huron and Superior, although in general, water quality in these lakes is good.

Increases in the dissolved solids of the Great Lakes have been observed over the years since routine water quality analyses first were initiated. Despite dissolved solids concentrations not having impaired water uses seriously, local problems influenced by population and industrial growth are experienced near points of large waste discharges. The dissolved solids problem probably will be reduced somewhat through recently adopted State water quality standards. Because most bacterial contamination can be directly traced to man, it can be remedied more easily.

The accelerated aging of the Great Lakes is not the sole cause or symptom of deteriorating water quality. However, because other pollution effects are intimately linked to this phenomenon, measures to prevent accelerated aging and to restore water quality help solve other problems. An example is lessening oxygen depletion caused by the biodegradation of organic wastes.

Oxygen can be depleted through addition of organic substances to a body of water and the proliferation of algae. Most organic pollutants can be controlled by treatment methods consistent with water quality standards.

## B. Causes of Pollution and Accelerated Aging

To define the necessary action and formulate restorative methods, it is essential to understand the nature of causative factors. The following factors contribute to the accelerated aging of the Great Lakes:

### 1. Municipal Wastewater

Municipal sewage is the principal source of nutrients, especially phosphorus; 75 per cent of the phosphorus added to Lake Erie comes from municipal wastewater, and 66 per cent of the phosphorus is derived from detergents. Two-thirds of the phosphorous is retained in the lake, principally in its bottom sediments. Needless to say, the effects of municipal wastewater discharges have had a drastic effect on aging. There is no doubt that domestic sewage is a predominating contributor to the deterioration of water quality because of its nutrients, as well as its bacterial and organic contamination.

## 2. Combined Storm Sewage

Combined storm sewage sometimes is a greater problem than municipal wastewater. Combined storm sewage from a heavy rainfall can overtax the capacity of a treatment plant; hence, substantial volumes of untreated wastewater are bypassed to receiving bodies of water.

## 3. Industrial Wastewater

Often industrial wastes are routed to municipal treatment systems for the mutual benefit of the community and its industry. These wastes generally have the effects discussed under Municipal Wastewater, paragraph 1 above. However, many large industries bordering the Great Lakes find it more economical to accomplish treatment within their own complex. Many do not effect a suitable degree of treatment, thus contributing to accelerated aging. Nutrient-laden effluents, organic contaminants, noxious chemicals, and sediments or inorganic residues are contained in industrial wastewaters.

## 4. Watercraft Wastes

Wastes from watercraft are not treated to the extent of municipal wastewaters, or most often not at all. In the United States, recreational watercraft wastes are equivalent to that discharged by a community of 500,000. However, this contribution to water quality deterioration of the Great Lakes is insignificant by comparison with other nutrient sources. While its treatment is beneficial, especially to public health, it is very doubtful that watercraft wastes alone would accelerate aging of the Great Lakes. However, on a very local basis—at a marina, for example—it may cause very serious

problems. Of course, the problem will grow as water transportation and recreational boating increase.

## 5. Oil Discharges

Oil discharges are undesirable, for they cause ecological inbalances and drastic effects on aesthetics. On the other hand, special oils could have limited beneficial effects by reducing the penetration of the sunlight, necessary for the growth of algae that contribute to eutrophication.

## 6. Dredging

For many years harbors and channels in the Great Lakes have been dredged to provide suitable channels for waterborne transport. The spoil, rich in nutrients, usually consists of sediments carried by tributary streams and rivers and of sewage and industrial waste residues. Dumping spoil in the lakes, the practice for many years, releases more nutrients than when sediments and residues are undisturbed. Hence, dredging causes an increase in the recycling of sediment-stored nutrients, especially phosphorous. Important benefits would accrue if the dredging spoil were deposited on isolated land so nutrients would not be washed again into the lakes.

## 7. Thermal Discharges

Thermal discharges can have both beneficial and detrimental effects on accelerated aging. Discharge of such heated effluents as industrial and power plant cooling water can induce extensive algal growth during seasons when water temperatures are normally too cold. Conversely, during seasons when water stagnates and becomes stratified in the Lakes, thermal discharges could help restore circulation. Stratification causes oxygen deficiencies in the bottom waters of a lake, in turn, causing vastly increased nutrient recycling from the bottom sediments.

## 8. Nutrient-Laden Inflow from Tributaries

Inflow from tributaries and impoundments add nutrients to the lakes. Because impoundments suffer the same aging problems, both the causes and remedies are essentially the same as for the lakes. This illustrates the need to treat the Great

Lakes as a total basin, implementing preventive and restorative measures for tributaries as well as the lakes themselves. (This aspect is discussed further below.)

## 9. Waterfowl

The Great Lakes, on an extensively used migratory flyway, are a resting and habitat area for large numbers of waterfowl. However, the birds' contribution to eutrophication of the Lakes is a part of the natural aging process.

## 10. Fisheries

That fisheries have suffered from water quality deterioration in the Great Lakes is well known. Actually, the annual catch of all species in Lake Erie has not decreased with accelerated eutrophication. However, less desirable species have supplanted the more desirable game fish, because spawning and rearing areas have been contaminated or destroyed. The bottom fauna have been changed by pollutants and sediments, altering the game fish food supply so only the more tolerant, less desirable species can thrive.

The predation of sea lamprey has had some impact, but this has been less important recently in Lake Erie than in Lakes Michigan and Superior.

The purposeful addition of nutrients is a common technique for increasing fish production in lakes, while catching or removing large quantities of fish constitutes a reduction of nutrients. This is important in the Great Lakes because planning and management of fisheries resources can benefit nutrient control. For example, nutrient removal as part of a restoration program requires that dead alewives which wash ashore from Lake Michigan be removed. Additionally, alewives can be a source of protein. Hence, two functions can be accomplished concurrently: nutrient removal by vigorous fishing for an undesirable species and production of a significant amount of protein.

## 11. Sediment Interchange

Sedimentation (including silt, erosion and agricultural runoff, dead biological life, and wastewater residues) constitute the second most important source of nutrients in the Great Lakes.

As silt and erosion runoff flow into the lake, nutrients are dissolved and are available for biological utilization. Land use practices, especially land development in urban and agricultural areas, have contributed to accelerated aging; measures must be undertaken to control this nutrient source.

## 12. Agricultural Runoff

Agricultural runoff, another very important source of nutrients entering the Great Lakes, consists of eroded soil, leached salts and fertilizers, and excess fertilizer. Measures to alleviate some of the nutrient contribution in the runoff include contour plowing and other land management techniques, judicious fertilizer application, and control of agricultural wastewater where possible. It is difficult to control nutrients in agricultural runoff, because treatment methods cannot be applied to point sources. It is a problem of, perhaps, the same magnitude as combined storm sewage. In the Midwest alone, it is estimated that the nutrients from animal wastes are equivalent to that from 300 million people. Obviously, only a fraction reaches the Great Lakes, but the potential from this source is enormous.

## 13. Urban Land Drainage

Although distinguished from combined storm sewage, this problem has many similar elements, assuming that a separate sewer system exists for storm runoff. Urban or storm drainage is composed of such nutrient materials as street sediments, grit, oils, salts, and street refuse. It usually is discharged directly to a receiving body of water, because the potential contamination by pathogens is quite low; yet, the nutrient concentration may not be low, particularly in rich soil areas.

## 14. Subsurface Waste Disposal

Rural areas and many development areas around the Great Lakes have septic fields for domestic wastewater disposal. Nutrients in substantial amounts drain to the lakes in areas having certain soil characteristics; however, these regions are fairly dispersed and do not constitute a major source of nutrients.

### 15. Atmospheric Quality Deterioration

The carbon dioxide content of the world's atmosphere has increased a small amount, and the temperatures of the atmosphere have increased likewise. Consequent temperature increases in the water cause a small drop in dissolved oxygen.

It is virtually impossible to predict what would happen to the eutrophication trend by removing any single nutrient source. While priorities should be established for preventive and restorative techniques, many methods must be implemented before restoration can be achieved.

Factors contributing to accelereated aging are ranked below according to their importance in the problem. Hence, they serve as the targets for both preventive and restorative measures:

*High Impact*

Municipal wastewater
Agricultural runoff
Sediment interchange

*Medium Impact*

Industrial wastewater
Combined storm sewage
Urban land drainage
Dredging
Nutrient-laden inflow from tributaries
Fisheries

*Low Impact*

Watercraft wastes
Oil discharges
Thermal discharges
Waterfowl
Subsurface waste disposal
Atmospheric quality deterioration

Can the eutrophication process in the Great Lakes be reversed? This is an extremely significant question, because the effort and funds expended on Great Lakes restoration will greatly influence the answer. In referring to Lake Erie, Dr. Ralph L. Brinkhurst of the University of Toronto said, "It's the healthiest corpse I've seen." He firmly believes that eutrophication can be reversed, citing specific studies that demonstrate eutrophication reversal

has occurred in other smaller lakes. The fact that the FWPCA and other agencies are working to control elements contributing to eutrophication and to restore water quality reinforces Dr. Brinkhurst's conclusion.

Technology to control eutrophication may be classified as preventive or restorative. Preventative measures remove nutrients from the water before discharge to a receiving body, and restorative measures remove the nutrients or the products of eutrophy from the affected body of water. Measures which reduce nutrients usually improve other water quality parameters, (e.g., bacterial content) which may have little effect on eutrophication.

### C. Preventive Measures

#### 1. Nutrient Exclusion

Most research has been to develop suitable methods to remove nutrients from municipal wastewater. Most methods, however, can be applied also to other nutrient-containing aqueous flows. The soap and detergent industry is seeking substitutes for the phosphate in detergent formulations, because detergents account for a substantial part of the phosphorus in municipal wastewater.

Activated sludge secondary treatment plants can be operated to optimize nutrient removal. Aeration rate, aeration time, aeration solids, and return sludge ratios are critical to effective phosphorus removal. These plants also can be operated to accentuate denitrification, employing a variety of operating procedures.

Capitalizing on the principle that nutrients in municipal wastewaters cause prolific growth of algae, algae are cultured under controlled conditions in the treatment plant. The algae then are harvested to remove the incorporated nutrients, leaving the effluent low in nutrient content. The limiting factor in the removal of nitrogen and phosphorus by this method is the efficiency of algal harvesting.

Chemical co-precipitation with lime and hydrous aluminum and iron oxides is highly effective in removing phosphorus from municipal wastewater, but nitrogen removal is less effective. Of all removal processes, ion exchange is the most effective for removing both nitrogen and phosphorus. Ammonia stripping also has been effective in removing nitrogen.

Spraying effluent on land has been relatively effective in removing nutrients from municipal wastewater, but drainage from the land must not be allowed to flow into a receiving body of water.

Membrane processes, primarily for dissolved solids removal, have some capability for nitrogen and phosphorus removal but are expensive.

Distillation is efficient for removing nitrogen and especially phosphorus.

Other methods have been proposed, but most are still in the research or developmental stages. Recent FWPCA hearings on Lake Michigan no doubt will accelerate efforts to evolve an efficient, inexpensive method for phosphorus removal. The Secretary of the Interior stated that phosphorus removal from municipal wastewater should be maximized, and municipalities that discharge effluents to Lake Michigan should accomplish 80 per cent phosphorus removal by 1972.

Agricultural runoff, a significant source of nutrients, is more difficult to control. However, some measures can be taken to exclude nutrients, including land management to prevent erosion and subsequent pollution by siltation.

Measures are being implemented to control watercraft wastes, including retention of wastes onboard for treatment ashore and onboard processing equivalent to secondary treatment and a corresponding degree of nutrient removal. Considerable research and development sponsored by the FWPCA, Navy, and Coast Guard is in progress.

Another measure that can be implemented to exclude nutrients from the Great Lakes is the cessation of dredge spoil, garbage, trash, and refuse disposal in the lakes. Of these, dredging has caused concern in localized areas because of the amount of nutrients associated with the spoil.

## 2. Nutrient Diversion

Diversion of nutrient-containing effluents (such as municipal wastewater) around bodies of water is a technique successfully employed in the past to prevent accelerated eutrophication. Despite its success, this method could prove shortsighted. The pollution problem merely is passed to a downstream impoundment, lake, bay, or estuary. This is not acceptable resource management unless substantial mitigating circumstances exist for which the long-term effects are thoroughly understood.

## D. Restorative Measures

Restorative measures are intended to remove nutrients from water. While prevention involves millions of gallons per day, restoration in the Great Lakes involves hundreds of cubic miles of water. This point should be carefully remembered when alternative courses of action are considered.

Some restorative techniques discussed below are based on limnological theory rather than actual experimental or developmental work. Others are based on applications to lakes of much smaller size than the Great Lakes.

### 1. Sealing Bottom Sediments

If the addition of all nutrients were terminated, recycling of nutrients from previously deposited sediments would continue accelerated eutrophication of the Lakes for a considerable time. One solution is to seal the bottom sediments from the overlying waters. This seal must be renewed periodically, perhaps annually, if accumulation of additional nutrients by natural causes continues.

### 2. Flushing with Low-Nutrient Water

Use of low-nutrient water to flush eutrophic lakes has been employed with some success to restore water quality. This method was used in Green Lake near Seattle, and similar experiments are planned for Moses Lake, Washington. The great quantities of low-nutrient water required make application of this method in the Great Lakes questionable. Further, downstream waters may be adversely affected by the flushed nutrients.

### 3. Nutrient Removal

Although two-thirds of the phosphorus introduced into Lake Erie is retained in the bottom sediments, significant amounts also are retained by fish, algae, and rooted vegetation. Removal of fish will be considered in later discussions. It is essential that algae and aquatic weeds be removed from the Lake. Cutting nuisance aquatic weeds and leaving them in the water effects no nutrient removal. Furthermore, the harvested algae and weeds must be removed so nutrients do not reenter the lake by leaching and drainage. One solution would be to utilize them for added benefits as sources of protein, fertilizer, mulch, or animal feeds.

### 4. Thermal Destratification

During seasons when oxygen deficiencies exist in the bottom waters of a lake, nutrient availability at the sediment-water interface is greatly increased. Oxygen deficiencies result largely from water stagnation in temperature layers and from biological decay on the lake bottom. Destratification or restoration of water circulation to allow oxygen to be absorbed from the air reduces the availability of nutrients in the bottom sediments, thereby arresting or retarding the aging process.

Destratification can be accomplished by mechanical mixing, aeration mixing, or thermal mixing. In the first, the lake is mechanically stirred so that zones of stratification are thoroughly mixed. In the second, the same mechanical mixing allows oxygen from the air to be absorbed in the water. In the third, mixing is accomplished by heating.

### 5. Dredging

Since bottom sediments are a potent source of nutrients, removal of the sediments has been recommended for restoring lakes. However, Great Lakes sediments are quite thick in certain areas. This and the expanse of the Lakes dictates exertion of Herculean efforts to completely remove the sediments. Care must be exercised to minimize release of nutrients during the dredging operation.

### 6. Biological Control

Biological control of algae and aquatic weeds is possible if suitable animal populations are discovered to graze on the blue-green algae and rooted vegetation. Developing strains of viruses or parasites to prey exclusively on the algae and aquatic weeds is an alternative. Research to attain these objectives has had very little success to date.

### 7. Chemical Control

Although copper sulphate has been very successful for almost a century in controlling prolific growth of algae, it is also toxic to other life forms. Research investigators are seeking highly specific algacides to kill only the noxious species. Chemical control, not being a nutrient removal method, treats only the symptoms of eutrophication; the dead algae settle to the lake bottom, increasing the potential nutrient reservoir in the sediments. Further, it is only a temporary measure that must be repeated at frequent intervals, and the chemicals could accumulate in fish and eventually be harmful to man.

### 8. Chemical Inactivation

Research is in progress for a method to chemically inactivate the nutrients by preventing their utilization by the algae. One promising method is to develop chelating agents which will complex with divalent ions that function as co-enzymes in nitrogen fixation by algae and to determine the types of algae growths which result.

### 9. Prevention of Light Penetration

The development of a substance to decrease the penetration of light into the Lakes by increasing either reflectance or opacity has been proposed. This substance must be nontoxic, biologically stable, and nonrestrictive to oxygen transfer into the water. No known substance satisfies these criteria and others required to maintain maximum beneficial use of the water resource. Further, during certain seasons photosynthetic organisms can provide measureable quantities of oxygen during hours of sunlight, so the addition of a light retarding substance must not disrupt this.

### 10. Rough Fish Removal

Part of the nutrient inventory in the Great Lakes is retained by the fish population, and removing the fish reduces the inventory. However, many fish species are highly desirable for game or commerce. On the other hand, substantial populations of rough fish, such as carp and alewives, are undesirable.

A concerted effort to remove these fish would result in reduced nutrients. It would be prudent to consider processing these fish for usable protein, as burial of the fish within the Great Lakes Basin could allow the nutrients to be washed again into the lakes.

Since desirable fish species are also a nutrient source, increased harvesting should be encouraged within the bounds of sound conservation practice.

### E. Other Measures for Water Quality Improvement

Accelerated eutrophication, the cause of the most serious long-range consequences, is not the sole cause of water quality deterioration in the Great Lakes. The following paragraphs discuss measures which will improve Great Lakes water quality. Most plans cited below are recommendations of the Federal Water Pollution Control Administration and others who are continually studying the Great Lakes Basin.

## 1. Municipal Wastewater Treatment

A minimum of secondary treatment should be provided by municipalities discharging wastewater to the Great Lakes. Treatment should be efficient and continuous, accomplishing 90 per cent removal of oxygen-consuming wastes. Limits should be established for such specific pollutants as suspended solids, settleable solids, ammonia, phenolics, oil, and those materials exerting a biochemical oxygen demand. The levels should be set commensurate with their ability to interfere with beneficial uses of water. Whenever possible, treatable industrial wastes should be processed by municipal systems, and master plans should be formulated for integrated treatment facilities in urban areas. Areas with septic tanks should be incorporated into sewerage systems as soon as possible. Continuous disinfection of all municipal wastewater also should be effected as soon as possible.

## 2. Industrial Wastewater Treatment

All industrial wastes should receive the equivalent of secondary treatment, and those industrial wastes causing chemical pollution should be excluded from the Lakes or should receive a suitable level of treatment.

Maximum reduction by the best available treatment should be implemented for acids and alkalies, oils, and tarry substances; phenolic compounds and other organics which produce objectionable tastes and odors; ammonia and other nitrogen compounds; phosphorus; suspended materials; toxic and highly-colored materials; oxygen-demanding substances; excessive heat; foam-producing compounds; and other materials which detract from aesthetics or other uses of water.

## 3. Agricultural Runoff

Pesticides and herbicides should be applied to minimize the amounts that drain into the Great Lakes in surface or subsurface runoff.

## 4. Thermal Discharges

Thermal discharges should be managed so that water quality standards are met and these discharges are beneficially employed wherever possible.

## 5. Oil Discharges

Treatment of oil and other hazardous materials should be undertaken to exclude them from the Lakes.

## F. Future Needs

The foregoing subsections have shown that:

—The causes of water quality deterioration in the Great Lakes are fairly well defined.

—Technology is available to prevent most water quality problems.

—Technology to restore the water quality of the Great Lakes is or can be developed.

To abate pollution substantially and to improve water quality before implementing restoration measures, ultimate standards should be established in cooperation with the States, the regions, and the Federal Government. Once fixed, the standards should be strictly enforced. Incremental compliance may be necessary in some instances to offset the economic efforts of the ultimate standards and to allow time for new treatment equipment to be incorporated. The Great Lakes should be used as an example for applying national standards.

It has been determined that significant preventive measures are being implemented to improve Great Lakes water quality. Undoubtedly Lake Erie will become truly dead if accelerated eutrophication proceeds unimpeded.

If only preventive measures are implemented and technology for improvement is only partially applied, the Great Lakes could be restored to a desired level of water quality, but only after considerable time. Some speculate that recovery would be measured in terms of geological time.

Even if technology for improvement is fully applied (i.e., full utilization of preventive *and* restorative technology), restoration of desirable water quality could take as long as a generation. This assumes that eutrophication is reversible—a point of considerable controversy. However, recent research appears to confirm that reversal to some degree is possible.

Therefore, in summary, if present resource management practices are not improved, Lake Erie will continue to accelerate toward its demise, and the other Lakes will likely succumb in the order: Ontario, Michigan, Huron, and Superior. If only preventive measures are taken, Lake Erie may recover in a few thousand years, and water quality in other Lakes will be maintained; Lake Ontario also may show improvement. If both preventive and restorative measures are implemented, marked improvement in Lake Erie might be observed within a generation.

These statements, however, are far too general to support the necessity for restoration. The question, "What is the desired level of water quality in the Great Lakes?" has never been specifically answered. The objective should be to optimize the benefits which would accrue because of enhanced water quality in terms of the cost of attaining such enhancement.

Within the general framework of a market system, there are clear-cut reasons to suppose that public intervention can control disposal of wastes into water bodies. Not only can government intervention improve efficiency as measured in terms of market values, but it can and should take explicit cognizance of extra-market values. Since the character of water courses in heavily populated areas is such that interdependency between uses is inevitable, a major problem confronting public policy is to gauge accurately the significance of various interdependencies and foster the efficient multipurpose use of the water resource.

The answer, then, to the question of how much restoration is enough can be determined through a detailed benefit-cost analysis similar to that which long has been used to evaluate the economic feasibility of large public projects.

Figure 49 illustrates the type of analysis required. At the outset, the costs of improved water quality probably will not be matched by the value of associated benefits. Eventually, the value of benefits will rise until incremental benefits equal incremental costs (Point A). Benefits will exceed costs from A to B, but the ratio will gradually decrease until the incremental benefits are again equal to incremental costs (Point B). Beyond that point, increments of cost will exceed increments

of benefit. Hence, Point B is commonly referred to as the most economically efficient project scale, because this point maximizes benefits in terms of associated costs.

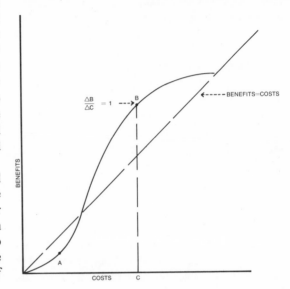

Figure 49. *Benefit-cost analysis.*

Since the degree of restoration can be directly implied from the derived optimum cost (Point C), a detailed benefit-cost analysis can identify how much restoration is enough.

Several benefits that can be quantified:

—Enhancement of land values.

—Reduced cost of water treatment for domestic, municipal, and industrial supplies.

—Enhancement of the fishery resource, both commercial and sport.

—Enhancement of water-based recreation activities and increased potential for water-based recreation opportunities.

—Minimized potential public health hazard.

—Improved aesthetic appeal of the Lakes and attraction of tourists.

Benefits derived from improved water quality change continually. For example, demographic and sociological trends as in increased population, leisure time, income, and mobility will put increasing pressure on the Great Lakes as a recreational resource. The change is compounded by the fact that as population density increases, social pressures arise to place a higher value on recreational opportunities. Therefore, the value to the individual of such opportunities in the future will be greater than today. By the year 2020, for example, the projected population in the Lake Erie Basin alone is expected to pass 23 million, compared to 9.8 million in 1960. The rate of increase in water-based recreation demand is estimated to far exceed this population growth.

There has been much speculation about the cost of a restoration plan for Lake Erie. The following example provides an order-of-magnitude estimate of cost for a potentially feasible method. It already has been shown that preventive measures must be implemented to remove the causes of accelerated eutrophication. Moreover, it has been stated that restorative measures must be implemented so that the time of lake recovery will be short enough to avoid forfeiture of substantial benefits. The example assumes that the recommendations for preventive technology will be implemented.

Earlier subsections on Prevention and Restoration (C and D) outlined the technology considered and, in some cases, tested on a small scale. The following is one approach involving a large engineering effort. It is a method to destratify Lake Erie by artificial recirculation. This example is not offered as the ideal solution. (Undoubtedly a complex of restoration methods will be required, and several techniques must be implemented.) It is intended to provide a reference concept that will assist in defining the necessary level of planning, effort, and funding in a more quantitative manner than previously. As such, the artificial recirculation case study can serve as a focus for further evaluation.

It must be emphasized strongly that restoration of a lake as large as Erie represents a major environmental modification and, hence, must be approached with caution. The analysis and evaluation required before such an undertaking is beyond the scope of this discussion. Although much information necessary to evaluate the feasibility, engineering requirements, and effects of an artificial recirculation project already exists, substantial additional work will be required.

As other restoration plans proposed earlier, this example is directed toward reducing the availability of nutrients from bottom sediments. It has been demonstrated experimentally that the availability of nutrients to the water mass is regulated by the oxygen content of a lake's deep waters. As these waters become oxygen deficient, decomposition of organic matter without oxygen results in chemically reducing conditions in the sediments. This further results in iron and manganese compounds being dissolved and sediment nutrients being released. Further study of this phenomenon is an integral part of the National Eutrophication Research Program wherein pilot scale tests in Klamath Lake, Oregon, will be used to determine the influence of sediment-water interchange on algae production.

A second effect of oxygen depletion in the deep waters is the marked change in the aquatic ecology. The demise of the mayfly nymph on the bottom of Lake Erie is related to the low oxygen concentration. Since the mayfly provided a major source of food for desirable fish species, these too have declined. A more direct effect of low oxygen concentrations is the gradual takeover of the Lakes by rough fish that are more tolerant of low oxygen levels.

In the Public Health Service 1965 report, *Pollution of Lake Erie and Its Tributaries,* the dissolved oxygen values in the bottom waters of the central basin of Lake Erie are described as having decreased during the past 35 years from about five milligrams per liter (mg/l) to less than two, with many areas near zero. Typically, severe late summer stratification can occur over an area of about 2,600 square miles or about 25 per cent of the entire lake. The total volume of the water column (average depth—12 fathoms) in this area is about 120 million acre feet or 35 cubic miles.

Carr[13] provides an excellent review of dissolved oxygen conditions in Lake Erie. Although it is difficult to generalize, Carr's work suggests that the oxygen-depleted hypolimnion occurs in the water column below 50 feet. For the particular configuration of Lake Erie, this condition prevails for about the last 10 feet of the central basin. If

[13]Carr, J. S., *Dissolved Oxygen in Lake Erie, Past and Present,* University of Michigan Great Lakes Research Division, Pub. 9, pp. 1-14.

so, about 20 to 40 million acre feet are oxygen deficient.

An alternate calculation based on a 270 million pound oxygen deficit suggests that 20 million acre feet could be seriously depleted.[14] These values are in sufficient agreement for purposes of this analysis.

The conclusion, then, is that artificial destratification of Lake Erie will require displacement of about 40 million acre feet of bottom water, which must be brought to the surface to be replaced with surface water during the summer months (i.e., about 100 days).

Artificial destratification is not a new concept, but application on the scale represented by Lake Erie requires new considerations. Numerous destratification tests have been conducted in the United States, Great Britain, and Europe. Whether any permanent installations have been made is unknown.

Results of these experiments have not always been predictable, probably due to the nature of sediments and the initial oxygen content. This experience emphasizes the obvious need for caution in any major effort to change the environment. A direct parallel can be seen in large-scale weather modification programs.

The use of airlift recirculators has been described, and detailed design methods have been developed. Airlift recirculators (vertical, open-ended pipes with compressed air introduced near the bottom end and discharging below the surface) are extremely efficient movers of water against essentially zero head. For example, air consumption rates are approximately one-hundredth of a cubic foot per minute per gallon of water circulated per minute. Velocities issuing from the circulator will be from five to six feet per second.[15]

Application to the destratification of Lake Erie obviously requires considerable extrapolation. This is particularly true of the induced circulation that occurs outside the circulator. Another expert estimated that the net induced circulation may be as large as 20 times that calculated by the design method; however, for purposes of this analysis, this value is not applied.

Using the design methodology of Cook and Waters[16] and the aforementioned volume of water to be circulated (i.e., 40 million acre feet in 100 days), the following values result:

### Engineering Parameters

| | |
|---|---|
| Volumetric water rate | 200,000 CFS[17] |
| Diameter of circulators | 10 feet |
| Length of circulators | 50 feet |
| Number of circulators | 500 |
| Compressed air volume (total) | 1,300,000 SCFM[18] |
| Compressor horsepower (HP), total | 600,000 |

### Cost Parameters

| | |
|---|---|
| Capital costs | |
| Circulators @ $200,000 | $100,000,000 |
| Annual operating costs | |
| Fuel (diesel) | 8,150,000 |
| Amortization (10 yrs. st. line) | 10,000,000 |
| Maintenance and repair | 5,000,000 |
| Personnel | 5,000,000 |
| | $28,150,000 |

For contingency purposes, this total value can be rounded upward to $30 million per year.

As presently conceived, airlift circulators would consist of vertical, open-ended riser tubes mounted on barges. Power for compressing the motive air introduced near the riser's bottom would be provided by diesel engines—approximately 1,000 hp per circulator. Each riser would be 50 feet in length with the upper end terminating about 10 feet below the surface. Blowable ballast tanks at the lower end of the riser will allow the riser tube to be elevated for moving into shallow water for repair and storage. With the ballast tanks flooded,

[14]Commoner, B., "The Killing of a Great Lake," *The 1968 World Book Supplement to the World Book Encyclopedia.*

[15]Cook, M. W. and E. D. Waters, *Operational Characteristics of Submerged Gas Lift Circulators,* U.S. Atomic Energy Commission Report HW-39432, Dec. 1, 1955.

[16]*Ibid.*

[17]CFS is cubic feet per second; 200,000 CFS is approximately equivalent to the average annual flow of the Columbia River at its mouth.

[18]SCFM is standard cubic feet per minute; standard refers to the conditions of average atmospheric temperature and pressure.

the riser tube will hinge down from the barge and lock into its operational position.

Mobility of the barge-mounted system will permit towing to mooring sites selected on the basis of water quality analyses.

## G. Institutional Arrangements

Well-founded restoration plans that incorporate the best available technology are of little value unless institutional arrangements provide means for successful implementation. All too often, desirable proposals for improved water management practices have not been implemented because constraints of existing water law, water management institutions, administrative regulations, and water use customs had not been considered adequately.

It takes only a cursory examination to discover that, in both the United States and Canadian parts of the Great Lakes Basin, there are a multitude of Federal, State, and local agencies, universities, research institutes, and industries with active programs related in some manner to one or more aspects of the quality of the Great Lakes resources. As one would suspect, there is considerable overlap in interest and activity among these programs.

In view of the rapidly deteriorating quality of some of the Lakes, particularly Lake Erie, it is apparent that existing institutional arrangements are not adequate to handle the problem. This raises the question—should a new organization be set up, or does an existing agency possess enough of the requisite characteristics that, given the necessary authority and funding, it could successfully formulate and implement restoration plans?

It is essential that full advantage be taken of the vast reservoir of knowledge and skills that exists among all the resources agencies and organizations active in the Great Lakes Basin. The problem is neither a lack of capability among available personnel nor a shortage of suitable technology with which to attack the water quality problem. Rather, it is the need for an effective vehicle with which to accomplish (1) needed leadership, coordination, and utilization of available talent including the special capabilities to be found in marine sciences and (2) successful implementation and management of a large-scale restoration program.

## H. Conclusions

This section identifies and focuses attention on the action required to restore Great Lakes quality to a desirable level. Accelerated eutrophication and other water quality deterioration are described with the contributing factors. Current technology to prevent water quality impairment resulting from man's activities and to restore water quality to a level that provides for optimum beneficial use is reviewed.

Also, the necessary economic analysis to identify the costs and associated benefits or restorative measures are discussed. Institutional arrangements are mentioned to identify the requisite characteristics of an agency to lead the planning and restoration programs.

Finally, restorative techniques of the Great Lakes are discussed with one example examined in detail to help identify the magnitude and cost of needed restoration actions.

Any plan to restore the Great Lakes will involve a tremendous undertaking because of the scale and nature of the resources involved. Technology to deal with freshwater environments is not oriented toward solving problems of the Great Lakes magnitude; however, technology developed in the marine sciences has been directed toward solution of large-scale problems. Therefore, experience in marine technology would be highly beneficial in formulating and implementing plans to restore this vast resource.

Two opinions often have been strongly stated in both the marine sciences and Great Lakes research. First, the experts agree that the application of marine science and technology skills to study the restoration of the Lakes would be highly appropriate. Second, and more importantly, almost all the experts contacted believed that this desirable relationship has not been exploited sufficiently.

Use of Great Lakes resources is limited by water pollution. Although a variety of classes of pollution are evident, the most serious long-range problem results from accelerated eutrophication or the aging process of these lakes. Lake Erie is not dead.

Suitable technology is presently available to successfully undertake measures to prevent further water quality deterioration and accelerated eutrophication.

**Recommendations:**

Implementation of measures to prevent water quality deterioration and accelerated eutrophication is essential before restoration can be achieved.

A detailed economic analysis should be undertaken: (1) to identify the quantifiable benefits accruing for various levels of improvement in the quality of Great Lakes resources and (2) to determine the associated costs of achieving these improvements. This analysis should include consideration of forfeited benefits if resource management practices are not improved and should encompass all significant aspects including domestic, municipal, and industrial water supply; power; irrigation agriculture; watershed management; and recreation and aquatic resources including pleasure boating. Without the knowledge that such an analysis would provide, the most desirable and justifiable level of water quality remains a matter of conjecture and debate, and any restoration program would lack direction and a defensible goal.

A restoration program, in addition to preventive measures, is necessary to improve the quality of the Great Lakes to any significant degree within an acceptable period. A detailed study of one part of such a program—artificially induced circulation—indicates that this part would cost about $30 million annually after a substantial initial capital investment. This provides a basis for which to examine and compare other aspects of a restoration program.

A goal should be set to halt substantially any further pollution and to improve the quality of nearshore waters. The goals of this program should be enforced by joint State-Federal ultimate standards to be fixed immediately. These standards should be tailored for incremental future compliance until the desired standards are attained.

A National Project tailored to the immediate needs of Lakes Erie and Ontario and southern Lake Michigan should be funded to test such promising restoration schemes as artificially induced destratification. Existing facilities should be used to the fullest extent.

A restoration project for Lakes Erie and Ontario and southern Lake Michigan should be undertaken as soon as the technology is available. The program should complement the implementation of existing pollution abatement technology in all the Great Lakes and must be managed to accommodate Federal, State, community, and private interests.

The technology of several domestic industries with major interest in the oceans or close to shore is discussed. These include the following resource industries:

—Living
  Fishing
  Aquaculture
—Non-Living
  Oil and gas
  Ocean mining
  Chemical extraction
  Desalination
  Power generation

Recreation, not treated separately here, is mentioned only for the sake of completeness. It is discussed more thoroughly in the Marine Resources Panel Report. Transportation and harbor development are discussed in Chapter 5 of this report.

Each industry subsection includes pertinent summaries and recommendations, with major findings and recommendations given at the front of the panel report. Each industry's technology is treated from the viewpoint of present status and trends, future needs, and recommendations, with emphasis on recommendations that can be implemented by the Federal Government.

There are tremendous differences in the industries' present and anticipated rates of growth. Further, widespread differences exist among the various segments of an industry, as in fishing.

Figure 1 depicts the present technological status of ocean industries in two broad categories—existing and future industries. Assignment of an industry to a given category has been somewhat arbitrary.

When development of an ocean industry is proceeding well, as in oil and gas activities on the continental shelf, only minor adjustments in Federal policies and programs are indicated.

When developments are in early stages of potential large-scale growth, as in desalination, the Federal Government's role can be decisive in maintaining the expected rate of growth. In the case of underwater recreation, the roles of State and local governments also are important (to insure access and availability of suitable areas and to zone for optimum multiple use of the resource).

## Figure 1
## PRESENT TECHNOLOGICAL STATUS OF VARIOUS DOMESTIC INDUSTRIES

| Type | Examples |
|---|---|
| *Existing Industries* Mature, healthy, and growing | Oil and gas on continental shelf Chemical extraction from sea water Mining of sand, gravel, sulfur Shrimp and tuna fishing Surface marine recreation |
| Early stages of growth | Desalination Bulk and container transportation systems and associated terminals Aquaculture, fresh water and estuarine Underwater recreation |
| Mature but static or declining | Most segments of fishing Shipbuilding Merchant shipping |
| *Future Industries* Nearterm promising (where nearterm is less than 15 years) | Mining of placer minerals Oil and gas beyond the continental shelf |
| Long range | Sub-bottom mining (excluding sulphur) Aquaculture, open ocean Deep water mining Power generation from waves, currents, tides, and thermal differences |

When development of an industry is not progressing, more drastic changes are recommended, including those of a fiscal, legal-regulatory, or technological nature—all of which are interrelated. For example, U.S. fishermen should be permitted to purchase vessels abroad and should not be required to pay excessive duty on foreign gear. This would help improve, for example, the technical position of the New England groundfish fishermen, enabling them to compete more effectively with foreign fishermen. In addition, technology's role in the Bureau of Commercial Fisheries should be upgraded considerably, with substantial emphasis given search and location techniques.

When an industry's development is yet to begin, as in offshore placer mining, special incentives to pioneers and special attention to removal of legal-regulatory and economic obstacles are needed. The Federal Government can do much prior to the beginning of a new mining enterprise, such as implementing a more comprehensive reconnaissance survey program of the shelves and encouraging broad basic engineering programs presently beyond the financial capability of most industries.

The nature of the encouragement for other potential ocean industries depends on the particular industry. Incentives for deep water oil and gas development, for example, would be somewhat different from deep water mining for many reasons, including:

—Availability of oil and gas industry venture capital is different from that of mining.

—The immediate past history of offshore oil and gas has created a more experienced industry.

—Extracting liquid or gas is far different from such mining operations as dredging nodules.

A common thread running through most ocean industries is the realization that aid in areas of basic engineering and in costly technology development facilities (available for lease) will be vitally useful. However, it is recognized that the mining and petroleum industries will wish to conduct their own detailed surveys and develop much of the final phase of the extraction technology. Both are important, but if the Government performs these functions, it will virtually eliminate the

incentive and competition necessary for resource development by free enterprise.

The Federal Government should keep a watchful eye on future industries with longer range potential and maintain close liaison with those industries and the academic community, as new developments may reverse the outlook. Two major recommendations emerge from a review of the industries' technological status.

Recommendations:

**National Projects such as the Fixed and Portable Continental Shelf Laboratories should be undertaken. Such projects would permit many users to lease and use these facilities to test the economic and technical feasibility of new undersea development options.**

**A statutory mechanism is needed through which the Federal Government, State governments, industry, and academic community can cooperate to provide responsible advice and planning for a truly national ocean program. Such a mechanism would help ensure that the overall program makes effective use of the competence and facilities of both Government and private organizations. In addition, it could be used to identify deficiencies in basic engineering disciplines, facilities, and manpower. Further, this mechanism could ensure consideration of important ocean programs not presently planned by industry or Government. Finally, this mechanism could monitor the progress of National Projects and the Government's fundamental technology efforts. The common need for this became apparent in hearings and interviews conducted with a broad cross section of marine interests.**

## I. FISHING

The case for a growing and stable fishing industry as a resource of employment and National income was vividly illustrated by the following:

*The annual catch is worth $438 million (1967) at dockside, but to the processor it is worth $1 billion. Fishermen have $500 million tied up in vessels that keep shipyards and gear manufacturers busy. The industry and closely allied shore activities provide half a million jobs. U.S. fishermen,* *whatever their present woes, would appear to be a national asset.*[1]

From a technological point of view, there is a current need within the industry to:

—Improve capital equipment (vessels and gear).

—Encourage more comprehensive and integrated use of marine technology.

The advance of a given industry is only partially dependent on scientific research and discoveries. It may be limited by lack of capital, technical knowledge, or proper complementary equipment. Environmental and institutional peculiarities pose problems in certain locations. The effects of fiscal, legal, and regulatory problems are discussed in detail in the Report of the Panel on Industry and Private Investment; this report concentrates on technology.

Research has been undertaken on a piecemeal basis, but the crucial interaction between components dictates that a more comprehensive approach is needed. Fisheries technology can be considered in terms of operational phases:

—Location, tracking, and identification of commercial species.

—Harvesting, including the concentration and control of species—preferably on a selective basis.

—Transporting catches from fishing ground to processing facilities at sea or ashore.

—Processing and preservation.

In location, tracking, and identification there are two major steps: (1) search for the general area in which commercial concentrations are to be expected and then (2) the localization or detection of the precise position of the fish. The long-range search involves broad-scale mapping with heavy dependence on environmental information. It ultimately could receive much support from satellites, buoys, and computers with appropriate instantaneous sensing equipment. Search is

---

[1] Senator E. L. Bartlett, *Congressional Record,* Jan. 30, 1968.

critical with respect to the pelagic fish. The localization step may rely on sonars, odors emitted by fish, lasers, etc. Localization is critical with respect to groundfish.

Each phase is dependent on basic data provided by biological research. However, it is not essential that such research be completed in order that technological advances relating to wild population production and harvesting be made more effective. Yet such research must be supported continually to optimize operations and to expand the number of species which can be fished economically.

## A. Fishing Vessels and Gear

### 1. Fishing Vessels—Present Status

The U.S. fishing fleet is numerically one of the world's largest—about 76,000 powered craft of all types exceeded only by Japan. About 60 per cent of U.S. vessels are over 16 years old, and 27 per cent have been in service over 26 years. While the fleet is in a continual state of renovation and replacement, there is much room for improvement.

The U.S. fish harvesting segment utilizes over 12,000 documented vessels of five tons capacity or larger, nearly 64,000 motor boats, and about 3,500 small unpowered boats. The 12,000 vessels total more than 415,000 gross tons. Estimated present market value of vessels alone exceeds $500 million. The range of individual vessel prices is from less than $1,000 to as much as $1,750,000.

There were 128,000 domestic fishermen on vessels, boats, and ashore in 1965 (U.S. figures), an average of less than two fishermen per boat. It is obvious there is a significant number of one-man boats.

Foreign fishing fleets off our coasts are dominated by large, complex craft capable of operating thousands of miles from home port. By contrast, most U.S. fishing vessels are small coastal craft. The small size in itself is not a deficiency because most fishing operations are close to our coast. (Figure 2 shows a departing fleet of coastal shrimp vessels.)

Although considerable variation exists among fisheries, 95 per cent of all U.S. fishing vessels are constructed of wood, while only five per cent are of steel. Of the 12,000 documented vessels of five tons or more, about 67 per cent have radio-

**Figure 2.** *Departure of shrimp fleet. (Bureau of Commercial Fisheries photo)*

telephones, 49 per cent have depth finders, 27 per cent have automatic pilots, 19 per cent have direction finders, and only seven per cent have radar. These percentages vary greatly by fishery.

The U.S. fishing fleet is not fully utilized, due partly to the seasonal character of fisheries and the inability of much of the fleet to participate in several fisheries. Some under-utilization results from the inability of a substantial portion of the fleet to compete with other more modern vessels in the U.S. fleet and with foreign fishing fleets. Many vessels are unable to locate and catch fish under conditions of changing resource availability. Figure 3 shows vessel utilization by fishery for the U.S. fleet. Regardless of the reason for idle time, the data indicate an inability to spread fixed costs by larger annual catches.

As indicated in Figure 4, 40 per cent of the documented vessels are part time (operating less than 120 days). The figure lists fishing vessels part time or full time by type of fishery in 1962. It should be borne in mind in interpreting these statistics that a large number of people fish commercially only in summer and for additional earnings, often encouraged by the low cost of commercial licenses.

## 2. Case Study of New England Ground Fishery

**a. The Demand** Many species of flatfish inhabit the U.S. Continental Shelves; some have such trade names as English sole, Dover sole, black back or yellowtail flounder, fluke, rex sole, etc. For the most part, however, in the United States they appear on restaurant menus or in food stores as fillet of sole. Such larger species as halibut often are steaked, finding ready retail market.

Flounder is taken primarily by otter trawls, the same gear that catch most of the cod, hake, haddock, pollack, ocean perch, and many other kinds of groundfish. This conglomeration of fish is the foundation for the most rapidly growing edible fish commodity in the world—the frozen fish block from which fish sticks are made. The demand at dockside for these fish has grown between 1948 and 1966 from 850 million pounds to 1,900 million pounds. To compete in this expanding market, U.S. fishermen must meet the price established by foreign competition.

**b. Strength of the Supply** Some species of groundfish off our coast are plentiful enough to meet domestic demand and provide a substantial export surplus. The supply of other species, however, has been considerably reduced by heavy fishing pressures, often by foreign fishermen.

**c. Domestic Production Decline** The New England otter trawlers at the end of World War II were the strongest and most vigorously growing branch of the United States flag fishing industry. However, the share of the domestic groundfish market claimed by the otter trawlers dropped from 74 per cent in 1948 to 29 per cent in 1966, causing a decline of U.S. position in the Northwest Atlantic fishery from first to eighth or ninth place.

U.S. Federal policy has been partly responsible for the decline in harvesting New England groundfish by encouraging other North Atlantic nations (particularly Canada and the Scandinavian countries) to increase their dollar earnings. In addition, Canadian fishermen have received liberal vessel construction subsidies and much related support from both their federal and provincial governments.

**d. Effects on Domestic Fishermen** Our fishermen have been forced, as a result, to restrict their activities to the higher priced resources of inshore flounder, Georges Bank haddock, and scallop. These species are taken by the smaller U.S. vessels with more ready access than foreign fishermen to the more lucrative but restricted U.S. fresh fish markets.

**e. Public Image of the Fleet**  It is precisely this fishery in New England (as well as California, Oregon, and Washington) which is the origin of the popular view that the entire U.S. fishing industry is decadent, declining, and composed of overaged,

inefficient, and obsolete vessels and men. It is this fishery that is the cause of the widely published reports that the Russians are catching all the fish and crowding U.S. fishermen off their own fishing grounds. The reasons for this, as indicated above, are not those generally stated. It should be emphasized that this decadence of the fleet is not due to negligence of the fishermen and is not typical of the entire industry.

## Figure 3
### VESSEL UTILIZATION BY FISHERY FOR THE U.S. FLEET, 1962

| Fishery | Average trips per year | Average days at sea per trip | Average days at sea per year | Average days vessel unutilized per year[1] |
|---|---|---|---|---|
| Gillnet/Drift . . . . . | 72 | 1.9 | 137 | 115 |
| N.A. Trawler[4] . . . . . | 17 | 12.1 | 200 | 52 |
| N.A. Dragger . . . . . | 80 | 2.8[2] | 223 | 29 |
| Oyster Dredge . . . . . | 21 | 4.4 | 93 | 159 |
| Clam Dredge . . . . . | 139 | 1.2 | 167 | 85 |
| Swordfish . . . . . . | 15 | 5.2 | 76 | 176 |
| Menhaden Seiner . . . . | 48 | 2.5 | 121 | 131 |
| Shrimp Trawler . . . . | 25 | 5.7[3] | 142 | 110 |
| Snapper Boat . . . . . | 18 | 5.3 | 97 | 155 |
| Tuna Seiner . . . . . | 7 | 18.0 | 133 | 119 |
| Salmon Seiner . . . . . | 14 | 5.7 | 80 | 172 |
| Halibut Boat . . . . . | 6 | 14.2 | 85 | 167 |
| Salmon Troller . . . . | 18 | 5.8 | 105 | 147 |
| Salmon and other Gillnet . | 16 | 4.4 | 72 | 180 |
| Pacific Dragger . . . . | 24 | 4.9 | 117 | 135 |
| Crab Boat . . . . . . | 53 | 2.3 | 121 | 131 |
| Herring Seiner . . . . . | 11 | 9.6 | 102 | 150 |
| Lobster . . . . . . . | 86 | 1.6 | 137 | 115 |
| Mackerel and Sardine . . | 14 | 5.6 | 80 | 172 |
| Industrial Fish . . . . . | 24 | 5.0 | 120 | 132 |
| Pound Boat . . . . . | 136 | 1.1 | 150 | 102 |
| Tuna Clipper . . . . . | 6 | 40.0 | 250 | 2 |
| Whaler . . . . . . . | 96 | 2.0 | 193 | 59 |
| Scallop . . . . . . . | 19 | 10.0 | 190 | 62 |
| Tuna Trollers . . . . . | 8 | 15.0 | 122 | 130 |
| Cannery Tender . . . . | 50 | 3.0 | 150 | 102 |
| Charter[5] . . . . . . | 21 | 3.7 | 77 | 175 |
| Longliner . . . . . . | 92 | 1.2 | 111 | 141 |

[1] Assumes a 252 working-day year. Saturdays, Sundays, and eight holidays have been excluded.
[2] 2.8 represents small draggers. Large draggers average 5.6 days.
[3] 5.7 represents medium trawlers. Large trawlers average 15.1 days.
[4] N.A. = North Atlantic.
[5] Vessels chartered for unspecified fisheries.
Source: Basic data from a private survey of the fishing industry by *Fish Boat* magazine.

**Figure 4**

**U.S. DOCUMENTED FISHING VESSELS CLASSIFIED AS PART-TIME OR FULL-TIME, BY FISHERY, 1962**

| Fishery | Number documented vessels | Part-time | | Full-time | |
|---|---|---|---|---|---|
| | | Number operating under 120 days | Per cent | Number operating over 120 days | Per cent |
| Gillnet/Drift . . . . | 633 | 266 | 42.0 | 367 | 58.0 |
| N.A. Trawler[1] . . . . | 177 | — | — | 177 | 100.0 |
| N.A. Dragger . . . . | 875 | 114 | 13.0 | 761 | 87.0 |
| Oyster Dredge . . . . | 599 | 282 | 47.1 | 317 | 52.9 |
| Clam Dredge . . . . | 264 | 66 | 25.0 | 198 | 75.0 |
| Swordfisher . . . . | 74 | 53 | 71.6 | 21 | 28.4 |
| Menhaden Seiner . . . | 222 | 167 | 75.2 | 55 | 24.8 |
| Sardine and Mackerel . | 72 | 52 | 72.2 | 20 | 27.8 |
| Shrimp Trawler . . . | 4,024 | 1,127 | 28.0 | 2,897 | 72.0 |
| Snapper Boat . . . . | 546 | 207 | 37.9 | 339 | 62.1 |
| Tuna Seiner . . . . | 106 | 31 | 29.2 | 75 | 70.8 |
| Tuna Troller . . . . | 391 | 168 | 43.0 | 223 | 57.0 |
| Tuna Clipper (large seiner) . . . | 66 | — | — | 66 | 100.0 |
| Salmon Seiner . . . . | 1,120 | 504 | 45.0 | 616 | 55.0 |
| Halibut Boat . . . . | 383 | 149 | 38.9 | 234 | 61.1 |
| Salmon Troller . . . | 1,421 | 710 | 50.0 | 711 | 50.0 |
| Salmon and Other Gillnet . . . | 752 | 466 | 62.0 | 286 | 38.0 |
| Pacific Dragger . . . | 152 | 12 | 7.9 | 140 | 92.1 |
| Crab Boat . . . . . | 480 | 197 | 34.0 | 283 | 66.0 |
| Herring Seiner . . . . | 25 | 3 | 12.0 | 22 | 88.0 |
| Longliners . . . . . | 53 | 40 | 75.5 | 13 | 24.5 |
| Lobster . . . . . . | 62 | 20 | 32.3 | 42 | 67.7 |
| Industrial Fish . . . | 206 | 52 | 25.2 | 154 | 74.8 |
| Pound Boat . . . . | 214 | 160 | 74.8 | 54 | 25.2 |
| Whaler . . . . . . | 5 | — | — | 5 | 100.0 |
| Scallop . . . . . . | 172 | — | — | 172 | 100.0 |
| Cannery Tender . . . | 260 | 260 | 100.0 | — | — |
| Charter[2] . . . . . . | 1,467 | 910 | 62.0 | 557 | 38.0 |
| Total . . . . . | 14,821 | 6,016 | 40.6 | 8,805 | 59.4 |

[1] N.A. = North Atlantic
[2] Vessels chartered for unspecified fisheries.

Source: Basic data from a private survey of the fishing industry by *Fish Boat* magazine.

# 3. Commercial Fishing Gear Types—Present Status

Commercial fishermen in the United States employ a variety of equipment and vessels to harvest fish and shellfish. Each fishery is characterized by its specialization of fishing gear and vessels. Commercial fishing gear design is dictated by the species to be harvested, its size, habitat, mobility, and by conservation requirements.

Commercial fishing gear may be classified as:

—Nets (seines, trawls, gill nets, etc.).

—Hook and line (hand lines, long lines, trolling lines, etc.).

—Gear for gathering immobile species (shovels, tongs, rakes, pumps, and dredges).

—Traps and barriers (pots, pound nets, wires, etc.).

Figure 5 lists the value of catch to the fishermen by type of gear for 1966. Figures 6, 7, and 8 are photographs of gill nets, a clam dredge and a snapper trap.

**Figure 6.** *Operation of gill net hauler aboard* R/V Oregon, *shown hauling 6-inch stretched mesh tuna gill net. (Bureau of Commercial Fisheries photo)*

## Figure 5
## CATCH BY GEAR TYPE, 1966

| Gear | Value of Catch to Fishermen ($ Million) | Principle Species Caught |
|------|------|------|
| Otter Trawls . . | 154 | shrimp, bottom fish |
| Purse Seines . . | 89 | salmon, tuna, menhaden, anchovy |
| Pots and Traps . | 54 | crab, lobster |
| Baited Hook & Line . . . | 51 | salmon, halibut |
| Gill Nets . . . | 42 | salmon, shad, perch, bass, mackerel |
| Dredges . . . | 33 | scallops, oysters, clams |
| Tongs and Rakes | 20 | oysters |
| Haul Seines . . | 4 | bait, herring |
| Pound Nets . . | 3 | herring |
| Hoes and Forks . | 3 | clams |
| Fyke and Hoop Nets . . | 2 | perch, alewives, catfish, bait |
| Trammel Nets . | 2 | pompano, mullet, weakfish |
| Other Gear . . | 15 | miscellaneous |
| | 472 | |

Source: Office of Program Planning, Bureau of Commercial Fisheries.

**Figure 7.** *Clam dredges being hauled aboard* R/V Silver Bay. *(Bureau of Commercial Fisheries photo)*

**Figure 8.** *Trap being hauled aboard with catch of red snapper. (Bureau of Commercial Fisheries photo)*

It is of particular interest that pound nets yielded only $3 million worth of fish in 1966; yet they once were the most efficient gear for catching salmon in Alaska and the Pacific Northwest. Only 20 years ago, more than 600 were in operation, catching salmon far more efficiently than any other gear since developed. The small fishermen, more numerous than the pound net operators, were successful in having legislation passed to outlaw these "overly-efficient traps."

An analysis of 9,251 fishing operations[2] indicates that 80 per cent of the vessels used were less than 60 feet in length, while only 4 per cent were greater than 90 feet. The following is a percentage breakdown of the gear type used in the 10,666 vessels represented by the analysis:

| | |
|---|---|
| Otter Trawling | 37.6 per cent |
| Troll Lines | 15.1 |
| Purse Seining | 11.9 |
| Gill or Trammel Nets | 9.8 |
| Dredging | 8.0 |

---

[2] A fishing operation is defined here as a company, partnership, or individual proprietor.

| | |
|---|---|
| Pots and Traps | 6.0 |
| Long Lining | 4.1 |
| Other Gear | 7.5 |

Although electronic gear has been well developed as navigational, safety, and fishing aids for the last decade, few vessels have installed the full array of available equipment.

Agriculture, road building, and other heavy equipment industries have long recognized hydraulics as a versatile, efficient means of transmitting power. Yet, only now is it beginning to find widespread use in the U.S. fishing industry. New developments are being implemented in the new tuna seiners and king crab vessels being built and converted on the West Coast for the Alaskan fisheries. The problem is not that fishermen, shipyards, or naval architects who design vessels are backward. Systems of this type usually must be built into vessels, and when a new vessel is built, it usually has this gear. However, hydraulic gear is an exception as it generally was added to tuna vessels (even old ones) during the purse seine revolution.

### 4. Trends of Fishing Vessels

Design trends are to:

—New hull shapes for greater speed, sea handling, carrying capacity, and safety.
—Introduction of more multi-purpose concepts.

Construction trends are to:

—Increased use of metals and less of wood, leading to stronger, more roomy vessels and greater versatility in layout of quarters and holds.

—Lower maintenance costs due to better materials such as steel alloys and anti-corrosive paints.

Propulsion trends are to:

—Greater horsepower for more speed. New engines have lower weight-to-horsepower ratios, requiring less space and increasing hold capacity. (Increased speed is especially important for tuna vessels.)

—Greater horsepower for better dragging power for trawlers (which in this case may be more important than greater speed).

Size trends are to:

—Larger vessels optimized for a particular mission.

—Crew quarters trends are to added space and comfort, including improved sanitation and mess facilities.

—Fuel capacity trends are to larger tanks to permit longer trips and additional time at the fishing grounds.

Fish hold trends are to:

—Larger capacity due to better construction techniques, smaller engine room requirements, and larger vessel size.

—Better insulation materials.

—Sanitation improvements by use of metal pen boards, improved covering materials, and refrigeration.

Safety trends are to:

—Inflatable life rafts, stronger rigging, non-slip deck materials, safety guards, firefighting equipment, etc., particularly in new construction.

—Features which reduce insurance rates and improve working conditions at sea.

## 5. Fishing Gear and Operational Aids

Current trends are toward:

—More sophisticated electronic gear for navigation and fish finding installed aboard new and existing vessels.

—More powerful deck gear to handle larger fishing gear being installed on new vessels and conversions.

—Larger fishing gear being employed on vessels with higher engine capacities.

—Larger fixed fishing gear (anchored in a single locality such as king crab pots).

—Greater use of snythetics in floats, pots, traps, trawls, seines and ropes.

—Greater use of hydraulic power throughout vessel for steering, deck winches, deck cranes, hoisting winches, etc.

—Increased mechanization of existing operations for faster handling of lobster traps, king crab pots, and clam dredges.

—Newly-designed nets and fishing techniques for faster and safer handling of fishing gear such as tuna purse seines, king crab pots, scallop dredges, and trawls.

In summary, fishing gear has changed measurably in the past decade. The king crab fishery has been aided by new crab pot design. Synthetic webbing, having swept through the entire industry, has been of great importance. The power block and large synthetic purse seines have revolutionized those fisheries using purse seines. The pound nets discussed earlier were enormously efficient devices, although their use is curtailed now by law.

## 6. Federal Effort

Exploratory fishing and gear research—closely related—provide the fishing industry with information concerning the location and extent of fish and shellfish resources and with knowledge of new and improved harvesting devices. These activities aid in meeting overall industry needs by:

—Reducing effort spent in locating concentrations of commercially useful fish stocks. It has been estimated that fishermen now spend an average of 50 per cent of time at sea locating fish, although this varies greatly among fisheries, and is considerably more in some.

—Providing a broader base for expansion to alternate fishery resources, thus reducing idleness and instability within the fishing community and increasing the variety of fish products available to consumers.

—Reducing harvesting costs, thus increasing the ability of domestic fishermen to compete with foreign imports and other domestically produced animal proteins.

—Providing efficient techniques and vessels to harvest resources not possible with existing gear.

—Disseminating through demonstration and technical services results of the above objectives.

Figure 9 lists the Bureau of Commercial Fisheries (BCF) budget in exploratory fishing Fiscal Year 1968.

Figure 10 shows distribution of BCF personnel engaged in exploratory fishing and gear research by position type and location, Fiscal Year 1968. It should be noted that there are no naval architects, only three mechanical engineers, and but three electronic engineers working on fishing fleet problems. With this low staffing level the Bureau cannot devote adequate attention to this subject.

Figure 11 shows Bureau of Commercial Fisheries exploratory fishing vessels and missions, Fiscal Year 1968. Figure 12 is a photograph of one of the newest exploratory fishing vessels operated by the Bureau of Commercial Fisheries.

**Figure 9**

**BUREAU OF COMMERCIAL FISHERIES, BRANCH OF EXPLORATORY FISHING, PROGRAM FUNDS, FY 1968**

| Region and Location | Total Funds ($ thousand) |
|---|---|
| 1 - Seattle, Washington . . . . | 550 |
| 2 - Pascagoula, Mississippi and St. Simons Island, Georgia . | 1,340[1] |
| 3 - Gloucester, Massachusetts . . | 450 |
| 4 - Ann Arbor, Michigan . . . | 265 |
| 5 - Juneau, Alaska . . . . . | 175 |
| Total . . . . . . . | 2,780 |

[1] Includes $400,000 non-recurring cost for outfitting new exploratory fishing vessel *Oregon II*.

Figure 10
BUREAU OF COMMERCIAL FISHERIES, BRANCH OF EXPLORATORY FISHING, DISTRIBUTION OF PERSONNEL, BY POSITION TYPE AND LOCATION, FY 1968

| Type of Position | Seattle Wash. | Pascagoula Miss. | St. Simons Island, Ga. | Gloucester Mass. | Ann Arbor Mich. | Juneau Alaska | Central Office | Total |
|---|---|---|---|---|---|---|---|---|
| Fishery Biologists . . | 9 | 14 | 4 | 5 | 8 | 3 | 4 | 47 |
| Fishery Methods and Equipment Specialists . | 4 | 4 | 1 | 2 | 4 | 2 | 0 | 17 |
| Mechanical Engineers . | 1 | 1 | 0 | 0 | 0 | 0 | 1 | 3 |
| Electronic Engineers . | 2 | 0 | 0 | 1 | 0 | 0 | 0 | 3 |
| Biological Aids and Technicians . . . . | 0 | 7 | 0 | 0 | 0 | 1 | 0 | 8 |
| Administrative Officers and Assistants, clerical personnel, Port Captains and Fleet Supervisors . | 4 | 12 | 3 | 5 | 2 | 1 | 2 | 29 |
| Vessel Crew . . . . | 7 | 15 | 10 | 13 | 3 | 5 | 0 | 53 |
| Total . . . . | 27 | 53 | 18 | 26 | 17 | 12 | 7 | 160[1] |

[1] Total number of authorized positions—includes several vacancies.

## B. Hunting and Harvesting

Many great fishery resources of the north temperate zone are fully exploited or overexploited. Marine harvest has definite limits, possibly much lower than theorized. During the past decade, fishing fleets have been expanded and new areas and new species fished. Overfishing may cause a serious decline of a species or an increase in population of another, possibly less valuable.

While true that many groundfish resources now in high demand are heavily exploited, many pelagic resources such as anchovy, thread herring, jack mackerel, Pacific saury, etc., are lightly exploited. Many midwater resources currently are practically unutilized off the United States. Thus, there is room to develop unexploited resources if technological developments and economic conditions allow this expansion. Potential areas of technological development are those concerned with fishing vessel design, fish detection systems, and new harvesting systems.

A concerted effort to upgrade the existing U.S. fishing fleet through improved capability of vessels and gear, more efficient hull forms, increased propulsion power, more effective deck hardware, and improved capturing devices—would play an important role in improving the competitive position of our fishermen. However, if the United States is to take advantage of the biological

Figure 11

## BUREAU OF COMMERCIAL FISHERIES, EXPLORATORY
## FISHING VESSELS AND MISSIONS, 1968

| Name of Vessel | Home Port | Length | Year Built | Mission |
|---|---|---|---|---|
| George M. Bowers | Pascagoula, Mississippi | 73 | 1956 | Inshore exploratory fishing and gear research, Gulf of Mexico |
| Oregon II | Pascagoula, Mississippi | 170 | 1967 | Exploratory fishing and gear research, Gulf of Mexico and Caribbean |
| Oregon | St. Simons Island, Georgia | 100 | 1946 | Exploratory fishing and gear research, North Carolina to Florida and Caribbean |
| Delaware | Gloucester, Massachusetts | 147 | 1937 | Exploratory fishing and gear research, Western North Atlantic |
| John N. Cobb | Seattle, Washington | 93 | 1950 | Exploratory fishing and gear research, N. E. Pacific |
| John R. Manning | Juneau, Alaska | 86 | 1950 | Exploratory fishing and gear research, biological research, Alaskan waters |
| Kaho | Saugatuck, Michigan | 65 | 1961 | Exploratory fishing and gear research, Great Lakes |
| Delaware II[1] | Gloucester, Massachusetts | 156 | 1968 | Exploratory fishing and gear research, Western North Atlantic |

[1] Replaced Delaware in late 1968.

productivity of the oceans, plans must be initiated for the orderly transition of fishing from basically a hunting process to one in which greater artificial control can be exerted. This transition should include:

—Perfecting the hunting process by maximizing fish detection capabilities.

—Minimizing escape of fish within the influence of fishing gear.

—Leading, herding, or aggregating fish to increase availability to harvesting systems.

Figure 12. *Exploratory fishing vessel* Oregon II, *operated by Bureau of Commercial Fisheries. (Bureau of Commercial Fisheries photo)*

—Developing techniques that allow harvest of the more abundant smaller organisms in the food chain.

It is felt by many that the most urgent needs are to apply existing technical knowledge and to secure adequate capital for new vessel construction. This should be done by making investment capital more readily available to fishermen willing to upgrade their equipment. This subject is discussed more thoroughly in the report on the fishing industry by the Panel on Industry and Private Investment.

## 1. Present Limitations

A recent report described how an engineer might be impressed with the modern electronic equipment available to locate stocks of fish, navigate precisely, and stay in contact with other fishermen and shore facilities.[3] However, he also might be disillusioned with the relative antiquity of the fishing gear and the fishing captain's almost total lack of information concerning its performance. He might ask several questions the captain would be unable to answer:

—Why do catch rates sometimes vary greatly between nets concurrently fishing the same species?

—How many fish are present on the grounds?

—What is the speed of the net over the bottom?

—What is the net's speed through the water?

—What changes occur to the net when towed fast or slow?

—How many pounds of tension are exerted on the webbing?

—What effect do wind, tide, and current have on gear performance?

—How long does it take for the net to reach bottom?

—When does it leave the bottom?

---

[3]McNeely, R. L., "Marine Fish Harvest Methods—Recent Advancements and Future Engineering Needs," *MTS Journal of Ocean Technology*, April 1968.

—Does the net catch as many fish in the first 15 minutes of towing as in the last 15 minutes of towing?

—How can it be determined whether the net is torn during a drag?

These are just a few examples to describe the trial and error procedures of fishermen. They show the need for additional development in fishing systems and imply that many problems are physical and, therefore, need engineering solutions.

## 2. Future Requirements and Possibilities

**a. Fishing Vessels** New concepts are foreseen in designing fishing vessels and deck machinery that would allow more time for fishing and require less time for handling gear. The major emphasis should be on developing entirely new vessels and fishing strategy. Perhaps such unconventional hull designs as hydrofoils and catamarans should be considered. Submersibles offer unique advantages in a supporting role, their ultimate uses yet to be determined.

Typical submersible advantages include freedom from the effects of sea surface conditions, ability to operate under ice, better fish detection capabilities, and the ability to observe the performance of fishing gear and fish reaction to the gear.

A systems analysis should be made of major U.S. fisheries to determine optimum fishing strategy, possibly introducing radical changes in fishing practices. For example, it could lead to high speed fish detector vessels or aircraft, highly automated fishing vessels capable of remaining on the fishing ground for long periods, high speed vessels to transport catches to shore, and floating processing plants.

**b. Search** *(1.) Predictions* The value of environmental information to the fisherman is well recognized. The value of predictions lies in effecting improvement in locating and catching fish. Even now, ocean environment predictions are of great economic value in the North Pacific albacore fishery, the Gulf shrimp fishery, and others. Yet the collection, analysis, and use of oceanographic information by fishing captains is seriously deficient. Fishing vessel masters make decisions daily as to where to fish, and the processor and distributor must act on their predictions of the success of the fishermen. The system's economic efficiency will be increased to the extent that scientific information leads to improved decisions. Even small improvements in the precision of fishermen's predictions can effect important monetary savings in the multi-million dollar fishing industry.

Predictive capabilities are closely related to variations in the ocean's circulation patterns which are, in turn, related to variations in incoming solar energy, outgoing earth heat, and associated phenomena. The lack of regularly received data from large ocean areas and lack of understanding the energy exchange between the atmosphere and the ocean prevent systematic analysis. Synoptic environmental observation requires costly and extensive collaboration among oceanographers, meteorologists, and space scientists. Until this energy exchange is understood, the quality of ocean current predictions will be poor.

Technology to provide the basic data is now available. Satellites and computers can keep the entire world ocean under instantaneous observation to provide data to help manage the harvest of the ocean.

*(2.) Satellites for Navigation and Detection*
Ocean upwellings (where schools of surface and near-surface fish congregate, and plankton, the basic food of fish, flourish) are directly observable by satellite.

The open ocean hardly has been touched by commercial fishermen except whalers and tuna long-liners. The old live bait tuna clipper did not range far because: (1) it was tied to coastal sources of live bait, (2) it traditionally remained in known tuna areas, and (3) flocks of birds, which do not venture far from land, were relied upon to indicate schools of tuna. However, modern tuna purse seiners now are working 500 to 600 miles offshore.

The fisherman frequently is led to tuna schools by porpoise schools that can be detected also by satellites. Possibly, satellites will be able to spot tuna schools directly. Fish school spotting by shipborne and shorebased aircraft has been a normal adjunct of tuna, mackerel, sardine, and anchovy fishing in the eastern Pacific and of menhaden in the Gulf and Atlantic for a genera-

tion. There should be nothing that an airplane spotter can see with the naked eye that a low orbiting satellite utilizing cloud-penetrating remote sensors cannot detect.

*(3.) Data Collection* The number of instrumented platforms established in the oceans must be increased greatly to make maximum use of satellites. Instruments should be placed on research vessels and on ships of opportunity. It will be necessary to provide by mass production sturdy, simple, inexpensive and reliable salinometers, current meters, bathythermographs, plankton samplers, and water pigment measuring devices.

Moored and drifting unmanned buoys to sense various ocean and atmospheric parameters and to telemeter the data to shore via satellite will revolutionize our understanding of the ocean. Buoys will be particularly useful in areas seldom traversed by ships. Production of inexpensive, sturdy, dependable buoys from which several meteorological and oceanographic parameters can be recorded continuously requires intensification of effort. Development of instrumentation for continuously recording biological parameters is strongly urged.

Figure 13 illustrates a system of satellites and buoys to collect and distribute data useful to the fisherman.

**Figure 13.** *Artist's concept showing satellites and buoys used for collecting and distributing data. (Bureau of Commercial Fisheries drawing)*

*(4.) Data Reduction* Greatly improved computer facilities will be required to assimilate, store, and convert into usable form the vast quantities of data gathered by satellites. The fishery scientist will become increasingly involved with ocean, weather, and space scientists in developing programs to provide data to fishermen. Initial collaboration is being developed by the U.S. Bureau of Commercial Fisheries with the National Aeronautical and Space Administration, the U.S. Navy, and other agencies working principally off California, in the Gulf of Mexico, and the tropical Atlantic.

*(5.) Satellites for Data Transmission* The satellite system also can relay computer data to fishermen at sea—the link in the chain requiring least development. Facsimile charts already are being transmitted by Japan for fishermen at sea. Receiver costs are reasonable for oceangoing fishing vessels, and communication satellites could provide this service to vessels far from port.

**c. Fish Detection Systems** Locating fish schools is very time consuming and costly. To reduce this time, methods to detect fish schools should be investigated, including acoustical systems, pulsed laser systems, chemical techniques to detect organic residues left by fish, and devices to detect electromagnetic and temperature disturbances caused by fish.

Active sonar for locating and passive acoustic devices for identifying marine life by characteristic noises are being used (the latter by the Russians). Underwater television might also be used for detection and identification. Except active sonar, such devices are not developed fully, and more importantly, are not in general use because of high costs. Successful application of current and improved technology will depend on mass production, volume purchases, and cost reductions.

**d. Harvesting Systems** Efficient harvesting of pelagic fish populations will require the capability to control the movement of species, and to concentrate them for capture. Various mechanical, chemical, acoustical, optical and electrical techniques have been used with varied degrees of success to fence in desirable species, to fence out predators and to attract and immobilize species for harvest. Present methods have been devised

through empirical trials; some are ancient concepts, including nets and traps; many are quite inefficient.

The combined talents of biologists, economists, engineers, and physicists must be applied to increase harvest efficiency. Passive fishing systems utilizing large automated traps with electricity, sound, or light to herd fish are but one example. Large pens or traps can be attached to the seabed where ground fish migrate. Mechanical or electrical barriers can help herd fish into traps for pumping into vessels or to processing plants ashore. Figure 14 illustrates this method. Floating traps can be used to harvest pelagic fish. Automated lift nets can discharge fish into holding pens.

**Figure 14.** *Artist's concept showing fish being pumped into a vessel. (Bureau of Commercial Fisheries drawing)*

A brief review of possible future techniques follows.

*(1.) Chemicals* Fish respond to chemical concentrations of considerably less than one part per billion. Chemicals have been used to attract or repel fish. It is possible chemicals can be developed to concentrate commercial species selectively and repel predators during harvesting.

*(2.) Acoustics* Little scientific effort has yet been exerted to develop acoustical devices to attract or repel fish. The Russians have repelled

schools of fish successfully by transmitting whale predator noises; the fish, seeking shelter, concentrated against the bottom. A trawl net, towed along the bottom, thereby yielded a greater catch. Bubble fences to repel predators or guide fish to entrapment devices may depend on acoustic effects. Considerable research into the principles of operation has been conducted without much success to date. Nevertheless, the industry has not exploited the results of acoustic gear research to the fullest. Undoubtedly, one reason is the inadequate means of communication among the researcher, the typical user of acoustic gear in other fields, and the fisherman.

*(3.) Optics* Lights to attract and direct certain species are well known and widely used in various forms to improve catch. These methods are empirical and not based on behavioral research which could permit optimizing such variables as intensity, spectral content, geometry, and direction. Current experience indicates that such research will be fruitful.

*(4.) Electricity* Electrical devices to fence, attract, and immobilize species have received much interest, and their potential appears promising. Immobilization is relatively predictable, and crude design criteria are available. An electro-trawl for shrimp developed under the Bureau of Commercial Fisheries is now on the market. An electric stimulus causes shrimp buried in bottom sediments to jump into the path of the trawl. Despite the interest in such devices, some feel its use in salt water will be confined in the near future to just a few fisheries because of economics.

Future harvesting techniques will make increasing use of underwater technology, including: (1) system designs to view catching devices in operation, (2) more effective catching devices resulting from redesign based on direct observations, and (3) submersibles for various supporting functions.

In the future, it should be possible to harvest whole communities of organisms, particularly those in the deep scattering layers. Typically these layers contain concentrations of 10 to 12 intermingled species from a half inch to two inches long that rise to the ocean surface at dusk. Technological developments should help in harvesting the larger organisms for volume production of protein concentrates.

Many excellent fishing grounds from the standpoint of size, reasonable depth, availability of fish, and nearness to port are not being utilized because of rough bottoms. One such area off the coast of Washington contains over 1,000 square miles made unfishable mainly by scattered small boulders. Explorations have located only a few small tracts through which fishermen can tow nets safely. The area could be a major fishing ground through use of pots, traps, and rugged trawling equipment.

A primary objective of technological improvements must be to reduce present fishery production costs. It should be economically feasible to: (1) fish in areas of low species concentration, (2) fish in depths not worked now by surface fishing operations, (3) harvest species lower on the food chain, and (4) fish ocean floor areas too rough for present gear.

## 3. Long-Range Future

**a. Fishing-Up** One long-range concept to help develop U.S. leadership in the world fishing community might be to fish-up (to fish waters above from a position on the ocean floor) on the U.S. Continental Shelf. Probably many of the techniques discussed earlier would be utilized in a fishing-up system. If successful, the Nation's fishing capability would be increased and the competitive position with foreign nations on our own shelf improved. Foreign countries, obviously, could develop a similar competitive advantage on their shelves.

**b. Modification of the Environment** Modifying the environment to improve productivity of selected species is not practiced on a commercial scale. However, the possibilities of increasing nutrient concentration through fertilizing or artificially-inducing upwelling, of providing artificial cover (artificial reefs or floating plastic kelp beds), and of improving or creating spawning conditions (probably in shallow bays, lagoons, and estuaries) should be considered.

Increased knowledge of the ecology and physiology of desirable species must be obtained if such modifications are to be economically feasible. Further, economic feasibility probably will require establishing systems to utilize organic wastes for nutrition and waste heat to induce upwelling or temperature control in confined waters. A much greater understanding of organic nutrients and the effects of organic wastes must be obtained before fertilizing can be effective. The technology to implement these operations is available if basic information can be obtained.

## C. Processing

### 1. Present Status

The object of research in processing technology is to ensure the greatest variety of fishery products of consistently high quality and nutritional value at lowest cost.

Processing the U.S. catch and raw imports is done in more than 4,000 plants throughout the country. The regional location and estimated number of workers employed in 1965 are shown in Figure 15.

**Figure 15**
**PROCESSING FACILITIES (1965)**

| Section | Establish-ments | Persons Engaged | |
| --- | --- | --- | --- |
| | | Average for season | Average for year |
| New England | 532 | 12,583 | 8,398 |
| Middle Atlantic | 488 | 6,787 | 6,008 |
| Chesapeake | 621 | 9,679 | 7,026 |
| South Atlantic | 443 | 7,826 | 5,541 |
| Gulf | 847 | 18,056 | 12,645 |
| Pacific Coast | 557 | 26,207 | 16,746 |
| Great Lakes | 256 | 2,923 | 2,429 |
| Mississippi River | 417 | 2,368 | 2,160 |
| Hawaii | 24 | 435 | 357 |
| Total[1] | 4,185 | 86,864 | 61,310 |

[1] These totals do not include U.S. Territories.
Source: *Fishery Statistics of the U.S., 1965,* Bureau of Commercial Fisheries, U.S. Department of the Interior.

Of 4,185 plants, 1,057 process and package fresh or frozen fish and shellfish products, 324 are fish and shellfish canning plants, and 160 manufacture industrial fish products. While many plants also perform a wholesale function, the remaining 2,644 firms are primarily wholesalers and brokers, performing minor aspects of processing but primarily concerned with distribution. With the exception of a few firms who dry and cure fish

products, most do not change the product form. Figure 16 shows a menhaden reduction plant, and Figure 17 illustrates frozen shrimp processing techniques.

**Figure 16.** *Menhaden reduction plant for fish meal. (Bureau of Commercial Fisheries photo)*

**Figure 17.** *Processing frozen shrimp. (Bureau of Commercial Fisheries photo)*

A summary of processed products from domestically caught fish for 1966 is shown in Figure 18.

While domestic *production* has been essentially static over the past 30 years, the domestic *consumption* has increased at a much faster rate than the population. For example, in 1945 the demand for fish and fish products in the United States was 5.3 billion pounds or 41 pounds per capita in terms of round weight, the same as the catch is

**Figure 18**

### WHOLESALE VALUE OF PROCESSED PRODUCTS FROM DOMESTICALLY CAUGHT FISH (1966)

| Item | ($ thousand) |
|---|---|
| Packaged | |
| Fresh . . . . . . | 118,329 |
| Frozen . . . . . . | 367,402 |
| Canned . . . . . . | 495,231 |
| Cured . . . . . . | 54,166 |
| Industrial . . . . . | 82,830 |
| Total . . . . . . | 1,117,958 |

given in. The domestic demand in 1967 was about 14 billion pounds or over 72 pounds per capita.[4] The major increase during this period was to augment domestic animal and poultry feeds. As the demand for animal protein continues to grow, the market for fish products should continue to increase rapidly.

The trends in production and consumption of fishery products are shown in Figure 19. Recognizing that U.S. exports have been minimal, one can estimate the round weight consumption by simply adding domestic catch to imports.

---

[4]Comparable BCF figures are in terms of edible meat weight per capita. Such figures show a static trend of 10-12 pounds per capita over the past 20 years.

**Figure 19**

### PRODUCTION AND CONSUMPTION TRENDS OF FISHERY PRODUCTS IN THE UNITED STATES, SELECTED YEARS, 1945-1967

| | 1945 | 1950 | 1955 | 1960 | 1965 | 1967 |
|---|---|---|---|---|---|---|
| Population, Millions[1] . . . . | 129.1 | 150.2 | 162.3 | 178.2 | 191.9 | 195.7 |
| *Edible Fish (round weight)* | | | | | | |
| Domestic Catch, Million pounds . | 3,167 | 3,307 | 2,597 | 2,498 | 2,586 | 2,385 |
| Imports, Million pounds . . | 680[3] | 1,128 | 1,332 | 1,766 | 2,576 | 2,683 |
| Total, Million pounds . . | 3,847 | 4,435 | 3,911 | 4,264 | 5,162 | 5,068 |
| Per Capita Use, pounds . . . | 29.8 | 29.5 | 24.1 | 23.9 | 26.9 | 25.9 |
| (meat weight)[2] . . . . | (9.9) | (11.8) | (10.5) | (10.3) | (10.9) | (10.6) |
| *Industrial Fish (round weight)* | | | | | | |
| Domestic Catch, Million pounds . | 1,431 | 1,594 | 2,230 | 2,444 | 2,190 | 1,677 |
| Imports, Million pounds . . | 31[4] | 639 | 980 | 1,515 | 3,182 | 7,442 |
| Total, Million pounds . . | 1,462 | 2,233 | 3,210 | 3,959 | 5,372 | 9,119 |
| Per Capita Use, pounds . . . | 11.3 | 14.9 | 19.8 | 22.2 | 28.0 | 46.6 |
| *Total Fish (round weight)* | | | | | | |
| Domestic Catch, Million pounds . | 4,598 | 4,901 | 4,809 | 4,942 | 4,776 | 4,062 |
| Imports, Million pounds . . | 711 | 1,767 | 2,312 | 3,281 | 5,758 | 10,125 |
| Total, Million pounds . . | 5,309 | 6,668 | 7,121 | 8,223 | 10,534 | 14,187 |
| Per Capita Use, pounds . . . | 41.1 | 44.4 | 43.9 | 46.1 | 54.9 | 72.5 |

[1]July 1 population eating from civilian supplies, excluding Armed Forces overseas: beginning 1950—50 states.
[2]Computed per capita consumption on edible or meat weight basis with allowances for exports and changes in beginning and end-of-year stocks.
[3]Estimate based on 1946 relationship of round to imported product weight.
[4]Estimate based on the 1946 ratio of round weight to industrial product weight.
Source: Office of Program Planning, Bureau of Commercial Fisheries.

A start has been made in developing less conventional uses for fish. For example, the United States can be credited with first using canned tuna, breaded shrimp, and the fish sandwich. Processes have been established to manufacture fish protein concentrate from lean species. New methods are being developed to preserve and increase shelf life of fishery products.

Two tables indicate the Federal effort in processing technology. Figure 20 lists the Bureau of Commercial Fisheries program funds in processing, Fiscal Year 1968. Figure 21 shows distribution of Bureau personnel engaged in processing research by position and location, Fiscal Year 1968.

## 2. Problems

**a. Inspection** With increasing mechanization and efficiency of handling and processing, factors affecting quality must be considered. The quality of U.S. fishery products varies greatly; only a small percentage is inspected by the Federal Government for quality or health hazards. Under the Department of the Interior's voluntary inspection services, 260 million pounds of fish and fishery products were inspected during 1967.

However, inspection may be conducted by such other groups as the States and the National Canner's Association. The latter inspects salmon

**Figure 20**
### BUREAU OF COMMERCIAL FISHERIES, BRANCH OF PROCESSING TECHNOLOGY, PROGRAM FUNDS, FISCAL YEAR 1968

| Location | ($ thousand) |
|---|---|
| Seattle, Washington . . . . . | 660 |
| Pascagoula, Mississippi . . . . | 135 |
| Gloucester, Massachusetts . . . | 470[1] |
| College Park, Maryland . . . . | 670 |
| Ann Arbor, Michigan . . . . . | 165[1] |
| Ketchican, Alaska . . . . . | 285 |
| Terminal Island, California . . . | 135 |
| Total . . . . . . . . | 2,520 |

[1] Includes contributed funds from other agencies.

canners of the Pacific Northwest under an agreement with the Food and Drug Administration. In general, the canners (particularly salmon and tuna) have relatively rigid standards and inspection systems. However, it appears that much more effective inspection is needed for fresh and frozen fish and for small-operator plants.

A small number of food poisonings involving fishery products have occurred and have been

**Figure 21**
### BUREAU OF COMMERCIAL FISHERIES, BRANCH OF TECHNOLOGY, DISTRIBUTION OF PERSONNEL BY TYPE OF POSITION AND LOCATION, FY 1968

| Type of Position | Seattle, Washington | Pascagoula, Mississippi | Gloucester, Massachusetts | College Park, Maryland | Ann Arbor, Michigan | Ketchikan, Alaska | Terminal Island, California |
|---|---|---|---|---|---|---|---|
| Chemist . . . . . . . . . . | 22 | 5 | 15 | 14 | 4 | 4 | 2 |
| Chemical Engineer . . . . . . | 3 | — | — | 4 | 1 | — | — |
| Mechanical Engineer . . . . . | — | — | 1 | — | — | — | — |
| Food Technologist . . . . . . | 1 | 1 | 6 | 1 | 1 | 1 | — |
| Physicist . . . . . . . . | — | — | — | 1 | — | — | — |
| Health Physicist . . . . . . | — | — | — | 1 | — | — | — |
| Microbiologist . . . . . . . | 3 | 2 | 1 | — | 2 | 1 | — |
| Statistician . . . . . . . | — | — | — | 1 | — | — | — |
| Animal Husbandry . . . . . . | — | — | — | 2 | — | — | — |
| Nutritionist . . . . . . . | — | — | — | 1 | — | — | — |
| Home Economist . . . . . . | — | — | — | — | 1 | — | — |
| Technician . . . . . . . | — | — | 1 | — | 6 | 1 | — |
| Miscellaneous Personnel (includes clerical, aides, and part time) . . . . . . . . | 17 | 4 | 10 | 30 | 6 | 1 | 1 |
| Total (179)[1] . . . . . . | 46 | 12 | 34 | 55 | 21 | 8 | 3 |

[1] Total number of authorized positions, including vacancies.

widely publicized. Instances involving other foods also have occurred but their public image has not been damaged as severely as that of fishery products.

The consumer is developing increased awareness of the need for quality and health protection in all classes of food—poultry, meat, and fish. As a result, mandatory inspection of fishery products soon may be instituted by Federal and State governments.

**b. New Products** Emphasis also will be placed on convenience products manufactured from currently abundant and under-utilized marine resources. It is estimated that over half the seafood products on the market today were unknown a decade ago. These include breaded fish portions, breaded shrimp, heat-and-serve fish sticks, frozen fish dinners, and other convenience items that are a basic part of seafoods used by the American consumer.

**c. Technical Barriers** A chemical change in the oil of stored, frozen, or processed fish is one major factor causing quality to deteriorate. As yet, successful control has not been developed. The antolytic enzymes in fish flesh rapidly bring about undesirable textural and flavor characteristics in frozen fish. Moderate quality is maintained for an average of only three months. Methods to control enzyme activity have not been developed. However, the use of anti-oxidants is reportedly extending the shelf life of fish meal and fish oil.

### 3. Promising Technological Breakthroughs

Controlled atmosphere storage could retard degradation of fresh fish and increase shelf life.

Such protein products as fish protein concentrate could become commercially available as supplements to foods nutritionally deficient in animal protein. They also could be used in gravies and soups.

Fish oil could become a component of human food in the United States. For example, fish oil in Europe is normally used to make margarine.

### D. Government Role

### 1. Technology Transfer

Until 1950 fishermen knew more about the ocean and fish than scientists did. Scientists were involved mostly with biological and conservation research, not having studied the environment on a scale of interest to fishermen. By 1960 the situation had begun to change. Now not only can the scientist inform the fishermen beneficially, but in the near future scientific data may reduce the fisherman's production costs substantially, enabling him to harvest a much larger percentage of the sea's living resources. However, no presently satisfactory mechanism exists to transmit data to the fisherman similar to the county agent organization in agriculture.

### 2. Environmental Effects on Fish Location

Pelagic fishermen in particular, but bottom fishermen increasingly, require a more precise appreciation of the effects of environmental changes on fish availability than any Government service can provide now.

Great emphasis frequently is put on the lack of precision in scientific prediction. However, each fisherman must make decisions daily whether scientific information is available or not. If scientific information, theory, and models improve the precision of predictions by five per cent, the effect on his economic success would be measurable.

### 3. Navigation and Bottom Charts

The fisherman has long used Government navigational and bottom charts to great advantage. However, fishermen need precision navigation beyond that now provided by Governmental services. Satellite navigation equipment is too expensive and bulky. Many fishing areas are not covered by Loran C; and Loran A, a system of reasonable price and bulk, does not adequately cover major fishing grounds to the south of the United States. It is of interest that a private navigation system is deployed along many foreign coasts and is used by the U.S. Navy for special applications. It has high accuracy, reliability, simplicity, and low cost.

Navigation by bottom type and character always has had great value to fishermen. Bottom trawlers require much better knowledge of the continental shelf and slope than is available on Government charts or likely in the near future. Most knowledge has been acquired by individuals through experience.

## 4. Emphasis in the Bureau of Commercial Fisheries

The Bureau of Commercial Fisheries has a small number of college trained engineers in exploratory fishing and gear research (Figure 10). The magnitude of engineering problems in the fishing fleet indicates that the Bureau should expand its ocean engineering and exploratory fishing efforts substantially.

The Bureau must expedite engineering of new vessels, gear, and equipment for search, detection, and harvesting. This should be closely coordinated with the Sea Grant College Programs, especially the at-sea technician training.

## E. Conclusions

The status of the domestic fishing industry can be summarized as follows: annual production of 4 to 6 billion pounds, static for nearly 30 years; market for about 14 billion pounds, growing much more rapidly than population; resources off the U.S. coast for a catch of at least 30 billion pounds per year. The question arises as to how the domestic fishing industry can leave the first figure, move toward the second, and prepare for the third.

As in other industries, technology in fisheries is applied to supply, demand and production problems. With respect to supply, technology is required to assess and assure the continued availability of fish stocks supporting traditional fisheries. In addition, it is required to assess and develop fisheries for under-utilized resources (e.g., Atlantic and Gulf thread herring, Pacific hake, etc.). Efforts directed toward traditional resources encompass the technology of supporting biological research, as in preventing overfishing and ensuring that conservation laws and treaties are based soundly on research, not emotion. Additional technological effort is required to prevent destruction of stocks by pollution. The effort directed toward under-utilized resources poses such new technology problems as harvesting species of low concentration or fishing in depths not now feasible, Aquaculture promises to increase the supply of edible fish in fresh water and estuaries, especially the luxury species.

With respect to demand, it is estimated that over half the fish products on today's market were unknown a decade ago (e.g., fish sticks, etc.). Fish protein concentrate (FPC) presents possibilities for vast increases in demand; process technology is a key factor here.

Production from the fishermen's viewpoint demands major consideration. Since the fishing industry is quite heterogeneous, it is natural that the fishing fleet should also be described in the same fashion. Some fisheries, such as those of tuna, shrimp, and Alaska king crab, have fairly modern fleets; but some are static or rapidly declining as a result of foreign competition or fishery depletion, giving the entire industry a similar reputation. Part of the New England groundfish industry is an example. The domestic fleet is second only to Japan in number of vessels; moreover an examination of gross tonnage shows the U.S. fleet is essentially a coastal and inland waterway fleet. However, this should not necessarily be regarded as a disadvantage, because the U.S. domestic fish production is obtained predominantly from fishery resources adjacent to our coasts.

In addition to the vessel, the production aspect involves search, detection, and harvest. Fish hunting has been estimated to require an average of 50 per cent of the fisherman's sea time, but in some fisheries it may be considerably more, thereby constituting a very costly factor. Hunting itself consists of two steps: searching for the general area of commercial concentrations and then detecting the precise position of the fish. Long-range search involves broad-scale mapping with heavy dependence on environmental information. Ultimately, it could receive much support from satellites, buoys, and computers with appropriate instantaneous (realtime) sensing equipment. Search is critical to pelagic fishing. Detection relying on sonars, fish odors, and lasers is critical with respect to groundfish.

There are many quite fertile under-utilized fish resource areas adjacent to our coasts. Because of this and the costly time expended in hunting fish, a concentrated effort should be made toward improving vessels and gear in the hunting process, resulting in an immediate financial return to our coastal fisheries.

The United States has paid relatively little attention to radically new fishing methods and systems linked to broad analysis of oceanographic variables. In this respect, we are far behind the Soviet Union, despite the inherently greater industrial and research capacity available to American industry.

Vessel and gear engineering (as distinct from biological science) and eventually the benefits of fundamental marine technology will play a larger role in general fishing technology. Benefits from advanced marine technology will arise from developments in such areas as materials, advanced sonars, exploratory submersibles, buoy networks, satellites, and underwater stations.

Recommendations:

Fishing technology should be directed toward maximum utilization of food resources and development of efficient means of exploiting them. The major portion of the effort should focus on maximizing efficiency in catching fish (as contrasted to the processing phase), emphasizing those fisheries not in danger of depletion.

To achieve a more immediate economic return, effort should be concentrated initially on problems more amenable to near-term solutions. This includes primarily learning how to reduce the time spent in search and detection. Methods showing promise include optical, infrared, electrical, and acoustical.

Additional improvements in harvesting gear and techniques should focus on:

—Minimizing escape of fish within reach of fishing gear.

—Leading, herding, or aggregating fish to increase their availability to harvesting systems.

—Developing techniques to harvest the more abundant smaller fish in the food chain.

High speed, automated vessels should be utilized wherever possible in coastal fisheries, in order to improve efficiency and become more competitive with foreign fishermen.

For some fisheries attention should be directed toward use of specialty vehicles for different tasks. This might include a high-speed vessel or aircraft for fish detection, another type vessel for harvesting and a third for transporting catches (as might be used in distant water fisheries). At present we combine all three functions in one vessel and thereby pay a penalty for it.

A field service mechanism should be established by the Federal Government analogous to the Department of Agriculture Extension Service to facilitate transfer of technical information to the fisherman at the county or fishing port level. For example, the Government should provide pelagic and bottom fishermen with information on the effects of environmental change on fish availability and knowledge of the latest domestic and foreign advances in fishing gear.

An updated survey should be completed of promising coastal fisheries and distant water fisheries, improving knowledge in the case of our traditional stocks and delineating resources in the case of under-utilized species. The survey should be updated continually and should include sport fisheries because of the ecological interactions.

Improved charts should be provided for bottom trawlers in particular to portray more information on the continental shelf and slope. The charts also should have overprints of predicted areas of fishery stocks.

The ocean engineering program in the Bureau of Commercial Fisheries should be expanded and adequately funded. A National Vessel and Gear Development Program within the Bureau of Commercial Fisheries should be established to conduct basic bio-engineering studies and provide technical support of biological research relating to new harvesting systems, new and improved fish detection systems, and improved performance of new fishing vessels. This should provide support and coordination to the activities of the present regional laboratories.

The staff of this national program should include engineers and biologists (or bio-engineers), naval architects, and other scientists to undertake basic studies and provide effective liaison with private engineering firms and academic institutions. A substantial share of the program's budget should be used for contract studies with industry and private institutions. A submersible should be available to study fishing gear performance, the reaction of fish to the gear, and to explore novel methods of detection. A modern gear research vessel capable of handling types of harvest systems likely to be developed would be necessary to demonstrate such systems to the fishing industry. A close working relationship should be established with Sea Grant Colleges, industrial firms, and the fishing industry.

## II. AQUACULTURE

Aquaculture today often is discussed as one part of a long-range solution to feeding the billions of people expected to inhabit the earth. Some authorities claim that (except in a few cases) aquaculture is not a viable solution to this problem. In this section acquaculture will be discussed as a potential supplemental source of food. Some of the technology needed to enhance aquaculture will also be described.

Aquaculture may be defined as a systematic and scientific farming program in restricted water areas including inland waters, coastal waters and open sea.[5] This definition of aquaculture is not intended to include advanced techniques for improved conventional fishing.

### A. Present Status and Trends

### 1. General Activity

Aquaculture, often discussed as impractical or too visionary in the United States, is no longer a dream. Examination of the status and success of aquaculture in other parts of the world reveals the practical applications of this source of food more clearly. A report by the Institute of Fisheries, University of British Columbia, states that Mainland China in 1960 produced 2,000,000 tons of fish by fresh water culture of a total 4,000,000 tons for the entire nation's inland fish catch, thus 50 per cent of inland fish production in Red China was by aquaculture. In the same period, the United States produced a total of 1,249,000 tons of fish for human consumption.[6]

In 1966, pond culture in Israel yielded 9,454 tons of a total 24,503 tons of fish produced by all methods. Pond culture realized approximately 40 per cent of total production in this small country.

Japan, long an aquacultural leader through the necessity of feeding her population, continues to be a leader. Today 13 per cent of the total value of Japan's marine products is derived from aquaculture.

---

[5] President's Science Advisory Committee, *Effective Use of the Sea,* Report of the Panel on Oceanography (Washington: Government Printing Office, 1966), p. 10.

[6] National Council on Marine Resources and Engineering Development, *Marine Science Affairs—A Year of Plans and Progress* (Washington: Government Printing Office, 1968), p. 224.

In the United States, there is a relatively small but intensive effort to advance the field of aquaculture, specifically for the most desirable species for the luxury market. Examples are shrimp, oysters, abalone, lobster, salmon, trout, pompano, clams, and scallops. Efforts to produce the more common fish are minimal, primarily because of consumer disinterest. In Hawaii, extensive studies are being conducted in breeding mullet, a highly prized fish food in the islands.

As a matter of interest, the U.S. shrimp industry grossed $96 million in 1966 and was our most valuable fishery. Oysters in the same year ranked fifth with a catch worth $26 million. Thus, the American palate seems to be better pleased by gourmet seafoods.

The pages following discuss examples of aquaculture being undertaken with certain gourmet species. This is not intended to encompass all areas of aquaculture interest but illustrates a few to show the promise in this field.

### 2. Shellfish

Shellfish farming, primarily oysters, clams, and scallops, has been practiced for many years in bays, estuaries, ocean shelves, and other shallow salty waters. A more intensive method of shellfish farming utilizing special methods of seeding, growing, and harvesting in ponds or sheltered enclosed areas is practiced also.

Shellfish cultivation equipment is quite different, depending on whether in large shallow ocean areas or small ponds and enclosed areas. In the ocean areas fish cultivation requires boats, dredges, nets, etc., and is to some degree a mechanized operation. In small ponds and enclosed areas cultivation is done where seeding, growth, and harvest can be regulated carefully. It is widely practiced in low labor-cost areas, as it currently requires considerable manual labor. Because this intensive cultivation achieves greatly increased productivity per unit area (or volume), and because it is now largely a hand operation, it is a fruitful field for new equipment development. Further, specialized heavy equipment is needed to prepare new growing areas.

### 3. Salmon

Another example of U.S. aquaculture is the salmon hatchery program on the Columbia River.

In 1967 the Columbia River system produced about 15 million pounds of salmon by aquacultural methods, contributing to a total U.S. salmon catch of 202 million pounds. While only seven per cent of total production, this contribution is indicative of the potential of aquacultural techniques.

The Bureau of Commercial Fisheries conducted a benefit-cost ratio (B/C ratio) analysis of the Coho and Chinook salmon produced at the Columbia River hatcheries in relation to salmon caught by fishermen and the results were startling. Coho ran as high as 7.8 to 1.0 and Chinook ran from 2.5 to 4.5 to 1.0. This ratio is conservative but represents a reasonable reflection of the advances aquaculture can provide.[7]

In addition to work progressing in the Columbia River, Dr. Lauren Donaldson at the College of Fisheries, University of Washington, is doing extensive work in aquaculture by breeding salmon.[8]

Dr. Donaldson's Chinook salmon data after eight cycles indicates some progress has been made. Studies of the returns of Chinook salmon to the University holding pond for 1960 through 1967 revealed increase in growth, length and weight, as well as a significant increase in fecundity for both the three-year-old and four-year-old females (Figures 22, 23, and 24).

The emphasis in selection has been on the three-year-old returning Chinook salmon. Although the variation from year to year is great, the increase in length for females—excluding the returns of 1966 with the pectoral mark[9] averaged about a centimeter per year over the past eight years (Figure 22). Also the average yearly increase in weight for three-year-old Chinook females was about 200 grams (Figure 23). In the past eight cycles, egg production for the three-year-old salmon increased at a fairly steady rate. The yearly

[7]This B/C ratio was based on the ex-vessel price (fish gutted and gilled but not headed and not processed).

[8]The material on Chinook salmon and trout in subsections 3 and 4 was taken from reports by Dr. Donaldson.

[9]For the brood years 1960 to 1966, the young salmon fingerlings were marked by amputation of a fin or the maxillary bone. This procedure handicaps the fish in varying degrees and makes exact interpretation of the results of the selective breeding difficult. Removal of the pectoral fins from the 1963 brood year fingerlings, which returned during the fall of 1966 as three-year-old adults, was especially damaging.

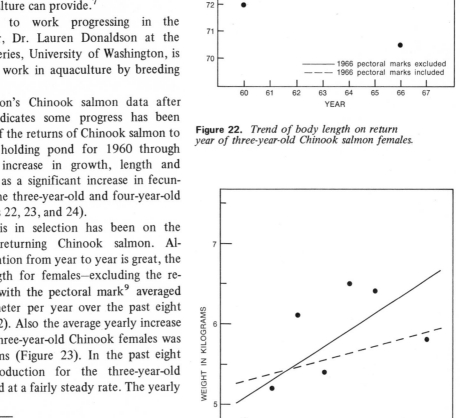

**Figure 22.** *Trend of body length on return year of three-year-old Chinook salmon females.*

**Figure 23.** *Trend of body weight on return year of three-year-old Chinook salmon females.*

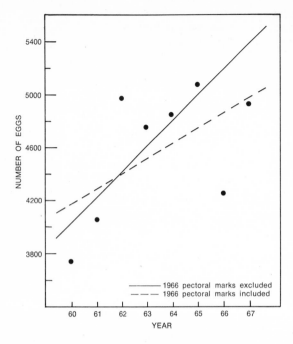

**Figure 24.** *Trend of fecundity on return year of three-year-old Chinook salmon females.*

has changed dramatically. In 1944, the first year a fair number of spawning fish of the two-year age class was available, the fish averaged 36.3 centimeters forked length. By 1968, the average length for two-year-old spawning rainbow trout had increased to 60.4 centimeters, an average increase of a centimeter a year. The three-year-old spawners in the past 14 years (1954 to 1968) have increased from 50.5 centimeters forked length to 68.1 centimeters, an average annual increase of 1.25 centimeters. An actual example (Figure 26) shows the results of controlled rearing techniques.

### B. Future Needs

There is a need to develop an integrated systems approach to the field of aquaculture, consisting of effective collection, trapping, hatching, stowage, and processing facilities. If such a system were adopted, industry would be able to contribute heavily to expand the program. An example of the systems approach is found in the oyster industry.

Suspended culture of oysters is performed now in small areas, the oysters growing on strings suspended from floating rafts or underwater racks. Seeding the oysters, setting the racks or rafts, and harvesting are hand operations. It is technically possible to make racks (with suitable oyster attachment materials already in place) to be installed by hand but seeded automatically from nearby seed beds. Properly designed, an entire rack could be conveyed to a harvesting device for removing the mature oysters mechanically or hydraulically, sorting them and packing them in one continuous operation.

The entire growing medium could be regulated, using three-dimensional units and controlling the oysters' growth with properly regulated water and nutrient flows. The engineer would work closely with the marine biologist who would determine optimum temperature, nutrient level, and water turnover required to maximize shellfish growth and quality.

He would treat the oyster farm as a system (including both the physical and biological parameters established by the marine biologist and the economic limitations imposed by product value and the local labor market) to achieve the best rate of return on investment. In a region of high labor costs, the environmental control system might

average increase was about 200 eggs per female, from 1960 through 1967.

Sea survival of the Chinook salmon has been good, returns exceeding 1 per cent of the fingerlings released (1.0 to 3.25 per cent). The program has now become stabilized; 250,000 select fingerlings are released each year and 2.5 to 5 million eggs are obtained when the fish return. Five to 10 per cent are selected to continue the select stock. Excess eggs and fingerlings are transferred to other streams, where we hope they will contribute to commercial and sport fisheries.

### 4. Trout

A program of selective breeding of rainbow trout has been carried on at the University of Washington's College of Fisheries for the past 36 years. Changes during the past 13 years have been pronounced (Figure 25). When the program was initiated in 1932 the trout reached maturity in their fourth year at an average weight of 1½ pounds and produced 400 to 500 eggs at their first spawning.

After 36 years, the males of select stock reach maturity in the first year and the females all mature in the second year. The rate of growth also

**Figure 25**

## SIZE AT SPAWNING AND NUMBER OF EGGS PRODUCED BY SELECTED RAINBOW TROUT BROOD STOCK

| Spawn- ing year | Age at recorded spawning | Number of females spawning | Fork length (centimeters) | | Number of eggs from each female at spawning | |
|---|---|---|---|---|---|---|
| | | | Average | Maximum | Average | Maximum |
| 1944 . . | 2 | 12 | 36.3 | 39.0 | 1,653 | 2,121 |
| 1946 . . | 2 | 39 | 41.9 | 48.0 | 2,011 | 2,982 |
| 1948 . . | 2 | 78 | 41.2 | 50.0 | 1,958 | 3,094 |
| 1950 . . | 2 | 129 | 35.5 | 45.5 | 1,315 | 2,097 |
| 1952 . . | 2 | 51 | 40.9 | 45.0 | 2,145 | 3,810 |
| 1953 . . | 2 | 27 | 38.9 | 43.5 | 2,032 | 3,631 |
| 1954 . . | 2 | 47 | 44.6 | 51.5 | 2,377 | 3,960 |
| — | 3 | 36 | 50.5 | 57.0 | 4,042 | 6,106 |
| 1955 . . | 2 | 28 | 50.7 | 56.5 | 3,894 | 5,123 |
| — | 3 | 28 | 59.6 | 67.0 | 5,029 | 8,850 |
| 1956 . . | 2 | 84 | 49.0 | 53.5 | 3,281 | 5,915 |
| — | 3 | 9 | 59.2 | 65.0 | 6,149 | 7,331 |
| 1957 . . | 2 | 58 | 46.4 | 55.0 | 3,161 | 9,639 |
| — | 3 | 14 | 67.4 | 72.0 | 7,117 | 11,475 |
| 1958 . . | 2 | 57 | 57.6 | 66.0 | 5,617 | 9,077 |
| — | 3 | 2 | 73.5 | 74.0 | 15,767 | 16,839 |
| 1959 . . | 2 | 39 | 60.0 | 63.0 | 5,224 | 6,960 |
| — | 3 | 6 | 70.2 | 73.0 | 8,689 | 11,580 |
| 1960 . . | 2 | 63 | 59.6 | 68.0 | 5,132 | 8,268 |
| — | 3 | 6 | 70.8 | 72.0 | 9,030 | 11,186 |
| 1961 . . | 2 | 29 | 52.9 | 59.0 | 4,809 | 6,838 |
| — | 3 | 5 | 67.1 | 71.0 | 9,092 | 13,515 |
| 1962 . . | 2 | 73 | 57.8 | 68.5 | 6,080 | 13,407 |
| — | 3 | 20 | 66.1 | 72.0 | 9,176 | 16,482 |
| 1963 . . | 2 | 83 | 52.5 | 63.0 | — | — |
| — | 3 | 8 | 67.6 | 70.5 | — | — |
| 1964 . . | 2 | 48 | 59.1 | 66.5 | 6,091 | 8,845 |
| — | 3 | 12 | 64.0 | 74.0 | 9,768 | 13,684 |
| 1965 . . | 2 | 81 | 58.5 | 65.5 | 6,274 | 11,826 |
| — | 3 | 30 | 68.3 | 78.0 | 11,556 | 16,160 |
| 1966 . . | 2 | 131 | 57.0 | 63.0 | 7,798 | 16,872 |
| — | 3 | 32 | 68.7 | 74.5 | 13,304 | 19,922 |
| 1967 . . | 2 | 36 | 60.7 | 67.0 | 7,335 | 13,707 |
| — | 3 | 29 | 67.2 | 73.5 | 11,090 | 20,602 |
| 1968 . . | 2 | 70 | 60.4 | 66.0 | 9,259 | 18,144 |
| — | 3 | 8 | 68.1 | 72.0 | 11,718 | 21,288 |

Figure 26. *Results of controlled rearing techniques with lake trout. Lower two fish grew under normal conditions.*

Figure 27. *Mackerel reared on plankton from ocean. Nutrient-rich deep waters brought to the sunlit surface support prolific plant life on which fish thrive. Waste heat from fossil or nuclear power plants may benefit aquaculture and selected fisheries. (Bureau of Commercial Fisheries photo)*

include pumps, temperature controllers, automatic monitoring of nutrients, etc. In a region having cheaper labor, the system might be largely a manual operation with a minimum of capital investment.

Artificial upwelling techniques, artificial reefs, and control of environmental temperatures can increase fish production further. As an example, the University of Miami has a research grant for raising shrimp, using waste heat from power generation plants at Turkey Point, Florida to control water temperatures. Thermal energy dissipated from nuclear installations offers a whole new field of development, particularly in aquaculture. The New England lobster population is declining becasue long-range climatic cycles have reduced water temperatures below the levels favorable to their growth.

Heat from man-made sources, if properly applied, potentially could benefit aquaculture and selected fisheries. Basic understanding of how waste heat can be used is being investigated in a Bureau of Commercial Fisheries project to rear mackerel artificially under controlled environmental conditions (Figure 27).

The United States can contribute substantially to development of new and improved techniques in aquaculture by applying its experience and competence in such fields as pathology, ecology, microbiology, nutrition, genetics, chemistry, and engineering. Application of techniques in developing countries could aid materially in the war on hunger. Immediate benefits to the United States would be increased production of food items now considered luxuries because of limited supplies.

Engineering aspects of shellfish farming (particularly equipment employed, means for enclosing farming areas, and methods for controlling the growth environment) need concentrated attention for improvement and economy. Very little has been accomplished in practical demonstration of open sea aquaculture techniques to date. With the proper encouragement to industry, the techniques needed will be developed, leading to increased catches, improved efficiency, and better fulfillment of needs for fish protein.

A concept of an open sea aquacultural operation is illustrated in Figure 28.

## C. Conclusions

Aquaculture can make a major contribution to the war on hunger, by applying recent scientific and technological advances to existing practices or by development of new techniques in such fields as pathology, genetics, nutrition, ecology, and engineering.

Aquaculture is practiced in the United States to various degrees in raising luxury crops or augmenting natural stocks. Aquaculture programs are scattered among several groups. Real progress will

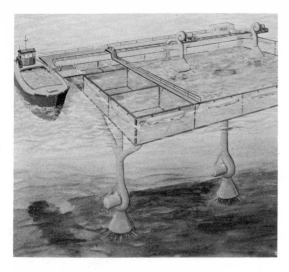

**Figure 28.** *Artist's concept of open sea aquaculture. (Westinghouse photo)*

require recognition of the need for a systematic approach and a cooperative relationship between Government and industry.

Widespread, low-intensity aquaculture, as practiced in many developing countries where large areas are available for the purpose, may result in relatively low yields and profits. The potential of aquaculture is greatest in these places where improved technology may be expected to increase yields greatly.

Recommendations:

**A program to coordinate and foster aquaculture should be established and managed by the Federal Government. This program should focus on technology needed for potential commercial applications. Use should be made of Government, State, academic, and industrial facilities. The program goals should be directed toward both domestic and world aquaculture needs.**

**An intensive program to strengthen and expand the scope of Federal laboratories engaged in aquaculture would be of great benefit to industry and would allow further research in fertilization, nutrition, population ecology, pathology, predator and pest control, soil chemistry and biology, and design and construction of ponds, lagoons, and estuarine impoundments.**

**In view of the improvement in salmon production, an economic, political and ecological inquiry** should be made of the rationale of changing escapement quotas in certain estuaries on the West Coast.

## III. OFFSHORE OIL AND GAS

### A. Scope of Offshore Industry

#### 1. Worldwide

**a. Investment** Cumulative investment, now near $18 billion, is likely to triple in the next decade.

**b. Production—Reserves** Free World offshore production, quadrupled since 1960, now represents about 8 per cent of Free World output. Offshore proven reserves, tripled since 1960, now account for about 14 per cent of the Free World total. If the figures include production from protected waters, (such as Venezuela's Lake Maracaibo, which alone produces 2 million barrels per day (b/d) and bays such as along the U.S. Gulf Coast) the percentage rises from 8 to 16 per cent. The Persian Gulf in the Middle East has most of the Free World's offshore oil reserves and provides about one-fourth of current world offshore production.

Figure 29 depicts offshore activity in the 80 Free World countries; it does not include protected waters but represents true continental shelf activities. Thus, whereas the figure shows 1967 Free World production at 2.4 million b/d, it is almost 5.0 million b/d if Lake Maracaibo and other inland water areas are considered. The Far East and Africa represent the fastest growing areas. It is estimated that by 1980 total over-water production from the continental shelves and protected waters will rise to 20 million b/d, or about one-third estimated total production.

Offshore activity ranges from early seismic work to full-scale production operations. The pace has been increasing sharply since 1960 in all geographic areas. Most jack-up and semisubmersible offshore rigs built in the past two years have gone into foreign service because of the expected increased offshore activity in those areas in the next few years.

#### 2. United States

**a. Investment** The petroleum industry has invested about $7.5 billion in offshore Louisiana,

**Figure 29**
**EXTENT OF OFFSHORE CONTINENTAL SHELF ACTIVITY IN THE FREE WORLD[1]**

| Category | Year | U.S.A. | Canada | Latin America | Europe | Africa | Mideast | Far East | Free World |
|---|---|---|---|---|---|---|---|---|---|
| Countries with Offshore Activity[2] . . | 1960 | 1 | 1 | 5 | 2 | 6 | 5 | 4 | 24 |
| | 1964 | 1 | 1 | 15 | 8 | 21 | 12 | 8 | 66 |
| | 1967 | 1 | 1 | 18 | 9 | 26 | 14 | 11 | 80 |
| Offshore Concession Acreage . . . . | 1960 | – | – | – | – | – | – | – | 300[3] |
| (Millions of acres) | 1964 | 7 | 154 | 87 | 48 | 56 | 34 | 422 | 807 |
| | 1966 | 9 | 202 | 125 | 69 | 127 | 53 | 760 | 1,345 |
| Geophysical Crew Months . . . . . | 1960 | 93 | 5 | 6 | – | 31 | – | – | 135 |
| (Marine seismograph) | 1964 | 273 | 22 | 12 | 133 | 45 | 26 | 35 | 546 |
| | 1966 | 461 | 26 | 18 | 103 | 33 | 47 | 140 | 828 |
| Crude-Oil Production . . . . . . . | 1960 | 190 | – | 25 | – | – | 181 | – | 396 |
| (Thousand b/d) | 1964 | 449 | – | 59 | 8 | 65 | 684 | 7 | 1,272 |
| | 1967 | 870 | – | 77 | 10 | 165 | 1,184 | 50 | 2,356 |
| Proven Crude Reserves . . . . . . | 1960 | 1,700 | – | 220 | 100 | – | 14,750 | – | 16,770 |
| (Million bbl) | 1964 | 2,200 | – | 260 | 100 | 1,050 | 32,300 | 100 | 35,910 |
| | 1967 | 4,100 | – | 330 | 220 | 3,150 | 43,350 | 1,400 | 52,550 |

[1] Does not take into account activity in such protected waters as Venezuela's rich Lake Maracaibo.
[2] Excludes countries where onshore concessions extend into offshore areas and where there is no offshore activity.
[3] Breakdown not available.
Source: *The Oil and Gas Journal*, May 6, 1968, p. 77.

and its operations have recovered about $3.5 billion in revenue from oil and gas sales—a $4 billion net deficit.[10] Yet, the U.S. industry still regards the offshore as its last big frontier.

**b. Production–Reserves** Latest figures from the American Petroleum Institute place U.S. offshore oil reserves total at 4.3 billion barrels, including 2.4 billion off Louisiana and 1.4 billion off California. U.S. offshore oil production has climbed from 335,000 b/d in 1960 to over 1,300,000 b/d in 1968. One major company reports that offshore Louisiana accounts for over one-third its total production; another reports that half its production increase in North American liquids will come from Cook Inlet, Alaska.

### 3. Natural Gas

**a. Free World** Six per cent of Free World natural gas production comes from underwater areas, compared to 16 per cent for oil. Outside the

United States, the Free World's only commercial offshore gas areas lie in the North Sea, off Australia, and in the Adriatic. Some however, will be large producers in the future. Britain's Gas Council estimates England's share of North Sea gas reserves at 25 trillion cubic feet; the search for gas is just beginning on the Netherlands' side of the sea.[11]

There is a strong possibility that the Free World offshore gas production will follow the trend of offshore oil with a sudden growth spurt in the next few years. Any offshore gas discovered near sizable market areas will find outlets.

However, expensive failures have occured off Norway and Sweden. All efforts in the German part of the North Sea ceased after about a dozen expensive dry holes were drilled.

**b. United States** In this country offshore natural gas is becoming big business, and much future growth in supply is expected to come from close-in offshore areas. For example, one company reports that its offshore Louisiana reserves represent over half the company's total.

[10] Wilson, J. E., "Economics of Offshore Louisiana," presented before the Louisiana-Arkansas Division, Mid-Continent Oil and Gas Association, Sept. 12, 1967.

[11] *The Oil and Gas Journal*, May 6, 1968, p. 77.

## 4. Technology—The Broad Picture

**a. Capability** Exploratory wells have been drilled from floating rigs in waters deeper than 600 feet, and exploitation wells have been drilled from huge fixed bottom-mounted production platforms in waters deeper than 300 feet. Recently, one company invested almost $200 million in lease bonuses for 47 tracts in the Santa Barbara Channel, of which 16 are in water deeper than 600 feet, six deeper than 1,200 feet, and one in 1,800 feet of water. Exploratory wells are presently being drilled in depths up to 1,300 feet, and production may be established in waters as deep as 400 feet during 1969. It is expected that by 1980 industry will have the capability to explore for and produce hydrocarbon reserves in almost any area of the world; however, alternate sources of petroleum probably will enter the energy market before petroleum deposits are exploited in deep ocean areas.

**b. Equipment** There are about 180 mobile drilling rigs throughout the world, valued at about $1 billion, 35 per cent floaters.[12] It is estimated that by 1980 there will be about 400 mobile units, about 60 per cent floaters. To reduce the cost of development drilling, it may be necessary to use multiple drilling rigs on a single floating platform.

In the Santa Barbara Channel it may be more economical on some leases to complete wells on submerged platforms connected to and controlled from operating platforms in shallower water.

Extensive tests with actual underwater wells, coupled with experiments to determine diver and diverless capability have provided confidence that the technology to install and operate underwater facilities in the Santa Barbara area can be developed. The method used for each lease will be governed by economics, safety, and environmental considerations.

Using Federal funds, a group of oceanographic institutions has contracted with industry to drill a series of core holes to 2,500 feet below the sea floors in waters to 20,000 feet deep in the Atlantic, the Pacific, the Gulf of Mexico, and the Caribbean Sea. This program, called JOIDES,

began in the summer of 1968 and shallow holes have been successfully drilled in 17,500 feet of water.

## B. Background of Offshore Activity

### 1. History

Offshore oil was first produced about 1894 in California from wells drilled from wooden wharves or from wells directed seaward from the beach. Petroleum operations in the Gulf of Mexico began in 1936. The first offshore well completed beyond the sight of land was off Louisiana in 1948; a typical early platform is shown in Figure 30. The first offshore pipeline was completed the following year. Today production has been established more than 70 miles from shore and in water depths to 340 feet. Production pipelines have been laid successfully in 340 feet of water. The first subsea well with all components under water was completed in Lake Erie in 1959; there are now 50 to 100 throughout the world.

**Figure 30.** *Early offshore platform beyond sight of land, in 50 feet of water. Designed to house a crew of 50, it was completed in 1948 and is still in operation.*

Drilling capability in the last 10 years has progressed from water depths of less than 100 feet to more than 600 feet. In addition, leases have been granted by the Department of Interior for petroleum exploration and production more than

---

[12]Rigs that do not touch bottom but maintain position by anchoring or dynamic positioning. The other two types of mobile drilling rigs are submersible and jack-up.

100 miles off the U.S. shores and in waters up to 1,800 feet deep. About 100 core holes have been drilled beyond the U.S. Continental Shelves, some in waters nearly 5,000 feet deep in the Atlantic Ocean and Gulf of Mexico.

## 2. Phases

Offshore activities are conducted in three phases:

*Exploration* consists of geophysical surveys to locate subsurface structures favorable for the accumulation of hydrocarbons, followed by exploratory drilling to determine the presence or absence of oil or gas under the ocean floor.

*Production* involves development drilling followed by installation of equipment for production, well service, and maintenance.

*Storage* of the product and *transportation* to shore is the final phase of offshore activity.

## C. Exploration

### 1. Geophysical Surveys and Geological Analysis

Exploration encompasses the broad reconnaissance surveys followed by more detailed surveys that actually delineate the geological structures that may contain oil or gas deposits (i.e., exploration activities involve locating promising areas for drilling activities). Exploration begins with geologists making a general study of the structure of the earth to select an area with characteristics possibly favorable for oil or gas recovery.

After selecting a promising area, tests pinpoint the site to probe further for possible reserves. These can be simple magnetometer readings taken from an airplane or ship. By showing a variation in the earth's magnetic field, the tests indicate geologic structures below the ocean floor. In addition, towed marine gravimeters can determine very small variations in the earth's gravity field. Both types of geophysical surveys can be made in any depth of water and at any distance from land. However, in themselves, they usually do not provide information of sufficient accuracy to permit siting an exploratory well.

The most successful technique to locate test drilling sites is seismic profiling. Such surveys require much more expensive equipment but because of the high speed at which the surveys can

be conducted, the actual cost per mile is about one-third as much as on land. A sound pulse is generated, a portion of which is reflected from the layers of sediment and rock under the ocean floor. The reflections when received at the surface are recorded on a graph showing an approximation of the depth and characteristics of underlying geological structures. In earlier surveys black powder or dynamite was used to generate the sound pulse. Today, electrical sparking systems, air guns, contained-gas explosions, mechanical boomers, and other nonexplosive energy sources are used. Seismic data are recorded routinely on magnetic tape and processed by digital computers, enhancing quality and reliability.

The above-mentioned geophysical techniques are indirect methods for examining structures under our continental margins. The most satisfactory method to date for obtaining geologic samples of rocks on or at shallow depths under the sea floor has been with small coring devices operated from a surface ship. These devices drill a hole several hundred feet into the sea floor and recover samples of rock for further study. Similar holes have been drilled in the U.S. continental margin beyond the shelves to 1,000 feet beneath the sea floor in waters from 600 feet to 5,000 feet deep. Coring in such depths has been accomplished from floating, dynamically positioned vessels. As long ago as 1961, several experimental core holes were drilled in 11,700 feet of water as part of the early phase of Project Mohole.

Exploration technology has made rapid strides in new seismic energy sources and receiving systems. Computers permit analysis of the data while under way at sea. The Navy Navigation Satellite System will permit seismic teams to determine more accurately survey locations in remote areas.

### 2. Exploratory Drilling

Determining the presence of oil or gas requires full scale drilling operations at the site, a much more difficult and expensive task than drilling shallow core holes. Multiple strings of casing must be set in the hole to keep it open. To control drilling fluids or fluids in the rock, large blowout preventers must be installed should high-pressure oil or gas be encountered. The drilling rig must maintain position at the wellsite for many weeks or months. More than 10;000 wells already have been drilled into the U.S. Continental Shelves.

Most of these are for exploitation purposes and have been drilled from fixed platforms, artificial islands, or directionally from shore.

The petroleum industry has more than $1 billion in offshore drilling equipment presently at work. Drilling contractors, hired by operating oil firms, generally bear the burden of the capital investments for this phase of the operation.

While the types of platforms used to support the drilling rigs vary greatly, the rigs are fairly standardized. They consist of: (1) a tall steel tower to hoist the bit, pipe, and other equipment in and out of the hole, (2) a system to rotate the pipe and bit, and (3) a system to circulate fluid to the bottom of the hole.

Fixed platforms supported by pilings were constructed in shallow offshore waters as the drillers followed the seaward extension of oil fields. As the industry moved into deeper waters, it continued using this type of foundation for exploitation drilling. However, for exploratory drilling, where the incidence of dry holes is inherently higher, fixed platforms soon became too costly.

The industry then began to develop mobile drilling platforms. This minimized the capital investment chargeable to each well site. The first mobile platforms were submersible barges for operation in 20 to 40 feet of water and evolved from the barge-mounted drilling rigs used in southern Louisiana marshlands. Later, jack-up mobile platforms were developed for greater water depths.

Figure 31 shows the categories of offshore drilling platforms, their cost, daily operating rate, and depth capability. There are three general types of mobile platforms—submersible, jack-up, and floating.

The jack-up rig is mounted on a buoyant hull to which extendable legs are attached. The legs are raised for moving the rig and lowered to the ocean floor to lift the platform above the ocean waves during drilling operations (Figure 32). The number of jack-up rigs has grown steadily, with about 75 in operation in depths to 300 feet. Designs have been proposed for jack-up rigs for 600 feet of water. Recent innovations include a self-propelled, jack-up rig resembling a ship, to operate in 300 feet of water.

The submersible rig is mounted on a submersible hull that is ballasted with water and sunk to the ocean floor for support during drilling operations (Figure 33). The largest submersible rig is designed to drill in 175 feet of water with 25-foot deck clearance; however, most submersible rigs are limited to 100 foot water depths. About 35 submersible rigs are in use currently, a number almost constant since 1958 due to depth limitation and the increasing popularity of jack-up rigs.

The advantage of the jack-up and submersible rigs is that they rest on the bottom while the platform stands clear of the highest waves, enabling them to operate in rough seas. The jack-up rig has more depth flexibility and capability while the submersible rig, a monolithic structure, can be towed more readily from one location to another.

### Figure 31
### COSTS AND DEPTH CAPABILITIES OF OFFSHORE DRILLING PLATFORMS

| Category | Initial Cost[1] ($ million) | Day Rate[2] ($) | Typical Operating Depths (Feet) |
|---|---|---|---|
| Fixed Platforms . . . . | 1.0 to 15.0 | 5,000- 7,000 | 0-300 |
| Mobile Platforms . . . . | | | |
|   Bottom Supported | | | |
|     Submersible . . . | 3.0 to 5.0 | 6,000-10,000 | 20-175 |
|     Jack-up . . . . . | 4.0 to 8.0 | 6,000-15,000 | 20-300 |
|   Floating | | | |
|     Semisubmersible . . | 7.0 to 10.0 | 12,000-17,000 | 130-600 |
|     Ship-shaped . . . | 3.0 to 7.0 | 10,000-15,000 | 50-600 |

[1] Depends upon soil conditions; wave, wind, and ice loading; and the number of wells supported by the platform.
[2] Includes rig, labor, transportation, routine daily services, and routine expendable materials.

**Figure 32.** *Self-elevating (jack-up) mobile drilling rig. Open fabricated legs increase strength without substantially increasing resistance to waves. (The Offshore Co. photo)*

**Figure 33.** *Submersible drilling rig. (Shell Oil photo)*

While floating platforms lack the stability of the bottom support type, they are not as restricted to a given depth of water and are cost-competitive at 200 feet or more. The floating platform includes two major categories: semi-submersibles and the ship-shaped type.

The semisubmersibles are floating platforms supported on tall columns which rise from buoyant barge-like hulls or cylindrical torpedo-shaped tubes (Figure 34). Upon arrival on location they are ballasted so that approximately one-half the unit is below water. Their advantage over drilling ships or barges is that the major structure is located above or below the region of most severe wave action. This configuration provides improved stability by its large inertia, and by having a vertical natural frequency of movement which is affected little by wave forces.

**Figure 34.** *Semisubmersible rig (SEDCO 135) measures 300 feet on a side and in drilling position displaces 16,800 tons. (Southeastern Drilling photo)*

The semi-submersibles can be raised by pumping ballast water from the tubes and columns. Finally, they can be used to drill while resting on the sea floor if in sufficiently shallow water.

Ship-shaped platforms consist of a drilling rig supported on a barge or self-propelled ship. A barge, because it is not self-propelled, must be moved by tugs to new assignments, but it has the advantage of low initial cost. The ship-shaped platform can transit at higher speeds and at less expense. A disadvantage of the ship-shaped vessel platforms is that much drilling time can be lost in bad weather due to vessel motion; however, this may not be an important consideration in protected drilling locations (Figure 35).

The floating platforms can drill in depths exceeding 600 feet, with some of the latest exceeding 1,000 feet. The floating drilling vessels normally are held over the drill hole by a system of anchors; however, some of the newer vessels are held by various types of multidirectional thrust systems (Figure 36). Most companies plan on conventional anchoring in depths to 1,300 feet. Drilling exploration wells often requires being on station for long periods (100 days, for example) and excessive fuel would be consumed if dynamic positioning were used. However, in comparatively sheltered waters with moderate winds and sea states, the costs of dynamic positioning systems compare favorably with conventional mooring systems.

**Figure 36.** *Artist's concept of dynamically positioned drilling vessel designed to maintain a fixed position without anchors. (Esso Production photo)*

**Figure 35.** *Self-propelled drilling ship* Glomar Sirte *measures 380 feet x 64 feet, displaces 9,500 tons, and is one of the largest drilling ships in operation. (Global Marine photo)*

Should a drill ship be compelled to abandon its station, upon return it must be able to relocate the seafloor wellhead and reinsert the drill string. Recently, acoustic systems have been designed and tested for hole re-entry. Sea floor pingers or transducers will be increasingly used for precise repositioning, for effectively relocating the wellhead, and for accurately guiding the drill string.

### 3. Delineation Drilling

Drilling a delineation or appraisal well (combination exploratory and development well) is becoming a common practice in the United Kingdom sector of the North Sea. The operators use the wells to define or appraise a geological structure once it has been confirmed by a successful wildcat operation. The practice has been to re-enter previously suspended delineation wells and equip them for gas production, thus realizing considerable capital savings.

### D. Production

### 1. Present Capability

Recently a fixed platform was installed in 340 feet of water in the Gulf of Mexico. At the time of installation this depth was a world record. This 2,900-ton structure, towering more than 550 feet from the bottom of its legs to the top of the drilling mast, can drill as many as 18 directional wells. Figure 37 is a photograph of this platform. Some companies believe permanent fixed platforms can be installed in depths of more than 600 feet. Generally, various well and production control equipment is located on the platform.

In some cases the subsurface reservoir is close enough to shore that the wellhead and producing equipment can be located on land; in other cases man-made islands have been built to support these facilities. Obviously, these approaches are confined to fairly shallow waters.

**Figure 37.** *World's largest fixed platform located in 340 feet of water in Gulf of Mexico off the mouth of the Mississippi River. (Shell Oil photo)*

## 2. Development Drilling

After oil is found through exploratory drilling (usually with a mobile platform), the exploitation cycle is begun. First is development drilling, almost all done from a fixed surface platform using land technology. Associated activities and problems involving separation and subsequent storage and transportation of the hydrocarbons generally dictate use of a surface platform as a base of operations.

Sometimes a contractor will be engaged different from the one involved in exploratory drilling, because of the changed nature of the drilling in the development phase. Usually several holes are drilled before the platform is established to pinpoint the oil pool in quantity and quality. The initial well usually is drilled vertically, but subsequent wells usually are drilled slanting out from the platform to cover a wider area. Depending upon depth and other considerations, reservoirs more than a mile horizontally from the platform can be reached in this manner. Such wells usually are completed conventionally with the wellheads above water on a platform.

With such a platform, it also is possible to connect more distant wells to production-handling equipment on the platform. Such wells cannot be drilled from the platform itself and require a floating rig. Some may be completed using existing underwater completion techniques. (Underwater completion is discussed in a subsequent section.)

## 3. Installation of Producing Equipment

After development drilling, the rigs are removed, and producing equipment is installed. Since crude oil usually is accompanied by large volumes of entrained and dissolved gases (and eventually water), a major purpose of the platform operation is to separate these materials. If there is too much gas or water mixed with the oil, it cannot be pumped ashore efficiently or economically. Provisions are made on the platform for:

—Measuring accurately and controlling flow rate from oil or gas wells.

—Cleaning the flow lines to remove sand and paraffin deposits.

—Injecting chemicals for control of corrosion, scale, or hydrates in the well and the flow lines.

—Separating entrained gases and water from the raw product. (Oil, gas, water, and natural gas liquids seldom occur as pure products in the field.)

—Accessibility for periodic maintenance.

—Storage before subsequent transportation.

—Facilities for supplementary recovery operations.

—Facilities for pumping the oil wells after they stop flowing by natural pressure.

### 4. Lag Between Exploratory and Production Drilling Capability

The ability to explore and drill for petroleum resources in deep water exceeds the capability to produce once it is found. Recent lease acquisitions in depths beyond 600 feet exceed present production capability. Also, the problems and expenses of underwater production and well maintenance are much more extensive than those of exploration.

Oil and gas in relatively shallow water are easier to produce on fixed platforms, because the production systems and pipelines are not significantly different from those on land. Many of these fields have been producing for years, but of hundreds of wells drilled in water depths greater than 200 feet, only a few have been brought into production. Costly production platforms on legs 200 to 300 feet high have rendered many recovery operations economically impractical. Wells in great water depths also present problems of maintenance, and the pipelines required to connect these distant platforms to shore are proportionally more expensive.

Some underwater wells in deep water already have been capped to await such developments as: (1) an increase in the price of crude oil and gas, (2) enough adjacent discoveries to justify a joint pipeline, or (3) technology advances that will make recovery from them profitable.

Costs in shallow water can approach those of deep water under special high risk conditions as in Alaska's Cook Inlet. Platforms in this location must withstand tidal currents up to eight knots which in the winter move pack ice as much as six feet thick past the installation four times a day. Each platform costs more than $10 million—an expenditure for a stable base that is a minimal cost on land.

The largest four-legged platform is a 3,200 ton, 43-well unit to be installed in 75 feet of water in Cook Inlet. Another unique platform rests on one column which stands on a base. Steel in the 28-foot diameter column ranges from one to two inches thick, the thicker sections being in the areas buffeted by the pack ice (Figure 38).

**Figure 38.** *The monopod located in Cook Inlet, Alaska. The single-leg platform, installed in 1966, has minimized effects of ice loading and lends itself to rapid installation in strong currents. (Brown and Root photo)*

### 5. Automatically Controlled Platforms

A completely automatic platform complex has been installed in the North Sea for gas extraction. The entire platform and all its generators, pumps, dehydrators, and other equipment run completely unattended with only occasional visits by supervisory and maintenance personnel. This platform is monitored from shore by closed circuit television that could also indicate fire or illegal trespassing.

Such offshore wells are remotely controlled through automatic valve actuators receiving instructions usually via microwave. In addition, these systems require communications equipment and an electric power source to operate the valve motors. Pneumatic or hydraulic valve actuators can be used, but these require continuous high-pressure air or hydraulic fluid.

### E. Pipelines

Pipelines are laid in an offshore field to gather the oil or gas produced from individual wells into a central collecting point where it is pumped ashore via a large pipeline or stored for loading onto a barge or tanker. In some cases, portable storage facilities are installed near the platform to allow production to begin before the pipeline is completed.

In the production phase, the offshore oil and gas industry is largely a single industry. Historically, additions to the gas reserves have come chiefly via the oil producers. Only in recent years has the search for gas as an independent commodity begun in offshore areas. The principal activity of the gas industry in the oceans has been related to pipelines. All offshore gas is brought ashore by pipelines.

### 1. Laying Techniques

Most offshore pipelines are laid using either of two methods: a long stinger stretching from the lay barge to or close to the bottom or a short curved stinger in conjunction with tensioning apparatus. Both have limitations. Figure 39 shows a conventional pipelaying barge with a long stinger which allows the pipe to follow a gentle slope to the bottom during the laying operation.

**a. Long Stingers** Unless efficient locating and control instruments are developed, the usefulness of the long stinger is limited, especially under adverse tide and weather conditions as in the Cook Inlet or North Sea. Frequently the stinger is dropped to the bottom during severe weather. In the Cook Inlet operation, shutdowns accounted for more than half the elapsed time.

**b. Short Curved Stingers** The use of a short curved stinger with tensioning devices is an alternative having the principal advantage of reducing laying stresses. The advantage of tension declines as pipe diameter increases, since the effect of tensioning is to lessen normal laying stresses which increase in proportion to the square of the pipe's diameter.

### 2. Present Status and Problems

Offshore contractors have developed methods of laying 12-inch diameter pipelines in depths up to 340 feet. Lengths of pipe are joined aboard specially designed barges. The joints are welded, x-rayed, primed, wrapped, and concrete-coated as the pipeline is fed off the end of the barge. An estimated 5,000 miles of pipe, ranging in size from small diameter flow lines to 26-inch trunk lines, now traverse the sea floor in the Gulf of Mexico; large-diameter lines have been installed in the Persian Gulf (to 48 inches) in depths of about 100 feet. Figure 40 shows a novel reel barge which was developed to lay up to six-inch diameter flow lines at high rates. Rollers straighten the pipe as it is laid. The tide-swept Cook Inlet has presented the toughest problem, and installation costs in this area have reached $500,000 per mile even for relatively small-diameter pipe.

**Figure 39.** *Conventional pipe-laying barge with a floating stinger allowing pipe to assume a gentle slope to bottom during laying operation. (Shell Oil photo)*

**Figure 40.** *Barge laying small-diameter pipe from reel at a high rate. Rollers straighten pipe as it is laid. (Shell Oil photo)*

Depth is probably the most immediate problem facing offshore pipelaying. Distance is also an important but less urgent problem. Crude oil pipelines have been laid in 340-foot waters. However, methods for laying the large diameter, high-pressure gas pipelines have not been tested for water depths greater than 300 feet. Pipelines have been laid up to 100 miles in shallow water in the Gulf of Mexico. An 88-mile, 22-inch line was laid recently in the Persian Gulf in 300 feet of water. A French firm demonstrated in 1966 that underwater pipelines can be laid in greater depths when they laid an experimental, small-gauge line in the Cassidaigne Deep near Marseille in waters as deep as 1,080 feet.

The low cost of tanker transportation may limit the laying of long-distance underwater lines. Before the Suez Canal was closed, oil could be shipped around the Arabian Peninsula from the Persian Gulf to the Mediterranean at the same cost as it was moved less than a third that distance across the peninsula by pipeline.

With costs declining as tanker sizes increase and with offshore lines costing two to five times as much as onshore lines, the probability of many long-distance underwater pipelines being constructed seems to be diminishing. On the other hand, the new supertankers have such deep drafts that they are unable to enter many major ports and must be loaded and unloaded offshore. In addition, mooring a large tanker is very difficult in open, unprotected waters. Finally, long-distance underwater lines require the same support facilities as onshore lines (e.g., stations, valves, operators, manifolds, etc.) plus much more expensive corrosion protection.

The problems of gas pipeline support appear similar to those of oil pipelines in the ocean environment and in some cases are intensified because of special characteristics of gas pipelines. For example, their greater diameters cause handling and fabrication to be more difficult and make the pipelines more vulnerable to disturbance and damage by subsurface ocean currents and deep turbulence created by storms.

## 3. Cost Factors

Laying an offshore line is at least twice and more often five times as expensive as laying an onshore line, making costs a major consideration.

Wall thickness and welding improvements offer promise of reduced costs.

**a. Wall Thickness** Wall thickness of onshore pipelines is governed by operating pressure. Offshore it is governed by stresses encountered in laying and heavy-wall pipe is used to lower such stresses. It is estimated that $2.7 million could be saved in the construction of a proposed 30 inch Red Snapper line offshore Louisiana if the wall thickness were reduced from 0.562 to 0.500 inch. Subsequent studies found that with adequate handling equipment, the 30-inch, 0.500 inch wall thickness pipe could be used safely in 150 feet of water and that the factor of safety during the laying operation could be increased by continuous applications of tension to the pipe. These findings emphasize the need for further improvement in pipelaying procedures.

**b. Other Factors** Increased acceptance of micro-wire and fully automatic welding will contribute to lower costs. The pace of welding is a predominant factor determining the rate of offshore pipelaying; the other is keeping the pipelaying barge supplied with pipe in rough seas. Any development that saves time and reduces delays will cut costs.

## 4. Forecasts

Since natural gas pipelines require large diameters, they are more expensive and present more difficult technological problems. Hence their depth and distance to shore are more restricted than oil pipelines. Tankers could be used when these depth-distance limits are exceeded; however, to do this the gas must be liquefied. Cryogenic liquefaction of natural gas is economical only for long-distance transportation and requires major installations for liquefaction, handling, and storage. Such a program is already planned or under way between Algeria and France, between Libya, Italy, and Spain, and between Alaska and Japan.

It is difficult to predict what, if any, future advances may allow production of natural gas from greater water depths or longer distances from shore. It appears that offshore pipelines will continue in use primarily to transport offshore production to onshore facilities over relatively short distances, less than 200 miles.

## F. Subsea Operations

### 1. Potential Advantages and Philosophy

The potential advantages of having an underwater operating capability are:

—Extension of production capabilities to greater depths than those for which fixed platforms are economical. Fixed steel platforms (similar to Figure 41) can be designed for very deep water, but there is an economic and technical limit to their maximum height. Moreover, to emplace them is extremely risky, particularly when the site is far from available fabrication sites.

—Removal of operations from the often turbulent surface environment to avoid loss of platforms in hurricanes or damage from severe storms and shifting foundations.

—Elimination of navigation hazards.

—Additional operational options in such hazardous ice areas as Cook Inlet.

**Figure 41.** *Two derrick barges installing section of fixed platform. Equipped with 500-ton capacity revolving cranes, barges are erecting a 650-ton crude oil storage deck on permanent drilling and production platform in Gulf of Mexico. (Brown and Root photo)*

The fact that the industry is buying leases in ever deeper waters implies that the bidders expect that it will become economically and technically feasible to produce in deep water.

Any discussion of subsea operations must be preceded by qualification of the type of field involved. Each field is different in water depth, size, and product nature; in closeness to shore; and in many other factors which must be taken into account.

The requirement for collection, storage, or transportation a few miles off Santa Barbara, California, is not expected to resemble those in areas distant from shore as in the Gulf of Mexico. In the Santa Barbara area a simple pipeline without underwater separation facilities may suffice, while in the latter, production and storage facilities may be necessary for intermittent delivery to shuttling tankers. In each case, however, it is possible that employment of some subsea completion, production, and maintenance features may enhance the system's economic appeal. It is difficult to predict which system will ultimately prove most practical, but it is likely that several different techniques will be employed.

In conclusion, future economical production in deep water will depend on a choice among surface, completely underwater, or some hybrid technology. It is reasonable to assume that the industry will continue in prototype technical work to:

—Make the best economical estimates of these options.

—Take maximum advantage of deep water opportunities found by exploration.

—Select an option that can be used side by side with its more familiar surface technology.

### 2. History

The first subsea wellheads were installed on gas wells by divers on the shallow bottom of the Great Lakes in 1959. The first oil well was completed in 1960 in the Gulf of Mexico in 55 feet of water. Underwater wells in the Santa Barbara Channel have been producing since 1964 in waters more than 250 feet deep. There are presently between 50 to 100 subsea completions throughout the world. They are still considered experimental in most cases. Limited subsea capability presently exists to ocean depths of 600 feet.

Subsea wellhead equipment may be used when directional wells drilled from a single, deepwater platform cannot reach all parts of a reservoir. In this case, satellite underwater completions could be used. However, almost all existing underwater completions are for wells producing directly to shore without a production platform; several such installations exist off the coasts of California and Peru.

### 3. Characteristics of Subsea Production

The industry already is studying and developing methods for sea-floor well completions, for production and collection techniques, and for separation, treatment, and storage facilities. The particular choices made by the operator depend on the size of the field, the location, depth, etc.

**a. Underwater Christmas Tree**  The heart of the well system is the underwater *christmas tree*—a series of pipes and valves at the wellhead used to control the well during drilling and production phases (Figure 42). It is installed on the subsea landing base by a mobile rig during or after drilling. Although most underwater trees are designed for installation by remote control, divers often must lend a hand. Recently an experimental robot was built to perform limited operations on a specially designed christmas tree.

**b. Divers**  The use of divers is being extensively investigated, and studies are under way to determine the usefulness of divers working with diver-lockout submersibles. Divers for years have had the capability to work at moderate depths, but only recently they have extended their operations considerably below 200 feet. Even so, diving at great depths is considerably more costly than in shallower water where decompression time is much less.

The choice of whether divers should be an element in the system also affects the choice of a specific technological system. Now that divers can work at 600 feet or more, it is possible to choose between diver-assisted completion methods, or automated or remote control completion systems. These choices also are available for subsea installation inspection and maintenance (Figure 43).

**Figure 42.** *Underwater christmas tree, installed after drilling and completion operations, being emplaced in Gulf of Mexico.  (Shell Oil photo)*

**Figure 43** *Diving bell and decompression chamber. Using saturation diving techniques, divers can perform useful work to depths of 600 feet.  (Ocean Systems photo)*

In deeper continental shelf areas, a fixed platform can be erected to extend up to shallower depths and hence be more readily accessible to divers and yet deep enough to escape the major effect of surface waves. Controls, instruments, power sources, etc. could be located on the platform to be tended by divers. Only that equipment absolutely needed at the wellhead would be located on the ocean floor.

Saturated diving techniques with diver lockout and decompression chambers have been utilized by the oil industry to the limit of diver capability. During tests in the summer of 1967, divers performed functional tasks on a simulated wellhead in 600 feet of water in the Gulf of Mexico, demonstrating man's ability to do useful work in such depths.

Diver systems will require development of power units to augment divers' underwater physical capabilities. Subsea oil field hardware is massive; useful work by divers is limited by lack of power tools and equipment for direct application to subsea hardware. The utility of divers in offshore petroleum activities will continue to be marginal until underwater work systems are developed.

c **Manned Submersibles** The need to place submerged wellheads deeper than routine diving depths opens new opportunities for submersible vehicles. Several one and two-man submersibles have been designed to operate at depths in excess of 1,000 feet and could be considered for use in future offshore oil fields. Many present submersible vehicles are unable to develop enough torque in their mechanical arms to flange-up wellheads or do other heavy work; however, their mechanical arms can operate small power tools and valves or make adjustments on instruments and controls. Submersibles are of limited usefulness in strong currents. Future vehicles can be designed to overcome most of today's limitations.

d. **Diverless Remote Control Systems** Many studies and successful tests already have been made on servicing underwater wells with remote controlled televiewing robots employing through-the-flowline treatment tools, hydraulically controlled surface lines, and acoustically controlled valving systems powered by conventional and isotope energy sources.

A recent report described an ocean-floor wellhead completion and production maintenance system.[13] Tests were made with an onshore

nonproducing well in which all normal operations were performed. Later, an ocean floor completion was made in 60 feet of water about one mile from an existing platform, and the tests were repeated.

Dual flow lines were run to the platform to provide for remote production maintenance operations in this simulated deep-water satellite well. Four hydraulic control lines also were run to the platform on the surface for remote operation of the underwater christmas tree valves. A submarine cable connected the tree with the production platform to transmit pressure and valve position data.

Another important feature tested satisfactorily was a remote flow line connector for independent installation and removal of both the christmas tree and the flow lines. The flow lines and the tubing strings were two inches in diameter to permit the use of pump-down tools; the flow lines provided access to the well tubing. The technology of remotely controlled tools demands much ingenuity to insure reliability. Thus, sending a tool to its properly intended location, locking it into place, testing it to insure proper seating, performing a task, and retrieving the tool are an important feat.

After completion of the test well, all production maintenance and well control operations were performed successfully from the remote production platform. The well produced at its full allowable rate over an extended period and successfully withstood several hurricanes with no damage whatsoever to the underwater christmas tree or the flow lines. Experience with the pump-down tools indicated good overall reliability of this system for remote production maintenance operations. This test demonstrated feasibility of such a system and will permit large oil fields on the ocean floor with only a few strategically placed platforms. A number of wells can be drilled within a radius of several miles, using the platform as home base.

Suitable power is needed to control ocean floor wellheads. An isotope unit to generate power at the location may be used or a battery pack designed for easy replacement by wireline methods from a surface vessel. A power source combining an isotope unit with batteries has been perfected to operate electric motor driven valves. This system has been installed, and has operated for several months. This, however, fulfills comparatively low power requirements only. An urgent

[13]Rigg, A. M., T. W. Childers, C. B. Corley, Jr.: "A Subsea Completion System for Deep Water," presented at Society of Petroleum Engineers of AIME Symposium, May 23-24, 1966.

need exists for a power unit in the intermediate range between the trickle chargers and the large stationary units on land.

**e. Acoustics**  Remote control and monitoring by a physical link to the surface have been described. However, there are obvious advantages of having no hard wire link, relying instead on a coded underwater acoustic link to command the subsea system to activate a particular valve mechanism. An acoustic interrogator could be used to monitor valve position, read pressure, and obtain other desired data. One acoustically controlled, isotope-powered wellhead was installed recently in the Gulf of Mexico.

Acoustic links also may find an important role during the drilling operation itself in conjunction with blowout preventers used to control the tremendous pressures in deep formations encountered during drilling. Figure 44 shows an underwater blowout preventer.

Acoustics also have been used with bottom-mounted transponders in water depths to 5,000 feet to enable a drilling ship to pinpoint the precise location of a subsea wellhead when returning to it for hole re-entry.

**Figure 44.** *Underwater blowout preventer.*
*(Shell Oil photo)*

**f. Floating Production Station**  A floating production station moored over a submerged platform or subsea wellhead could be used instead of a fixed platform.

## 4.  Underwater Drilling and Storage

Some petroleum operators foresee a time when drilling and collecting oil in water depths to 3,000 feet or more will be common. Indeed, recent reports suggest the possibility of petroleum deposits on the continental margin in waters as deep as 15,000 feet. Not everyone in the industry agrees on the direction in which the required technology will proceed. The large power requirements of the drilling rigs (several thousand horsepower) and the advances made in mobile rigs make the economics of underwater drilling controversial. Some feel that total underwater drilling will not be economically justified except for large, highly productive fields.

The French have developed a subsurface coring rig, remotely operated from a tender ship, which possibly could be extended to deep coring. A submarine drilling rig design of the late 1950's proposed an automatic drilling rig mounted in a submarine which would carry the necessary drilling mud, drill pipe, casing, and supplies to drill fullscale wells. Aside from the formidable problems of generating power for such a rig, the overall economics were so unfavorable that it was never seriously considered. It is possible that future coring rigs could be controlled acoustically; however, it is more likely that some type of hydraulic-mechanical control will be employed similar to that used by the French rig.

Nevertheless, various ambitious conceptual designs are being examined. At least one oil company is studying the feasibility of housing both the drilling equipment and crews in structures on the ocean floor One concept envisions an entire undersea community. The habitat, as described at a recent offshore oil conference, would enable 50 men to live and work in depths to 1,000 feet for extended periods.

The problem of oil storage arises when the pipeline investment becomes too high. One solution is to store the oil on or near the production platform and transport it to shore in barges later. In very shallow and well protected waters, barges often provide both storage and transportation.

Various portable tanks, similar to the submersible barge type of mobile rigs, have served as temporary oil reservoirs in depths to about 40 feet. If production increases or new discoveries justify a pipeline, these storage units then can be moved to another location. In the relatively calm waters of the Persian Gulf, a large tanker hulk was used to store as much as 250,000 barrels of crude, and a 360,000-barrel tanker was used to store oil off Nigeria. Transport tankers moved the oil from these storage tankers to the market.

Subterranean nuclear blasts below the ocean floor some day could carve out huge cavities to store petroleum as it is extracted from the earth. This might be far cheaper than storage methods now in use. Under one plan, the explosive for a million-barrel cavity would be lowered through a small diameter drilled hole 1,400 feet below the ocean floor and detonated from the surface. The blast would create a cavity approximately 200 feet wide and 600 feet high; all nuclear contaminants would be sealed far underground, preventing their escape into the atmosphere.

Summarizing, various oil companies anticipate that many installations in deep or hazardous areas by 1980 will be on the bottom of the sea, not on the surface. Drilling most likely will continue from the surface, but oil well operations and some temporary facilities will be on the bottom.

## G. Government Role

### 1. Legal-Political Environment

The Government should maintain a proper legal and political environment to assure the continuance of the necessary incentives as industry moves into the more speculative offshore areas. These incentives will encourage continuing development of the required exploitation technology.

### 2. Environmental and Hurricane Predictions

Hurricane Betsy in 1965 churned a path through investments by the oil and gas industry valued at $2 billion, causing damage exceeding $100 million. In the preceding year Hurricane Hilda raged through an area involving $350 million in capital, causing over $100 million in damages. While Hurricanes Betsy and Hilda were large storms, fortunately the industry has not experienced a maximum intensity hurricane moving through a highly developed offshore area. Such a storm will involve a combination of extremely high winds and low barometric pressure with slow storm progress causing tremendous wave forces which will persist for several hours, as with Hurricane Carla. One can only speculate about the extent of damages such a storm could cause.

Problems involving environmental prediction and modification, therefore, continue to be the prime category in which Federal Government efforts could have a major benefit to industry. Progress in hurricane research has been disappointingly slow; better predictions of path and energy dissipation would be of great value. A reasonable goal would be to attain considerably improved hurricane understanding within the next five years and limited hurricane modification within 10 years. Improved accuracy of weather information, wave data and predictions, and ocean current measurements would be extremely useful. Measuring wave heights during an actual hurricane is a promising subject for investigation. There is a critical need for this data. It is extremely expensive to install wave measuring equipment at fixed locations and then to wait possibly for years for the arrival of a large hurricane at the particular site. Seeking out a hurricane and taking wave measurements from an airplane, for example, would yield much more information on platform storm damage criteria than years of monitoring waves from a fixed platform.

### 3. Information and Technology Transfer

a. **From Industry** The petroleum industry has developed independently a technology for working at sea. Many companies engage in cost-sharing programs under unique arrangements encompassing research and basic engineering on environmental prediction, platform design, underwater completion, materials studies, welding techniques, and other subjects. Cooperative work is being performed among elements of the industry, universities, and Government. Much engineering knowhow evolved by the industry could be of great value to the Government. In addition, many companies continue to encourage the Government to make use of their platforms for immediate and historical measurements.

**b. From Government** While most Federal efforts in ocean technology were not intended to provide benefits to any particular industry, there have been developments of particular value to the offshore oil industry. As the Nation accelerates its ocean programs and as the industry continues to move into deeper water, increased technological knowhow will augment greatly oil company efforts. Such Government efforts should hasten the day when the petroleum industry will engage technically and economically in total or partial subsea operations. For example, the Government should encourage development of basic scientific and engineering data and knowledge beyond the economic scope of an individual industry but justified by multi-industry and Government needs. Examples include meteorology, oceanography, power sources, materials, and life support systems. Each industry would further develop and apply the technology peculiar to its own business.

### 4. Technology Requirements for Major Oil Spills

The petroleum industry is concerned with preventing and combating disasters such as the *Torrey Canyon* grounding, and it has supported coordinated efforts with the Government to solve such problems. In fact, the industry provided considerable information on the subject to the joint pollution study conducted for the President by the Departments of the Interior and Transportation.

Improved methods must be developed to minimize the probability of major oil spills. to optimize countermeasures, and to develop technological means to identify the parties responsible for pollution. Joint efforts of the industry and the Federal and State governments must be accelerated. International restrictions against pumping bilges and slush tanks into waters anywhere—in harbors or at sea—must be established and enforced.

### 5. Navigation and Positioning Systems

Many do not consider this subject to have the high priority of environmental forecasting. Nevertheless, more emphasis must be placed on positioning accuracy and repeatability in the order of 50 feet as far as 200 miles from shore. Such accuracies are required when delineating boundaries and

locating a well site. The release of the Navy TRANSIT System is an excellent first step.

### 6. Traffic Control

Development of marine traffic control methods for congested waters should be accelerated. Better delineation of shipping lanes would be an excellent first step.

### 7. Surveys

The petroleum industry makes a very strong distinction between broad regional and detailed exploratory surveys. Detailed exploratory surveys should be left to private enterprise. In general, the traditional guidelines established by the U.S. Geological Survey (USGS) on land are believed to represent an appropriate separation of the proper Government and industry responsibility in the sea. Thus, it is felt that the USGS should step up its reconnaissance mapping program of our Continental Shelf. The modest USGS program of subbottom mapping is also of value to the industry and should be continued.

Environmental Science Services Administration's (ESSA) bathymetric charting of our Continental Shelf also should be continued, with completion of most of the shelf within two years. In addition, ESSA should start now to make plans for extending bathymetric chart coverage of the continental slope and rise.

### H. Conclusions

Free World production from offshore fields is about five million barrels of oil per day, about 16 per cent of total land and offshore production. By 1980 this should climb to 20 million barrels per day, about one third of the projected total Free World production. The Far East and Africa are the most rapid growth areas. The Middle East holds most of the Free World's offshore oil reserves and provides about one-fourth of current offshore production.

Offshore oil was first produced in 1894 in California; petroleum operations in the Gulf of Mexico began in 1936, and the first subsea well was completed in Lake Erie in 1959. Today production has been established more than 70 miles from shore and in depths of 340 feet, and more than 50 subsea wells have been completed.

Production pipelines have been laid successfully in 340 feet of water.

Drilling capability in the last 10 years has progressed from water depths of about 100 feet to more than 600 feet. Leases have been granted by the Department of the Interior for petroleum exploration and production more than 100 miles off U.S. shores and in waters to 1,800 feet deep. About 100 core holes already have been drilled beyond the U.S. Continental Shelves, some in waters nearly 5,000 feet deep. It is expected that in 1969 production will be established in waters as deep as 400 feet, and exploratory wells will be drilled in the Santa Barbara Channel in water depths ranging to 1,300 feet.

The fact that leases already have been sold in water exceeding 1,800 feet does not necessarily mean that the industry now is prepared to buy leases this deep in other world areas. Many favorable factors pertaining to the Santa Barbara Channel more than compensated for the depths: the prospective fields are close to land; the oceanographic and meteorological conditions are less severe than in such other locations as the Gulf of Mexico; oil is in short supply in that area; and there are no allowable restrictions.

Underwater operation offers the following potential advantages:

—Extension of production capabilities to greater depths than those for which fixed platforms are economical.

—Minimization of damage to platforms because of hurricanes, severe storms, and shifting foundations.

—Elimination of navigation hazards.

—More flexibility in operating under ice.

Many studies and successful tests already have been made to service underwater wells with remote controlled televiewing robots, with through-the-flowline maintenance and treatment tools, with hydraulically controlled surface lines, and with remote acoustically controlled valving systems operating from conventional and isotope energy sources. The technology of remotely operated tools in itself has required ingenuity to insure reliability.

Most remote control and monitoring tests have employed a physical link to the surface; however, there are obvious advantages to having no physical link. An acoustic link has been used to command a subsea system to supply electric current to operate a particular valve, to monitor the position of a valve, and to obtain various data such as pressure. Acoustic links also are beginning to find an important role during the drilling operation when used in conjunction with blowout preventers. Acoustic bottom mounted transponders are being evaluated to enable a drilling ship to return to the precise location of a subsea well head and as an aid to re-enter a hole on the sea floor.

The fact that the industry is buying leases in ever deeper waters implies that the bidders expect it will be economically and technically feasible to produce in deep water. However, each field is different in water depth, reserves, size and nature of the reservoir, closeness to shore, value of the product, production rate, and many other pertinent factors.

For collection, storage, or transportation a few miles offshore a simple short pipeline system generally will suffice; in a distant sea, storage may have to be provided for intermittent delivery to shuttling tankers. In either case, some subsea completion, production, and storage features may enhance the system's economic capability. In any particular area it is likely that several different techniques will be employed.

Future economical production in deep water will depend on the most favorable choice of surface, completely underwater, or some hybrid technology. The industry will continue to engage in prototype undersea operations in order to make the best estimates of cost and benefit trade-offs and to take maximum advantage of deep water reserves.

In summary, various oil companies believe that by 1980 an increasing number of installations will be on the bottom of the sea, not on the surface. In these areas drilling will continue to be conducted essentially from the surface, but oil well operations and some temporary storage facilities will be on the bottom.

**Recommendations:**

**The Government should maintain a proper legal and political environment to support industry as it**

moves into the more speculative offshore areas. These incentives will encourage continued development by industry of much of the required exploitation technology, provided that the incentives are advanced sufficiently ahead of the need for the technology. It must be clearly understood that a lag of five to 10 years exists from the time a large field is discovered until volume production is achieved.

A mechanism should be established to ensure optimum information exchange between Government and the petroleum industry. This industry has successfully developed a major technology on its own for working at sea. Considerable engineering experience accumulated within the industry could be of great value to the Government. In addition, many oil companies continue to encourage the Government to make use of their platforms for realtime and historical measurements. The Federal Government should take full advantage of these opportunities.

The Government should seek a considerably improved understanding of hurricanes within 5 years and capability for limited hurricane modification within 10 years.

Problems involving physical environmental prediction and modification continue to be the prime technological area in which Federal Government efforts could have a major impact on the industry. Progress in hurricane research has been disappointingly slow. Two hurricanes in successive years, 1964-1965, caused over $200 million in damage to the industry. Efforts to improve accuracy of weather information, wave data predictions, and ocean current measurements would have a significant impact on offshore economics.

Improved methods must be developed to minimize the probability of major oil spills, to optimize countermeasures, and to develop technological means of identifying responsible polluters. Contingency plans should be established to permit immediate action to contain and clean up major oil spills.

More emphasis must be placed on achieving positioning accuracy in the order of 50 feet at distances as great as 200 miles from shore.

The U.S. Geological Survey should accelerate reconnaissance mapping of our Shelf. The modest USGS program of sub-bottom mapping is also of value to the industry and should be continued.

Detailed exploratory surveys should be left to private enterprise.

The ESSA bathymetric charting of our Continental Shelf also should continue, adhering to its schedule of completing most of the shelf within two years. In addition, ESSA should start now to make plans for extending bathymetric chart coverage to the continental slope and rise.

## IV. OCEAN MINING

### A. Introduction

#### 1. Interest in Ocean Minerals

The following are the primary reasons for the development of a domestic ocean mining industry.

a. **Act of Congress** Strong national impetus toward development of an ocean mining industry on the U.S. Continental Shelf is provided by two objectives stated in the Marine Resources and Engineering Development Act of 1966:[14]

*The accelerated development of the resources of the marine environment.*

*The encouragement of private investment enterprise in exploration, technological development, marine commerce, and economic utilization of the resources of the marine environment.*

b. **Income to Nation** The Presidential Proclamation of Sept. 28, 1945, and more recently the 1958 Geneva International Conference on the Law of the Sea, effectively added, with respect to natural resources, about 810,000 square miles to the area of the United States or approximately 25 per cent of total U.S. dry-land area. The Nation should gain knowledge of the potential resources of this tremendous area and should expect income from leases and royalties on the exploitation of its wealth. Ultimately, the stimulation of a new industry will result in expenditures for salaries, capital, and taxes, contributing greatly to the Nation's economy. This income should exceed many times any expenditure for Government services to support this exploitation.

---

[14]Public Law 89-454, Section 2(b).

**c. Potential Shortage of Metals** It is to the Nation's interest to promote and encourage ocean exploitation not only to support population increases but to supplement dwindling land resources. It has been predicted that total demand for metals between 1965 and the year 2000 will amount to more than the total metals consumed by all nations cumulatively until the present time. Therefore, technology will have to be developed to obtain minerals from such new locations as the ocean. Thus, companies mining sulfur and tin already are forced to look more to the sea.

**d. Dependence on Foreign Sources** It is advisable for the United States to have alternate sources of supply so that in an emergency it will not be overly dependent on foreign sources for critical metals.

**e. Industry Growth** Mining companies are interested in the sea for various reasons. They must keep abreast of the technology of offshore extraction if for no other reason than to have a good working knowledge of the competitive position of those marine minerals that eventually might enhance or jeopardize their business. In addition, they must be able to make rational decisions in choosing between ocean and land resources for investment in new production facilities.

## 2. Present Activity

Not counting coal and iron presently mined from on-shore openings, about $200 million of mineral products is mined world-wide directly from the ocean floor annually. This includes sand, gravel, oyster shell, sulfur, and tin and iron ores but does not include minerals extracted from the water column. If one excludes sand, gravel, oyster shells, and sulfur, the remaining ocean mining is only about $50 million per year for tin and iron sands, heavy minerals, and diamonds.[15]

For the most part, the present market represents unique local deposits that serve local markets. The notable exceptions are tin and sulfur. It is believed that once a substantially rich deposit is found, technology to exploit it will be readily

developed—at least for the continental shelves. However, unless a deposit large and rich enough to offset the higher cost of underwater operations is found, ocean mining development will continue to move rather slowly.

The mining industry on the U.S. Continental Shelf consists of little more than dredging non-metallic deposits and sulfur extraction. The latter is mined through a drill hole and is related to petroleum in its exploration and recovery techniques and problems. There are, however, successful ocean mining operations in other parts of the world where the legal and economic climate is more favorable and where the existence of sizable deposits has been established.

There is or has been *exploration* for gold off Alaska (depth of 200 feet), phosphorite off North Carolina and California (to 600 feet), and manganese and phosphorite nodules and crusts on the Blake Plateau (depth of 2,400 to 3,600 feet) and at even greater depths, especially in the Pacific.

## 3. Types of Mineral Deposits

Ocean minerals can be divided broadly into two categories encompassing those minerals found on the bottom and those that might be found in the sub-bottom (within bedrock), as shown in Figure 45. Within one or the other category is a diversified group of minerals such as copper, iron, gold, manganese nodules, oyster shells, etc.

Each involves variations in the exploration and recovery types of equipment required. Hence, the industry's needs will be of a heterogeneous nature. Sea water column mining is discussed in Subsection V, "Chemical Extraction".

The principal operations involved in ocean mineral exploitation follow: (1) exploration and evaluation, (2) recovery, and (3) transportation and processing. These will be discussed below. However, prior to this a brief description is given of some of the basic technological differences between hard mineral mining and the recovery of oil and gas.

### B. Hard Minerals vs. Oil and Gas

The geology controlling the occurrence of oil and gas commonly extends predictably offshore, and the technology and techniques used to find and recover oil offshore have, for the most part, been very similar to those on land. Exploration

---

[15] Barnes, S., "Mining Marine Minerals," *Machine Design*, April 25, 1968, p. 26.

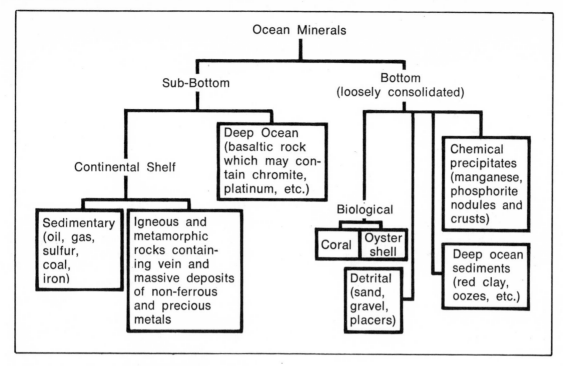

**Figure 45.** *Categories of ocean minerals.*

costs are high because the target (deposit) is concealed, but the industry has had long experience on land in searching for concealed targets. Once an oil or gas target is discovered, the discovery hole can be converted into a producing well more readily than for hard minerals. Moreover, because of highly developed geophysical and geological techniques used in locating oil and gas reservoirs, the ratio of target discovery holes to total exploration holes is high—on the order of one in five in the Gulf of Mexico (one in 13 countrywide, onshore and offshore).

On the other hand, the hard mineral explorer is faced with an entirely different set of problems than the oil explorer. Most rich ore deposits that have sustained our Nation to the present time were exposed at the surface and discovered by surface prospecting. Only in the last 15 to 20 years has the mining industry seriously attempted to find deposits not indicated by surface characteristics.

Techniques to discover concealed subsurface mineral deposits on land are less developed than those for oil and gas. Offshore, virtually a whole new technology to discover sub-bottom lode and bedded deposits will have to be devised. Further, if

a mineral discovery is made offshore the drill hole cannot be utilized as a producing unit. At that point, the explorer must decide whether to risk investing a large amount of capital to delineate the deposit to determine its potential profitability.

The transition from discovery drill holes to an operating hard rock mine will require either development of a very large open pit or the penetration of the ore body by a vast underground network of tunnels and excavations.

Oil and mineral targets differ in relative size. Oil targets may be tens of miles across, while some great metal deposits are tiny by comparison. For example, one of the largest copper deposits in the world is only about one square mile in horizontal area. This compares with an average of more than three square miles for the more than 200 oil reservoirs that have been developed in offshore Louisiana. Thus, the ability to discover deposits in certain formations and structures appears to be greater for oil than for hard minerals.

Whereas a single test hole can indicate the oil and gas potential of a formation over a comparatively large area, hard mineral exploration requires extensive close-spaced drilling to determine potential. In addition, such indirect measurements as pressure and electric logging may be very helpful in evaluating fluid (oil and gas) potential, but direct measurements of recovered samples are required in most cases to evaluate the amount and quality of mineral deposits.

Placer deposits and nodule deposits are easier to explore for than concealed sub-bottom bedrock deposits but still pose considerable difficulties. Placer deposits may not extend across the shore line, and in many cases, the beach separates environments containing different kinds of mineral occurrences.

A great many samples must be taken to define a placer deposit. As with gold and diamonds, the best material is often in cracks and depressions in the bedrock and is difficult or impossible to reach. Placer or nodule mining in deep water requires relatively expensive equipment, and operating costs also are high, especially where sea state conditions are frequently unfavorable.

The ratio of ore discoveries to targets explored may be as low as one in 1,000 onshore and may be even lower offshore. Exploration of the shelf for hard mineral deposits will be very speculative for the foreseeable future, and mineral explorers will require strong incentives to apply their energy and skill in an activity where good fortune will also be required.

## C. Exploration and Evaluation

### 1. Types

Mineral exploration in the ocean requires a sequence of activities, many similar to those on land. These include bathymetric, geophysical, and geological surveys, followed by sample analysis.

### 2. Bathymetric

Modern echo-sounders can, when used with shipboard recorders and underwater devices, determine details of bottom relief to within one fathom in deep water and even more precisely in shallow water. Bottom contours, representing such features as submerged river channels (frequently a favorable location for placers), can be detected. Interpretation of echogram characteristics also helps to identify the type of sea bottom; i.e., rock, sand, or mud. Although side-looking sonar represents a start towards more effective scanning of

bottom profiles, much more highly developed devices and techniques will be needed.

### 3. Geophysical

Geophysical survey methods used on land have proved readily adaptable to the marine environment.

Magnetic anomalies discovered in marine surveys can indicate the major rock types, faults, and other structural features below the ocean floor. They also indicate the occurrence of magnetic ores. Marine magnetometers allow accurate measurements while under way.

The gravity survey also is useful in locating anomalies. Marine gravimeters have been developed recently for shipborne surveys and for use near the sea floor. While the accuracy of a ship mounted unit is an order of magnitude lower than that of analogous sea floor equipment, more data can be provided in less time. Gravity data is useful in broad reconnaissance studies for interpreting large subbottom structures. However, such data is best used together with the results of other geophysical data.

Seismic surveys indicate structure, stratification, and sediment thicknesses. In addition, submerged beaches, which may contain placer concentrations, may be indicated. Present sub-bottom profiling techniques, however, cannot evaluate mineral deposits. Sophisticated methods may be able to provide much higher resolution information including acoustic velocities, densities, and acoustic impedances, thereby helping to identify a particular material.

Recently, electrical methods, such as measuring resistivity characteristics of rocks, radiometric techniques, and heat flow methods have been suggested as additional tools for detecting anomalies.

For more efficient exploration, mathematical search models have been used in laying out grids for geophysical surveys, sampling, drilling, and other exploration work.[16] Efforts also have been made to apply computer techniques and mathematical models to the probability of finding minerals

----

[16] United Nations Economic and Social Council, "Resources of the Sea, Part One: Mineral Resources of the Sea Beyond the Continental Shelf," Feb. 19, 1968, p. 44.

in certain areas. Such approaches are as applicable underwater as ashore.

## 4. Geological

Confirmation of the actual minerals present can be accomplished only by sampling and subsequent analysis. Methods of direct observation on-site are limited in usefulness to such items as outcrops, type of bottom (sand, mud, etc.), and nodules.

Methods of direct observation include those by divers and observers in deep submersible vehicles. Deep towed vehicles provide indirect continuous monitoring by television and by still and motion picture photography. Observation supplemented by bottom sampling is the most likely method of evaluating occurrences of manganese nodules on the sea floor by estimating area coverage, nodule size, and shape.

Because of the overriding importance of coring, major emphasis should be given to techniques for taking more samples and deeper cores. Coring provides samples for chemical and mineralogical analysis.

Much sampling today employs conventional tools originally developed for oceanographic research. Excluding core drilling systems, many bottom sampling devices cannot probe deeper than about 20 feet, although cores of up to 90 feet have been taken in very soft sediments. More recently, a vibratory corer has been developed that can take a 100-foot core six inches in diameter. This has proven very useful in evaluating mineral concentrations on the shelf.

Commonly used sampling devices are:

—Free fall grab sampler—useful for deep nodules.

—Wireline dredge samplers—used since the Challenger days; the disadvantage of dredging procedures is the lack of knowledge concerning the exact location of the sample.

—Free fall corers—cannot penetrate rock or gravel; remote controlled rotary corers powered and controlled from a mother ship, will enable obtaining short cores from rock.

—Jet lift corer—using water or air pumped down a pipe.

—Vibratory corer—newest type developed.

Petroleum core drilling systems with steel bits penetrate softer rock to 20,000 feet. Small diameter diamond core drills have penetrated harder rock to about 14,000 feet, although most conventional rigs are equipped to penetrate 4,000 or 4,500 feet.

## 5. Shipboard Integrated Survey Systems

Shipboard integrated geophysical systems have become available recently, including automatic sensing and recording devices. These measure simultaneously many parameters from magnetometer, gravimeter, echo sounder and seismic readings with reference to a synchronous clock, navigation fixes, and ship's course and speed. The data can be produced in both analog and digital form, including recordings on magnetic tape, for computer processing often while still underway.

## 6. Required Supporting Technology

Aside from ships currently used for mineral survey work, the role of submersibles is beginning to be appreciated. Newer versions will have greater depth and cruising range capabilities, permitting them to survey and sample. As an example, the *Alvin* has been used to recover sea floor specimens and perform geological studies in the West Indies and near Woods Hole.

An accurate navigation fix is critical in undersea prospecting, and as the search becomes more detailed, less error in positioning can be tolerated. The tolerable error also depends on the distribution of the mineral deposits. When distribution is broad and uniform, positioning requirements for exploitation are reduced, and at least initial exploitation will be little concerned with precise positioning. If distribution is patchy and concentrations are localized, precision positioning is essential both for evaluating deposits and for exploiting them efficiently.

## D. Recovery

## 1. Dredging

Onshore placers and other various unconsolidated deposits have been exploited commercially for many years throughout the world. Underwater mining recovery can presently be accomplished for a number of ore deposits at depths of as much as 150 feet. Current recovery techniques include the clamshell dredge, the bucket-ladder dredge, and dredges employing air-lift or suction hydraulic systems.

**a. Clamshell Dredge**  Clamshell or wireline dredges use large grab buckets, clamshells, and other digging and lifting tools lowered to the sea floor on flexible steel cables. They have the advantage of being adaptable to work in water depths to 350 feet. Having flexible cables, they also can be used in areas of high currents or wave motions. The main disadvantages of this method are the cost of operations in deep water because of the cycle time (which increases directly with water depth) and uncertainty in continuity of successful withdrawals. Clamshell dredges have been used in Thailand to recover tin ore from depths of 90 to 130 feet.

**b. Bucket-Ladder Dredge**  The bucket-ladder dredge employs an endless chain of steel buckets to dig into the bottom. The dredged material is drawn continuously up the ladder and dumped. The material is then fed to various screening and concentrating devices. Bucket-ladder dredges have good digging capability, making them especially useful for placer mining, but are limited to water depths of about 150 feet. Because of the rigid dredging ladder, this method is confined to protected waters or fair-weather operations. Several bucket-ladder dredges mined tin deposits in 1967 off Indonesia in 60 to 100 feet of water.

Bucket-ladder dredges were first used in the United States in the late 19th century. They have seen major service in inland waters. By digging the mineral deposit at the bow and depositing all barren materials (waste) at the stern, the dredge automatically advances to new reserves.

Figure 46 shows a front view of the bucket-ladder dredge, *Yuba No. 21*. Still in operation on the Yuba River, California, mining placer gold, it is one of the last gold mining dredges in operation in the United States. With a mining depth capacity of 107 feet and 18 cubic foot capacity buckets, it has an excellent record of efficiency.

Figure 47 is a rear view of the 14 cubic foot bucket-ladder dredge, *Rasep*, shown mining to a depth of 100 feet on the island of Singkep, off Sumatra.

**Figure 46.**  *Front view of bucket-ladder dredge* Yuba No. 21 *(C. M. Romanowitz photo)*

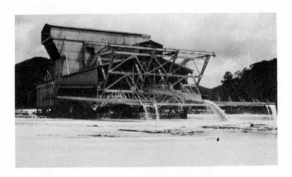

**Figure 47.** *Rear view of bucket-ladder dredge* Rasep, *shown mining to a depth of 100 feet off island of Singkep, off Sumatra. (C. M. Romanowitz photo)*

**c. Hydraulic Dredge**  The hydraulic dredge uses either air-lift or suction techniques. Using air-lift, air is injected into the bottom of a pipe which is submerged more than half of its length in water. A density differential is produced in the pipe, forcing the column of air-water mixture to flow upward in the pipe. This flow creates a powerful suction at the bottom of the pipe, bringing up silt, sand, and gravel suspended in a large volume of water. The mechanism consists of two pipes which may be constructed on the site with limited shop facilities and which require only compressed air to operate. However, air-lifts are extremely inefficient when operated without the assistance of water jets and other devices. The depth at which airlifts can be used efficiently is a function of the cost of supplying compressed air at the depth of dredging.

With the suction dredge, a movable suction pipe with a support ladder and a discharge line are mounted on a floating hull. When digging in semi-consolidated sediments or soft to medium hard rocks, a cutter head (normally of the rotating hollow bit type) usually is employed. The head is mounted on the lower end of the suction pipe to break up the ground and direct the flow of solids into the suction pipe.

The suction dredge method is best suited for recovery of large quantities of unconsolidated material. For example, this technique is used for channel maintenance as well as mineral recovery. Its water depth capability is up to 200 feet. Dredges using a rigid ladder are limited to protected waters or fair weather operation.

Recent improvements in size and capacity of hydraulic suction dredges for engineering construction work have caused renewed interest in their application for offshore mining. Preliminary designs have been made to recover sea floor nodule deposits at depths greater than 4,000 feet by this method. At such depths it probably will be necessary to establish additional submerged pumping capacity. Hydraulic dredging will almost certainly be applied in deep sea mining.

## 2. Deep Ocean Mining

The mining of deep sea manganese nodules has attracted serious evaluation and interest. It has been asserted that nodules constitute a renewable resource, their estimated renewal rate exceeding the present world rate of consumption for the elements contained in them (chiefly copper, nickel, cobalt, and manganese).

However, this may not be of practical significance because in the limited areas economic to mine, the rate of renewal is not adequate to sustain continuous mining. Technology for the economic exploitation of deep sea nodules has not yet been demonstrated. The problem is not only that of economic recovery but also of economically separating the elements from the raw nodules.

Various design studies have been made on nodule recovery. One such method conceives of an air lift or suction dredge mounted on a wheeled vehicle or sled towed along the ocean floor by a flexible pipeline secured to a surface vessel. The direction and speed of the mining device would be controlled by the heading and speed of the surface ship. An underwater acoustic transponder system would monitor the position of the mining device

relative to the bottom mining area. The ore could be dredged and piped to the surface for loading into ore barges for transportation to shore facilities. The ore might be concentrated at sea to lessen the amount of material that must be transported.

A similar system designed in Canada recommends a light-weight medium (such as kerosene instead of airlift or suction) to actuate a very high velocity upward flow through the conduit, lifting the heavy nodules faster than they can sink through the stream.

One of the more sophisticated ocean mining approaches is a self-propelled bottom mobile mining system in which a suction dredge is mounted on a bottom mobile crawler or wheeled vehicle. The power required for mobility, navigation, and dredging is supplied by cable from the mining control vessel at the surface. The product must be lifted to the surface by supplementary equipment.

Deep ocean mining will require development and evaluation of many new types of equipment heavily dependent on marine technology advances. Examples include: (1) submarine crawlers and bottom hovering vehicles to explore for and recover deposits, (2) stationary or neutrally buoyant platforms, (3) drilling rigs on the ocean floor, (4) submarine dredges, (5) high capacity, low cost vertical transport systems, and (6) high capacity equipment for horizontal transfer.

Typical basic engineering needs of deep ocean mining: (1) sufficient power to lift thousands of tons of minerals from great depths, (2) ultra-high strength, corrosion-resistant hoisting cables, (3) long, flexible pipes for deep water that can withstand the anticipated bending and shearing stresses, and (4) the ability to provide three-phase flow through long pipes. Further, very high ascending water velocities probably will be required to lift even small manganese nodules, requiring larger manganese nodules to be broken into small pieces on the sea floor or retrieved differently. Other difficulties may be encountered where a solid crust of manganese or phosphorite covers the sea floor.

## 3. Sub-Bottom Mining

Except for sulfur (Frasch process) and coal and iron (tunnels from land) the task of extracting ores from rocks beneath the continental shelf is an order of magnitude more difficult than dredging shelf depth, on-bottom deposits. Yet this type of mining justifies continuing attention.

Present sub-bottom coal and iron mining operations extending out from land under the bottom involve only incidental marine problems, seepage the main concern. As mining progresses, the horizontal distance from the surface entrance increases, accompanied by corresponding cost increases. When the economic limit of such mining is reached or as deposits far from shore are discovered, mining through a sea floor entrance must be considered.

Although openings in the sea floor have been made for tunnels and dam foundation caissons, water depths at the sites rarely exceed 150 feet. Opening the sea floor for a permanent shaft serviced from a surface platform or a submerged base presents formidable engineering problems and costs, especially at depths beyond practical diving limitations. Ultimately such objectives may be accomplished with sea floor entrance and undersea transfer capabilities, much of which may result from technology developments funded under military programs.

The techniques to recover offshore sulfur are similar to those for offshore oil production, making use of fixed above-surface platforms in shallow water. The platform supports drilling rigs, power plants, shops, warehouse, heliport and living quarters. The power plant heats the sea water used to melt the sulfur, supplies the compressed air to lift the sulfur to the surface and provides the electric power to operate the rigs and other equipment.

Wells are drilled directly from the platform into sulfur-bearing formations. Hot water is forced through pipes into the formations to melt the sulfur, which is then lifted to the surface by compressed air. Molten sulfur must be maintained at a temperature above 240 degrees Fahrenheit during handling operations.

### E. Processing and Transportation

### 1. Techniques

Problems of processing and transportation will be different for ores recovered from shallow water very near to land compared to ores recovered in deeper water remote from land bases. Immediate processing or enrichment of the ore generally will not be necessary if storage facilities are adequate, although desirable if transportation costs are high. Transportation from the sea surface to land can be by surface vessel or barge, by pumping slurry or liquid through a pipeline, or by conveyor belt. Floating or underwater storage tanks are possible, and transfer to transport ships or tankers can be accomplished in the same manner as tankers are loaded or discharged today.

Mining operations conducted completely independent of land (as in the deep sea or remote shallow banks) will result in entirely different processing and transportation problems. Ore will be loaded directly into barges, tankers, or ore transports. Immediate initial beneficiation or processing may be necessary at sea to reduce weight or bulk although this may require large processing equipment on the dredging ship. If all operations are conducted from a single vessel, this will further reduce the amount of ore collected on each trip. If multiple vessel operations are anticipated, one collecting and processing vessel could operate continuously while transport vessels shuttle to port.

### 2. Attractiveness of Transportation at Sea

The relative economy of transporting bulk materials at sea is an attractive economic characteristic of working at sea. High density cargoes can be transported in bulk carriers, in large quantities, and at low unit costs. Thus, a high-grade deposit in a remote location on land could be unprofitable because of the costs required to construct roads and community facilities for workmen. By contrast, an offshore deposit might be more feasible economically. These considerations already have influenced sand and gravel operations where transportation costs are high relative to product value.

Mobility of recovery platforms at sea is another attractive feature. Since dredging equipment is limited to a few basic types, many systems may be applicable to other operations. This might provide an opportunity for flexibility for a company mining certain minerals in the northern latitudes in the summertime but forced to disband operations due to winter weather. The mining ships could move to a warmer climate and mine a different material. In addition, economic fluctuations in the values of minerals being produced could make mining certain bottom deposits more attractive than another.

## F. Forecast

Figure 48 represents an estimated forecast for economic ocean mining endeavors. To date ocean mining has not attracted significant private capital for noteworthy domestic commercial operations. There is, however, sufficient international activity to serve as a foundation for future domestic commercial ventures. However, before any sizeable commercial ventures are attempted, much additional exploration of the ocean is required. There is not enough knowledge to motivate even the boldest managements to commit the large sums required for a deep ocean venture. The assurance of attractive ocean bottom deposits is simply too meager for more than exploratory company commitments. Stimulus would be added if Government-sponsored bathymetric and geological survey programs provided enough information to enable managements to make confident decisions leading to serious ocean prospecting and subsequent commitments to mining system hardware.

## G. Government Role

The present Government program to encourage the development of an ocean mining industry considers the vital need to provide information for sound economic evaluation of ocean mineral deposits. Because of technical difficulty and high cost, it is most logical that the Government should sponsor the initial broad surveys. When sufficient data are accumulated to warrant further action, the emphasis should shift to assistance in developing fundamental technology useful for exploitation. However, major hardware commitments should be the responsibility of industry.

As far as the Department of the Interior is concerned, the task of broad-scale location and delineation of mineral deposits is divided between the Geological Survey and the Bureau of Mines. The former is concerned principally with general geological characterization, while the latter is concerned with techniques for resource evaluation and recovery technology.

There has been increased emphasis in the Bureau of Mines program for marine minerals because of immediate needs for new sources of

### Figure 48
### ESTIMATED OCEAN MINING TECHNOLOGY TIME TABLE[1]

| | Depth of Water (feet) | | | |
|---|---|---|---|---|
| | 50 | 300 | 600 | 1,000 |
| Underwater Photographic Reconnaissance (analogous to aerial photographs) . . | 1960 | 1964 | 1970 | 1975 |
| Submersible (for exploration coring) . . . . . . . . . . | 1965 | 1967 | 1970 | 1970 |
| Barge Dredge (ladder) . . . . . . . | 1900 | 1970 | — | — |
| Barge Dredge (suction) . . . . . . . | 1930 | 1970 | 1980 | 1985 |
| Stationary Mining Platform . . . . | 1960 | 1970 | 1975 | 1980 |
| Mining Using Air Lift Device . . . . | 1960 | 1970 | 1975 | 1980 |
| Mobile On-Bottom Mining Platform . . | 1970 | 1972 | 1975 | 1980 |
| Buoyant Submersible Platform . . . . | — | 1975 | 1980 | 1985 |
| Solution Mining (Sulfur, Potash) . . . | 1960 | 1980 | 1985 | 2000 |
| Hardrock Mining (tunneling from land, approximate dates) . . . . . . . | 1900 | 1920 | 1950 | 1960 |
| Shaft Mining . . . . . . . . . . | 1950 | 1970 | 1980 | 2000 |
| Underwater Open Pit Hardrock Mining . . . . . . . . . . | 1968 | 1980 | 1990 | 2000 |

[1]*Mining* in this table refers to the recovery operation.

Source: Adapted from Pehrson, G. O., "Mining Industry's Role in Development of Undersea Mining," MTS Transactions, *Exploiting the Ocean:* 1966, p. 195.

what are called heavy metals, represented most importantly by gold. The program is handicapped by the sketchy nature of pertinent information derived as a by-product of studies directed towards other aspects of oceanography. It also is restrained by the need for more advanced and more reliable tools and techniques for ocean bottom sampling.

A most urgent need is for research and development in delineating and evaluating marine mineral deposits. Most of the Bureau of Mines' present effort is concentrated on (1) data collection and analysis and (2) sampling equipment and methods. In the former, liaison is being established to obtain from the oceanographic community data on known and potentially mineralized areas.

Development of equipment and techniques to sample sea bottom mineral deposits will proceed much faster and more efficiently as a Government-industry partnership venture. Here, industry already is a principal participant, and its involvement can be expected to increase. Figure 49 shows the *R/V Virginia City*, a Bureau of Mines research vessel. Once a naval ocean fleet tug, this vessel has been completely refitted by the Bureau of Mines Marine Minerals Technology Center for research on marine mineral problems.

**Figure 49.** *Bureau of Mines research vessel* R/V Virginia City, *shown operating off coast of Nome, Alaska. (Bureau of Mines photo)*

The recent Director of the Bureau of Mines, W. R. Hibbard, has identified several key problems, examples of which are:[17]

[17]Hibbard, W. R., "The Government's Program for Encouraging the Development of a Marine Mining Industry," MTS Transactions, *Exploiting the Ocean,* 1966, pp. 202-203.

*Determining the topography and physical character of the sea floor.... Some of the existing geophysical tools such as—density probes, underwater cameras, and manned submersibles, will be utilized and, with modification, doubtless can be made more useful for mineral deposit delineation. But the precision that will be required in making these determinations, and the necessary measurement of additional properties such as particle size, hardness, and strength make it inevitable that new tools will have to be developed....*

*Research leading to efficient methods for breaking sea-bottom ores... [However], the urgency of this problem cannot be determined now. It is probable that, for some time, attention will be directed principally to unconsolidated sediments....*

*[M]aterials handling, or the gathering and transporting of minerals from the ocean floor. As with fragmentation, details of the research that must be done will become clear as work progresses in the exploration and delineation phases of the program....*

*Research on the problems of waste disposal.... [U]nwise dumping of the tailings, if not carefully planned, could quickly foul a mining operation. Furthermore, the compatibility of a marine mining operation with exploitation of the other resources of the sea, particularly the food resources, will depend principally on the effectiveness of the tailings-disposal system.*

Ultimately, the bulk of the Bureau's research in the marine minerals field should be concerned with the technology and economics of production. Now, however, the state-of-the-art and lack of adequate knowledge of the resources make it necessary that most of the effort be devoted to acquiring information that will enable defining the mining possibilities.

## H. Conclusions

Ocean mining is a heterogeneous industry. It can be divided broadly into minerals found on the bottom and in the sub-bottom (within bedrock).

Despite intense interest in ocean mining, most recent activities have been conceptual and exploratory. In fact, not only is information on ocean floor mineral deposits sparse, but the tools and techniques for sampling in sufficient quantity and quality require further development. During the decade of 1970-1980 there will continue to be many gaps in the required technology. The greatest current need is to characterize the geology of our Continental Shelf as it is critical to planning economic exploitation. It is anticipated that most major technical problems could be solved by the recommended decade of aggressive technological development during the 1970's.

Sand, gravel, and oyster shell dredging (local enterprises oriented to local situations), and sulfur extraction (related to petroleum in its recovery techniques and economic problems) essentially comprise the mining industry on the U.S. Continental Shelf. There are, however, successful sea mining operations in other parts of the world where the legal and economic climate is more favorable and where the existence of minable deposits has been established. Nevertheless, there is or has been activity involved in exploring for gold off Alaska (depths of almost 200 feet), phosphorite off North Carolina and California (depths of almost 600 feet), and manganese and phosphorite nodules and crusts on the Blake Plateau (depths of 2,400 to 3,600 feet) and at even greater depths, especially in the Pacific Ocean.

Except for coal and iron, mined from tunnels started on land and extending out under the seabed, there is essentially no sub-bottom mining of solid minerals. Present mining concentrates on bottom deposits that require dredging operations. Of dredges in current use, a modified air lift hydraulic dredge presently has the potential to operate to 1,000-foot depths; conceptual designs have been made of suction dredges capable of recovering nodules at 4,000-foot depths.

Mining deep sea manganese nodules has attracted serious evaluation and interest. However, mining technology for economic exploitation of deep sea nodules does not exist. The problem is not only that of economic recovery but that of economically separating the elements from raw nodules.

Small scale sampling of the deep sea floor to locate mineral deposits and secure samples for specific laboratory analyses only recently has been conducted. Sampling of the deep sea floor still is so time consuming that a discouragingly small number of samples come from a day's work.

Of various design studies made on nodule recovery, all require making use of advanced undersea technology. The problems of providing sufficient power to lift thousands of tons of minerals from great depths; the need for ultra-high-strength, corrosion resistant hoisting cables; the requirement to design long, flexible pipes or hoses for deep water that can withstand the ocean current drag and the resulting bending and shearing stresses; and the problem of three-phase-flow through such long pipes are typical of basic engineering problems.

The task of extracting ores from rocks beneath the continental shelf is an order of magnitude more difficult than that of dredging shelf depth bottom deposits. Yet this type of mining justifies continuing attention. In contemplating sub-bottom mining far from land, mining through a sea floor entrance must be considered. Ultimately, such objectives may be accomplished with sea floor entrance and undersea transfer capabilities, much of which may result from technology developments funded under military programs.

The shaft required for mining production is much larger than a mining core drill hole or a petroleum production hole. Furthermore, to bring a mine located by coring into production requires the cutting of many thousands of feet and even miles of costly tunnels and underground excavations radiating from the mine shaft. In addition, the process of bringing up tons per day of solid minerals requires very expensive hoisting equipment.

In conclusion, deep ocean mining will require development of many new types of equipment heavily dependent on marine technology advances. Possible examples include: (1) submarine crawlers and bottom hovering vehicles for exploration and recovery of deposits, (2) stationary or neutrally buoyant platforms, (3) drilling rigs on the ocean floor, (4) submarine dredges, (5) high capacity, low cost vertical transport systems, and (6) high capacity equipment for horizontal transfer.

### Recommendations:

**Many mining spokesmen have indicated that industry will undertake the costs of detailed surveys and development of mineral recovery technology. The Government's role should be to provide the following:**

—Proper legal-political-fiscal environment to permit the industry to develop on its own much of the required recovery technology.

—Reconnaissance scale bathymetric, geophysical and geological maps.

—Technical services encompassing large-scale facilities, technology transfer, and environmental monitoring and prediction.

Identification of basic engineering problems associated with exploration and exploitation and development of tools and instrumentation required for exploration should be undertaken jointly between the private sector and the Federal Government in a properly coordinated program.

Specific technology needs identified for Government support of the ocean mining industry are as follows:

—Characterization of the geology of our Continental Shelf as a guide to further and more specific delineation of mineral deposits in particular areas by industry.

—Development of devices for rapid underwater exploration for minerals. Examples include equipment analogous to airborne magnetometer equipment employed for large-scale explorations on shore and devices for more rapid deposit sampling.

—Information on soil properties of continental shelves and deep ocean bottoms in areas in which undersea mining operations may be undertaken or facilities constructed. This includes load-bearing capacity, stability, possibility of submarine landslides, etc.

—Provision of large facilities for simulating deep ocean environments to develop, test, and calibrate materials, instruments, and other devices.

—Development of materials for cables having exceptional strength-to-weight ratios, high fatigue resistance, and the ability to retain strength in seawater.

—Improvements in predicting, monitoring, and controlling major storms, earthquake waves, and other environmental hazards to vessels and structures.

—Provision of topographical and sub-bottom maps of our Continental Shelf overprinted with gravimetric, magnetic, bottom type, and other geological information.

—Provision of topographical maps and characterization of the deep ocean basins.

—Establishment of a mechanism to accumulate and disseminate technical data applicable to offshore mining problems, including Navy data, available to industry with as little restriction as National security permits.

—Establishment of improved systems for precise location at the sea surface, mid-depth, and on the bottom.

## V. CHEMICAL EXTRACTION

### A. Introduction

#### 1. Elements in the Ocean

The total volume of the oceans is estimated to be 320 million cubic miles.[18] Although salinity of the several seas varies somewhat, the average is approximately 35,000 ppm of dissolved salts, equivalent to 165 million short tons per cubic mile. The world oceans, therefore, represent a storehouse of about 50 million billion tons of dissolved materials.

Figure 50 lists a few of the more important dissolved elements. Some 77 elements, including atmospheric gases, have been detected. It is quite likely that all naturally occurring elements exist in the ocean. The lack of detection of the trace components is due to analytical limitations. As can be seen from the table, the first eight elements account for over 99 per cent.[19] (Oxygen and hydrogen elements are not included.)

#### 2. Extent of Present Extraction

a. Overall Production    The chemical industry extracts various chemicals from the sea water column in commercial operations. The processes

---

[18] Shigley, C. M., "Minerals from the Sea", *Journal of Metals*, January 1951, p. 3.

[19] McIlhenny, W. F., "Chemicals from Sea Water," *Proceedings of the Inter-American Conference on Materials Technology*, May 1968, p. 120.

Figure 50

## PER CENT CONCENTRATION OF DISSOLVED ELEMENTS IN SEA WATER[1]

| Element | Per cent of Total Dissolved Elements |
|---|---|
| Chlorine . . . . . | 58.3 |
| Sodium . . . . . . | 32.2 |
| Magnesium . . . . . | 4.1 |
| Sulfur . . . . . . | 2.7 |
| Calcium . . . . . . | 1.23 |
| Potassium . . . . . | 1.17 |
| Bromine . . . . . | 0.20 |
| Carbon . . . . . . | 0.09 |
| All others (about 70 different elements) . . | Trace |
| Total . . . . . | 100.0 |

[1] Excludes oxygen and hydrogen.

are well developed and economically competitive. This oceanic area of interest has probably received much less attention by the public than is justified. As can be seen from Figure 51, nearly $400 million of chemicals or chemically related materials are recovered from sea water each year.[20] This includes desalinated water as well as the four types of minerals listed in the table.

[20] *Ibid.*, p. 119.

The mineral with the largest tonnage and the greatest value is sodium chloride—common salt—accounting for about 45 per cent of the total value. The other four products include, in order of dollar value: magnesium metal, desalinated water, bromine, and magnesium compounds. No materials other than salt, water, bromine, magnesium, and its compounds are extracted now in commercial quantities from sea water. It is also of interest, looking at this table, to note the importance of sea water as a source of magnesium metal and bromine. About two-thirds of these minerals are obtained from the ocean.

Figure 52 indicates the analogous figures for production in the United States.[21] The value of annual output of these minerals and desalinated water is $135 million. Magnesium metal, magnesium compounds, and bromine account for almost 90 per cent of the value of materials extracted in the United States from salt water (today salt and desalinated water make up only a small portion of the value of products recovered from sea water in the United States).

**b. Salt** The technique of obtaining common salt by means of solar evaporation is an ancient process dating back to 2200 B.C. when it was first recorded in Chinese writings.[22] It was discovered

[21] Information supplied by W. F. McIlhenny.
[22] Shigley, C. M., *op. cit.*, p. 3.

Figure 51

## WORLD PRODUCTION OF CHEMICALS THAT CAN BE OBTAINED FROM SEA WATER[1]

| Production \ Chemical | World Annual (million tons) Total | World Annual (million tons) From Sea Water | Per cent from Sea Water | Value from Sea Water Sources ($ million) |
|---|---|---|---|---|
| Salt . . . . . . | 118.6 | 34.6[2] | 29 | 173 |
| Magnesium Metal . . | 0.17 | 0.11[3] | 65 | 75 |
| Desalinated Water . | 241.0 | 142.0 | 59 | 51 |
| Bromine . . . . | 0.15 | 0.10[4] | 67 | 45 |
| Magnesium Compounds | 11.4[2] | 0.69[2,3,4] | 6 | 41 |
| Total . . . . | | | | 385 |

[1] Estimated values for each commodity based on values reported in *1965 Minerals Yearbook*.
[2] Estimated, figures not available.
[3] Includes magnesium from dolomitic lime.
[4] Includes sea salt-bittern.

Figure 52

## U.S. PRODUCTION OF CHEMICALS THAT CAN BE OBTAINED FROM SEA WATER[1]

| Production / Chemical | U.S. Annual (million tons) | | Per cent from Sea Water | Sea Water | |
|---|---|---|---|---|---|
| | Total | From Sea Water | | Annual Value from Sea Water Sources ($ million) | Per cent U.S. Value of Total World Value |
| Salt . . . . . . | 35.0 | 1.4[2] | 4 | 8 | 5 |
| Magnesium Metal . . | 0.09 | 0.081[3] | 90 | 57 | 76 |
| Desalinated Water . | 60.6 | 22.9 | 38 | 8 | 16 |
| Bromine . . . . | 0.14 | 0.068[5] | 50 | 30 | 67 |
| Magnesium Compounds[4] . . | 1.37 | 0.47[5] | 34 | 32 | 78 |
| Total | | | | 135 | 35 |

[1] Mostly 1966 figures.
[2] Includes solar sea salt and other solar salt.
[3] The only U.S. sea water magnesium facility is at Dow in Freeport (1965 figures).
[4] Includes magnesium chloride which, in turn, is used for magnesium metal.
[5] Includes sea salt-bittern.

quite early that salt helped prevent decay in many foods. Present chemical usage for sodium compounds is so extensive that salt is one of the primary raw materials upon which the chemical industry rests. About two-thirds of the salt consumed in the United States is by the chemical industry. Salt is produced from the ocean in commercial quantities in about 60 countries. More than 29 per cent of total world production is from sea water. In the United States, the production from sea water is centered in California and accounts for only about four per cent of the U.S. grand total.

c. **Magnesium Metal** Magnesium is the third most abundant element found in sea water. Over 90 per cent of magnesium metal produced in the United States is obtained from sea water. It is estimated that a cubic mile of sea water contains roughly six million tons of magnesium. However, this is equivalent to about only one-sixth ounce per gallon, worth about 0.4 cent.[23] The first U.S. magnesium metal from sea water was produced in

1941, extracted from the Gulf of Mexico by the Dow Chemical Company. The process was adapted and improved from a Dow Chemical metallic magnesium extraction plant near Midland, Michigan, using brine from inland wells. Some 65 per cent of the world's production comes from the only two magnesium metal plants that process sea water. These are the Texas Division of Dow Chemical at Freeport, Texas, and the facilities of Norsk Hydro-Elektrisk in Norway.

In order to furnish the needs of Dow plants and the adjacent bromine plant of the Ethyl-Dow Chemical Company, almost two million gallons per minute of sea water are pumped, *an amount equal to that pumped by all other process users of sea water in the world combined.* Since this figure includes water required for cooling, it may be said that the Dow plants pump approximately one cubic mile of sea water per year, equivalent to almost three billion gallons per day. This is approximately equal to what would have been pumped by the Bolsa Island dual purpose power and 150 mgd desalination facility had it been approved and constructed.

Demand for magnesium is high during wartime, as it is used extensively in airplane construction and also is employed in incendiary bombs. Magnesium is outstanding in its use as a sacrificial anode

[23] Spangler, M.B., "A Case Study Report on the Extraction of Magnesium from Sea Water," National Planning Association Report to the National Council on Marine Resources and Engineering Development, Sept. 11, 1967.

to protect metal surfaces against sea water corrosion, and as a widely used constituent of aluminum alloys.

The factors involved in extracting magnesium from sea water are somewhat different from those of bromine.[24] From an oceanographic or climatic standpoint, location is not as critical. For example, water temperature has little effect on the magnesium recovery process. More important is a location favorable to the supply of raw materials and power. The proximity of abundant natural gas, the fuel for Dow's electrical power generation, is paramount. The process also requires a cheap source of lime. For this, Dow purchases oyster shells dredged inexpensively from nearby Galveston Bay (Figure 53). Another raw material, sulfur, also is produced in south Texas and needs to be shipped only a short distance.

**Figure 53.** *Oyster shells from Galveston Bay serve as a cheap source of lime, required in the magnesium extraction process. (Dow Chemical photo)*

One aspect of extracting magnesium from sea water, *vis-a-vis* extraction from inland brines, is of special interest. The lower concentration of magnesium in sea water requires more water to be pumped. However, since the Freeport plant is only nine feet above sea level, the water does not need to be pumped as high a vertical distance as Dow's inland wells which are about 5,000 feet deep.

That lower sea water concentrations represent no handicap was demonstrated by comparative costs published after World War II. The Velasco, Texas, plant built for the Federal Government bettered by nearly 30 per cent the lowest cost of other Government plants using more concentrated magnesium sources from inland brines.

**d. Magnesium Compounds** Magnesia (magnesium oxide) is the principal product of the magnesium compounds industry. It is widely used as a basic refractory for metallurgical furnaces. A moderate percentage of these compounds is still mined from old geological basins in Ohio, Texas, and Michigan, with wells being drilled as deep as 5,000 to 6,000 feet.

There are at present eight plants in the United States producing magnesium oxide and depending on the ocean as a source of raw material. One plant produces these compounds from sea-salt bitterns, although such operations are expected to stop soon.[25]

As Figure 52 shows, the United States produces 78 per cent of the world-wide output of those magnesium compounds extracted from the sea water.

**e. Bromine** Of all the minerals extracted commercially from sea water, bromine is the least concentrated, about 65 parts per million.

All facilities directly processing sea water use a modification of the blowing-out process developed originally for use on underground brines.[26] In 1931 the process was modified to use sea water as a raw material. The Ethyl-Dow facilities at Freeport, Texas, have been operating since 1940. Large sea water plants are also in operation in France, Sicily, and England.

There are a few inland brines, as in Arkansas, having very high concentrations of bromine approaching 5,000 ppm. Bromine also has concentrations approaching 5,000 ppm in the Dead Sea. Inland brines are subject to depletion allowances, but this is not true of sea water sources, as they are considered unlimited reserves.

---

[24] Shigley, C. M., *op. cit.*, p. 7.

[25] McIlhenny, W. F., *op. cit.*, p. 123. A bittern may be defined as a bitter solution remaining in saltmaking after the salt has crystallized out of sea water or brine.

[26] *Ibid.*, p. 124.

Though bromine exists in the ocean with a concentration only one-twentieth that of magnesium, its price per pound is one-third less than magnesium. This apparent anomaly is due to the fact that the bromine extraction process is much less costly in power, labor, and capital equipment.

Favorable oceanographic and climatic conditions are paramount in extracting bromine from sea water.[27] The following requirements are necessary:

—High and constant salinity conveniently available.

—Source free from organic contamination and undiluted by major fresh water rivers.

—Favorable circumstances to dispose of large quantities of processed water without mixing with unprocessed water.

—Location in a warm climate since bromine can be removed at a greater rate from warm sea water.

—Location near economical raw material and power. For example, in Freeport, chlorine, sulfur, heated sea water (cooling water from other Dow production facilities), and natural gas are in relatively good supply.

## B. Present Techniques for Extraction[28]

Techniques for extracting salt and magnesium compounds from sea water were mentioned on previous pages. Almost 30 per cent of world salt production is from sea water, chiefly by solar evaporation in open ponds. While some magnesium compounds also are produced in this way, most are from a process similar to the first steps employed in magnesium metal recovery. Being more complex processes, the extraction of magnesium metal and bromine is described below.

### 1. Magnesium Metal

The only two plants that extract magnesium metal from sea water (in Norway and Freeport, Texas) employ electrolytic processes, although each is different. However, both depend on initial

precipitation of magnesium hydroxide from sea water; oyster shell is used in Texas and dolomitic limestone in Norway.

In the Dow process in Texas, sea water is brought into the plant through a system of flumes and intakes and then is screened and chlorinated for control of biofouling (Figure 54). Either calcined oyster shell or caustic soda from a caustic-chlorine electrolytic cell is used to precipitate magnesium hydroxide. The precipitated

**Figure 54.** *Sea water intake for magnesium extraction. Incoming sea water passes through a screen to prevent fish and debris from entering canal. (Dow Chemical photo)*

**Figure 55.** *Outdoor settling tanks for magnesium extraction. Lime is slaked with water, added to sea water, and pumped to outdoor settling tanks. Soluble magnesium in sea water reacts with lime to form insoluble magnesium hydroxide, which settles to bottom and is removed for further processing. (Dow Chemical photo)*

[27] Shigley, C. M., *op. cit.*, p. 5.

[28] McIlhenny, W. F., *op. cit.*, p. 123.

hydroxide is settled in large ponds, collected, filtered, and washed (Figure 55). The hydroxide is neutralized with byproduct hydrochloric acid and dried in fluo-solid driers to produce a dry, free-flowing hydrous feed for the magnesium cells. Electrolysis is conducted in large, bathtub-shaped, electrolytic cells filled with a fused salt mixture upon which the molten magnesium (liberated during electrolysis) floats (Figure 56). The molten magnesium is transferred in large crucibles for casting metal ingots.

**Figure 57.** *Ethyl-Dow bromine plant at Kure Beach, North Carolina, as it appeared in 1940. (Dow Chemical photo)*

**Figure 56.** *Electrolytic cell for magnesium extraction. Cells operate at about 700°C, using greater than 100,000 amps of direct current. Each cell rests in a brick-lined furnace. Magnesium chloride is fed to cell and electrolyzed to magnesium metal and chlorine. (Dow Chemical photo)*

## 2. Bromine

All facilities directly processing sea water brines use a modification of the blowing-out process developed originally by Dr. Herbert H. Dow for underground brines. In about 1927 when it became apparent that additional production facilities would be required, the process was modified to use sea water as a raw material. A plant was constructed at Kure Beach, North Carolina, in 1933, was expanded several times, and operated until 1946. Figure 57 shows the Kure Beach plant as it appeared in 1940. The present Ethyl-Dow bromine production facilities at Freeport, Texas, have been operating since 1940 and have been enlarged several times.

In the blowing-out process, incoming sea water is screened and acidified to pH 3.5. Chlorine is added to oxidize the bromide to bromine, which is stripped from the sea water by a countercurrent stream of air. The bromine-laden vapor is led into a baffled mixing chamber where sulfur dioxide is added, and the reaction products are absorbed in an aqueous acid solution. The acid solution is rechlorinated and steam-stripped to produce a high quality bromine which can be reacted with ethylene to produce ethylene dibromide.

## C. Future Extraction of Other Chemicals

### 1. Future Possibilities

Figure 58 shows the abundance of several critical elements contained in sea water. Magnesium and bromine also are shown for comparison. Uranium is by far the most valuable element per cubic mile. Bromine, the least concentrated of the commercially produced elements, is over 30,000 times as plentiful as uranium and over 10 million times as plentiful as gold.

Several sequential operations are required to produce a chemical from a raw material like sea water. The desired element must be separated, concentrated, and processed to a marketable quality. Processes have been proposed or developed to recover almost all the dissolved elements. However, when all costs are considered (e.g., handling the large volumes and the amortization and maintenance of the necessary equipment), they cannot be supported by the value of the chemicals recovered.

## Figure 58
### ABUNDANCE OF SOME CRITICAL ELEMENTS IN SEA WATER

| Element | Average Concentration Mg/Liter[1] |
|---|---|
| **Presently produced:** | |
| Magnesium . . . . . . | 1,350 |
| Bromine . . . . . . | 65 |
| **Not Produced:** | |
| Uranium . . . . . . | 0.003 |
| Silver . . . . . . . | 0.00004 |
| Tin . . . . . . . . | 0.0008 |
| Gold , . . . . . . . | 0.000004 |
| Zinc . . . . . . . . | 0.01 |
| Titanium . . . . . . | 0.001 |

[1]Note that 1 part per million equals 1.026 Mg/Liter.
Source: Goldberg, E. D., "Minor Elements in Sea Water," *Chemical Oceanography*, vol. I, J. P. Riley and G. Skirrow (ed.), Academic Press, London, pp. 164-165.

Most dissolved elements found in the ocean are being recovered more economically from other sources. Possibly the next material to be extracted commercially from sea water will be uranium. The English are reported to be experimenting with a uranium process, but prospects for its commercial utilization are not known.[29]

The economics of bromine versus magnesium extraction is a good illustration of why one should not be too pessimistic about the commercial possibilities of extracting less concentrated elements. Sea water contains only 65 ppm (parts per million) bromine versus 1,300 ppm magnesium. Yet bromine sells for about 25 cents per pound versus 35 cents for magnesium. The bromine extraction process is less costly than the magnesium process because it requires only 2 process steps to extract and convert the bromine to a salable form, whereas 10 steps are required for magnesium metal.

This indicates that other elements, even though less concentrated than bromine, may be produced at lower costs per pound than bromine if the technology can be developed along with the required market.

[29]Spangler, M. B., *op. cit.,* p. 9.

## 2. Long-Range Technology

To obtain minute quantities of elements it is necessary to modify the present philosophy of processing 100 per cent of sea water, 96.5 per cent of which is water, to recover only very small amounts of chemicals. It may be preferable to remove desired solids from the sea water at sea and then handle only the useable material.

Present desalting methods concentrate brines by a ratio of about two to one. However, concentrations of up to three to one have been reported feasible, and pretreatment processes such as ion exchange may allow concentration ratios as high as five to one. Future techniques may further increase the ability to concentrate brines. Improved extraction processes using concentrated brines (as may be available from desalting facilities) will permit more economical recovery of various chemicals.

Extraction directly from the sea using natural processes, another potential method of recovery, will require considerable additional basic research into sea water chemistry, biology, and extraction processes. For example, iodine has been extracted commercially from certain seaweed that concentrates the element. Some marine organisms concentrate trace elements in ratios as great as 100,000 to 1, as with vanadium. Lead is concentrated as much as 20 million to 1 in certain fish bones.

Biological concentration suggests future techniques of recovering valuable trace elements by learning which organisms can concentrate the desired elements best, culturing them in sea water, harvesting them, and extracting the elements, or learning the processes and adapting them to industrial practice.

## D. Conclusions

Extraction of magnesium compounds, magnesium metal, bromine, and salt from sea water is highly successful. World-wide, salt is the most important product. Almost 30 per cent of the total world production of salt is from sea water.

U.S. industry has been profitably extracting magnesium and bromine from sea water for over 25 years. About 90 per cent of all magnesium metal and 50 per cent of all bromine production in the United States is derived from sea water.

The concentration of magnesium in sea water is 1,300 parts per million. By contrast bromine is only about 65 ppm, or one-twentieth that of magnesium. Yet the cost per pound of extraction of bromine is one-third less than magnesium despite the lower bromine concentration. These lower total costs for bromine are due to fewer processing steps and to lower power, labor, and capital equipment costs. Bromine is released directly from sea water as an element while magnesium is not. Thus the experience with bromine encourages a belief that, if the technology can be developed, other elements with even lower concentrations may be economically extracted from the sea.

To obtain other elements from sea water, it will be necessary to modify current extraction techniques. For example, brines in desalting processes are reaching increasingly higher concentration ratios. Eventually this may permit economical recovery of additional chemicals.

Attention should be given to the possibility of local concentrations in the ocean environment that may have future economic importance. For example, gold concentrations in sea water have been as high as 60 milligrams per ton, compared to an average sea water gold content of 0.04 mg per ton. More recently, attention has been focused on the *hot spots* at the bottom of the Red Sea, where bodies of stagnant or semi-stagnant waters have been found to contain zinc, copper, and other mineral constituents in concentrations ranging from 1,000 to 50,000 times normal.

Extraction of elements directly from the sea using natural processes is another potential method. Some marine organisms concentrate trace elements in ratios as high as 100,000 to 1, as with vanadium. Lead is concentrated as much as 20 million to 1 in certain fish bones. Biological concentration suggests future techniques of recovering valuable trace elements. One could learn which organisms concentrate the desired elements best, culture them in sea water, harvest them, and extract the elements; or better yet, imitate the biological technique and synthesize it industrially.

Recommendations:

**Further research and development on ion exchange and biological techniques should aim at extracting elements with low concentration.**

**Techniques for concentrating brines from desalting plants will improve the possibility of by-product recovery. Hence the technology to permit commercial utilization of these techniques should be encouraged to allow recovery of chemicals either now or projected to be in short supply. Examples include potassium compounds, uranium, and boron.**

## VI. DESALINATION

Sea water can be used for human consumption if its saline content is reduced from 35,000 parts per million (ppm) to 1,000 ppm or less. However, the U.S. Public Health Service has established standards that good drinking water should not contain more than 500 ppm. The term desalting actually refers to more than just extraction of salt. It also encompasses removal of other impurities, such as those found in brackish inland water and, pollutants from waste water. Salt is one of the most highly soluble pollutants, and any process designed to remove salt from water usually removes other contaminants.

In contrast with extraction of minerals from sea water, desalination has received much attention by the public and the Federal Government, especially through the establishment of the Office of Saline Water (OSW). Desalination is important because an adequate fresh water supply is essential for life—for drinking, cooking, cleansing, diluting, irrigation, industry, fish, wildlife, etc. Despite its recognized importance, the total effort in desalting has been small compared to many other research and development programs.

The Honorable Stewart Udall, Secretary of the Interior, stated that:[30]

*We are directing our efforts to the solution of two separate problems simultaneously. A way must be found to supply the water needs of large metropolitan areas near the coast where conventional water is in short supply. Equally important, we need to develop a process that will improve the quality of brackish and minerally charged waters for inland communities at prices that will make this improvement economically feasible.*

[30] Hearings before the Senate Subcommittee on Irrigation and Reclamation of the Committee on Interior and Insular Affairs, 89th Congress, First Session, on S. 24, May 1965, pp. 5, 9.

The Secretary went on to say:

*The new program that has been devised to advance desalting technology will change the character of the program by placing greater emphasis on engineering problems and the development of hardware for prototype plants ranging up to 50 million gallons per day.*

The increase in water use in the United States has been phenomenal. At the turn of the century, 40 billion gallons per day (gpd) were used. By 1920 use had doubled; it doubled again by 1944 and still again by 1965. The use of water now is estimated at 375 billion gpd. It has been predicted that by the year 2000 our population will double, and within another 35 to 40 years it will double again, but the problems involved in maintaining an adequate supply of water are compounded by the fact that per capita demand is constantly increasing.

Thomas K. Sherwood, Professor of Chemical Engineering at the Massachusetts Institute of Technology, testified in 1965 that:[31]

*The most significant water statistic is the rate of "consumptive" use of water. This refers to water withdrawn from streams, lakes, and aquifers, used once, and then lost by evaporation or in other ways so as not to be available for reuse. The consumptive use of water within the continental United States is not known accurately, but is evidently between 10 and 20 per cent of the total fresh water which might sometime be obtained from natural sources by present technology. Not only are the demands increasing steadily, but water supplies vary enormously with time and place, so to me this is a frightening figure. I am further convinced that desalination is one of the several practical approaches to the problem. Two-thirds of the population lives in the 25 states which border on the oceans, and many of the other 25 states have large supplies of brackish water.*

With respect to the importance of water, Mr. Frank Di Luzio, former Assistant Secretary of Interior, has stated that:[32]

*It is not always practical to attempt to assign a reasonable market value to water. One thing is absolutely clear—there is no water as expensive as no water. . . The cost of water itself becomes less important when considered in the light of the economic impact of water rationing. Many industrial plants require great volumes of water for processing, and water use restrictions can cause production cutbacks which diminish profits and paychecks. But even more important than economic consideration is the relationship of water supply to human needs, especially the detrimental effects on health that can result from water shortages. Inadequate supplies of fresh water serve to compound pollution control problems. Without sufficient water for dilution of the effluents we pour into our rivers and streams, they can become so choked with pollutants as to lose their natural ability to regenerate the water to a usable condition. To alleviate this adverse situation, we suggest that it is now time for saline water conversion plants to be considered as a practical supplemental source of fresh water supply.*

## A. History and Trends

### 1. Past Activities

For many years desalination equipment was of major interest only to the maritime industry. For this use there were two principal criteria: reliability of operation and the space required for the equipment. Cost of conversion was a minor consideration.

In 1952, the Congress, through the Saline Water Act of 1952 and by subsequent legislative amendments, authorized the Secretary of the Interior through the Office of Saline Water to conduct a research and development program for new or improved low-cost desalination processes. Primary objective was to lower the cost of desalted water so that desalination will be a feasible alternate source of fresh water to meet future needs. Generally, the U.S. Government program has been conducted by supporting research and development grants and awarding contracts to individuals, universities, private research organizations, industrial firms, and other government agencies.

Desalting processes were improved as they advanced through laboratory and pilot plant stages to prototype and operation. In 1958, Congress

---

[31] Senate Hearings, May 1965, *op. cit.,* p. 212.

[32] *Ibid.,* p. 144.

authorized $10 million for construction of several demonstration plants. Each plant was to utilize a different promising desalting process. By recent legislation these plants are now designated as test beds for experimental operations.

During 1952 to 1967, public funds totaling approximately $88 million were invested in efforts to develop desalting processes and to lower costs.[33]

## 2. Current Status

The present value of desalinated water from world-wide sea water plants is about $50 million a year, accounting for about 15 per cent of the world's total production of chemicals from sea water. By contrast, the value of desalinated water produced in the United States is about $8 million, representing only six per cent of the total chemicals produced from sea water.

Figure 59 indicates there are over 150 land-based desalination plants throughout the world using sea water. Actually there are more than 600 plants, but as in the United States, most are for powerhouse boiler water production and operate on brackish or slightly saline water.

---

[33] Letter to the panel from W. F. Savage, Assistant Director, Engineering and Development, OSW, Dec. 20, 1967.

Figure 59 shows three separate groups: (1) world total, (2) world total built by the United States, and (3) total located in the United States, including U.S. possessions and military bases.

While there are only 28 sea water feed plants located in the United States, there are almost 100 U.S.-built plants around the world, indicating that U.S. investments are located mostly abroad. In fact, more than 50 per cent of all sea water desalination plants throughout the world were built by the United States. Figure 60 shows the geographical distribution of desalting plants and plant capacities as of Jan. 1, 1968.

Government activities have been focused on the operation of demonstration plants and special processes as the key to economic desalting. Four plants in the continental United States have capacities of at least one million gallons per day (mgd); three are OSW demonstration plants. The largest, with a capacity of 2.6 mgd, became operational in 1967 in Key West, Florida.

Overall, Government has recognized the following examples of how desalting facilities can help meet water needs in the United States and the world:

—To supplement an inadequate existing water supply by furnishing water as in the arid zones and supplementing existing sources to meet the de-

## Figure 59
## PRODUCTION CAPABILITY OF DESALINATED WATER, 1966

|  | Number of Plants[1] | Annual Production Value ($Million) | Capacity (Million GPD) |
|---|---|---|---|
| All Feed Water Sources[2] | | | |
| World Total . . . . . . . . | 669[3] | — | 158.6 |
| Built by U.S. . . . . . . . | 376[3] | — | 74.8 |
| Located in U.S.[4] . . . . . . . | 289 | — | 40.9 |
| Sea Water as Feed Source | | | |
| World Total . . . . . . . . | 153 | 51 | 94.1 |
| Built by U.S. . . . . . . . | 87 | 24 | 45.2 |
| Located in U.S.[4] . . . . . . . | 28 | 8 | 15.1 |

[1] All greater than 25,000 GPD.

[2] This includes plants which operate on brackish or slightly saline water.

[3] Approximate capital investment: $200 million, and $115 million respectively.

[4] Includes U.S. Territories and military bases.

Source: Unpublished information compiled by W.F. McIlhenny, based on Appendix E of the 1966 OSW Saline Conversion Report.

mands of rapidly growing major population centers.

—To improve the quality of an existing supply by upgrading water where a supply is adequate but of substandard quality (mixing desalinated water with the natural supply), supplementing water in inland or coastal areas where pumping ground water has resulted in brackish or sea-water intrusion, and serving as one of several tools to convert polluted water into usable water.

Mr. Frank Di Luzio, in this regard, has stated:[34]

*It is anticipated that cost competitiveness with water from conventional sources will not always constitute the first limiting factor to the utilization of saline water resources. Eventually, every major water utility may incorporate a desalting unit in its treatment plant. A water-quality conscious population is likely to insist on higher-than-minimum water-quality standards.*

---

[34]Senate Hearings, May 1965, *op. cit.*, p. 146.

## 3. Future

**a. Near-Term Forecasts**  During the past 7 to 10 years, the growth rate of commercial facilities has been approximately 30 per cent per year. At this rate it is estimated that the total commercial capability should be about one billion gallons per day by 1978. With this capacity, the sale of desalinated water would exceed $250 million per year (based on 75 cents per thousand gallons), approximately five times the 1966 value. Total investment in 1978 should approximate $1 billion (estimated at the rate of $1 per gallon per day). Figure 61 shows construction starts of desalting plants world-wide during 1967 by number and capacity.

**b. Role of Distillation Plants**  Future giant facilities obviously could alter greatly the figures given above. Although firm plans are difficult to pin down, a list of giant facilities being contemplated is shown in Figure 62. As presently foreseen they will be based on the distillation principle.

To help delineate the role of future facilities OSW has been conducting studies on the potential usefulness and feasibility of desalting as a way of drought-proofing northern New Jersey and New

### Figure 60
### WORLDWIDE GEOGRAPHICAL DISTRIBUTION OF DESALTING PLANTS AND PLANT CAPACITY, IN OPERATION OR UNDER CONSTRUCTION AS OF JAN. 1, 1968 - 25,000 GPD CAPACITY OR GREATER

| Continent or Country | Number of Plants | Total Plant Capacity (MGD) |
|---|---|---|
| 1. United States | 288 | 39.6 |
| 2. U.S. Territories | 15 | 7.5 |
| 3. North America except U.S. and its Territories | 11 | 8.4 |
| 4. Caribbean | 24 | 16.9 |
| 5. South America | 20 | 3.7 |
| 6. Europe (Continental) | 77 | 26.3 |
| 7. England and Ireland | 62 | 14.1 |
| 8. Australia | 7 | 1.9 |
| 9. Asia | 18 | 2.1 |
| 10. Middle East | 63 | 50.1 |
| 11. Africa | 35 | 10.8 |
| 12. Union of Soviet Socialist Republics | 7 | 40.9 |
| Grand Total | 627 | 222.3 |

Source: Information supplied by OSW.

York City involving 100 to 300 mgd facilities. The metropolitan areas of eastern Pennsylvania, New Jersey, and New York City experience cyclic drought during which the water supply is inadequate to meet demands. The study indicates that appropriately placed desalting plants in this size range, integrated with the existing water system, could provide the additional supply needed.

One of the most ambitious studies is that being conducted jointly with Mexico under the auspices of the International Atomic Energy Agency. Water requirements of portions of the states of Baja California and Sonora in Mexico and of California and Arizona, with needs for electrical power, are being projected through 1995. At present, parts of this area are irrigated with water from the Colorado River and from underground aquifers. It is anticipated that the prospective dual-purpose, nuclear-powered electric generation and one billion gallons per day desalting plant will satisfy the power needs as well as providing irrigation water to irrigate the vast arid region and to support growing municipal and industrial needs. Additional comments on the possibilities of desalination for irrigation are made in Subsection C, Projection of Water Costs.

**c. Role of Membrane Processes**  It is predicted that within the next 10 years numerous inland communities in the United States may have to shift to some new, more effective form of water purification for their progressively more brackish water supplies. Estimates indicate that over 3.5 million people in 1,150 U.S. inland communities have water supplies exceeding 1,000 ppm total dissolved salts; over 6,000 communities with a population of more than 40 million have waters that do not meet the 500 ppm Public Health Service recommended water standard.[35]

Dr. Donald F. Hornig, Director of the Office of Science and Technology, in testimony before the Senate pointed out:[36]

*One of the complicating features of research on desalting brackish and waste waters is the wide diversity in the chemical composition of these waters. A process which is highly successful in one application may encounter serious difficulties in others. That is not an insurmountable obstacle,*

---

[35] *Water Desalination Report,* Vol. IV, No. 24, June 13, 1968, p. 2.

[36] Senate Hearings, May 1965, *op. cit.,* p. 31.

**Figure 61**
**DESALTING CONSTRUCTION STARTS IN 1967**

| Continent or Country | Number of Plants | Plant Capacity (MGD) |
|---|---|---|
| United States and Its Territories . . . | 13 | 10.63 |
| Canada . . . . . . . . . . . | 1 | 0.20 |
| Mexico . . . . . . . . . . . | 1 | 7.50 |
| Bermuda . . . . . . . . . . | 1 | 0.10 |
| St. Martin/French . . . . . . . | 1 | 0.13 |
| Honduras . . . . . . . . . . | 1 | 0.17 |
| Gibraltar . . . . . . . . . . | 1 | 0.23 |
| Europe (Continental) . . . . . . | 7 | 14.10 |
| England and Ireland . . . . . . . | 3 | 1.24 |
| Australia . . . . . . . . . . | 1 | .22 |
| Middle East . . . . . . . . . | 10 | 15.72 |
| Ascension Island/British . . . . . | 1 | .03 |
| Canary Islands/Spanish . . . . . . | 1 | 5.28 |
| Asia . . . . . . . . . . . . | 3 | 2.83 |
| Grand Total . . . . . . . | 45 | 58.38 |

Source: Information supplied by OSW.

**Figure 62**
## CONTEMPLATED NEW PLANT CONSTRUCTION FOR DESALTING
### (Greater than 10 MGD)

| Location | Size (MGD) | Owner | Operation |
|---|---|---|---|
| Gulf of California . . | 1,000.0 | U.S.-Mexico | — |
| Israel-Jordan . . . . | 1,000.0 | Israel (public-private corp.) | — |
| Bolsa Island . . . . | 150.0 | Metropolitan Water District of Southern California | (Cancelled) |
| Almeria . . . . . . | 130.0 | Spain | 1970 |
| Donbass Region . . . | 130.0 | U.S.S.R. | — |
| Sidi Kreir . . . . . | 100.0 | U.A.R. | 1970-1972 |
| Athens . . . . . . | 50.0 | Pueblo Power Corp. | — |
| Escombreras . . . . | 26.0 | Spain | 1970 |
| Kuwait . . . . . . | 12.0 | Kuwait | 1970 |
| Kuwait . . . . . . | 10.8 | Kuwait | 1970 |

Source: *Water Desalination Report,* Vol. IV, No. 1, Jan. 4, 1968, p. 3.

but simply another variation that must be coped with.

The membrane processes may also prove useful in processing waste water from industries and municipalities for reuse. Some 60 billion gallons of such waste waters are produced daily. They contain from a few hundred to perhaps 2,000 parts per million of salts. These waters because they are already at centers of use, may be reclaimed at costs competitive with the cost of providing "new" water in many instances.

In the long run, it seems likely that membrane processes can be developed to the point where they will become the most efficient means of desalting sea water. This possibility is certainly not practicable now, but the membrane research which is currently aimed at small-scale plants is likely to provide the technological base for future generations of large-scale plants.

**d. Potential of By-Product Recovery** A question arises as to the potential value of solids removed as byproducts from the concentrated brine in the desalting process. Dr. Jack Hunter, Director of OSW, has answered this point in the following way:[37]

When we concentrate ocean water, for example, about twice its natural level of salt concentration we still do not have a brine that has great value as a source of by-product recovery. If our technology continues to improve, that is, our ability to prevent scale formation, our ability to minimize corrosion, and we are able to go to higher concentration ratios, we will come to a point where by-products can be effectively recovered.

I think it must be kept in mind, however, that if we depend upon by-product recovery as a means of making desalting plants economically valuable, we are chasing an ever diminishing circle, because with the chemicals from the brine we could saturate a good portion of the earth with chemicals, and obviously they would become less valuable as supply overtakes demand.

It does have potential, but it is not a solution.

[I]n the west coast test center near San Diego we have made an arrangement with a sea water salt company to take our brine effluent, which is concentrated by a factor of two, and somewhat warmer than ocean temperature. In that operation we will determine whether there is economic benefit to the production of sea salts.

We have also conducted some examination, and industry has on its own conducted additional investigation of the economics of extraction of by-product chemicals.

---

[37] Hearings before the Senate Subcommittee on Water and Power Resources of the Committee on Interior and Insular Affairs, 90th Congress, First Session, on S. 1101, March 1967, p. 22.

In general, where we now have concentration ratios of two, studies indicate that we begin to have economic potential if we reach concentration ratios of about 5 to 7. The principal chemicals in which we are interested are phosphates, chlorine, bromine, sodium, and magnesium.

As a result of continued research in this area, it has been demonstrated that it is feasible to raise concentration ratios to around four to five.

**e. Long-Range Estimates**  Long-range estimates indicate that by the year 2000 world desalting production should be about 30 billion gpd compared to about 0.10 billion gpd today.[38] This long-range forecast is significant in stating the unquestioned need for at least this much additional fresh water above and beyond the natural supply. The 30 billion gpd capacity, while seemingly large, is about eight per cent of U.S. domestic consumption today and presumably less than one per cent of present world consumption. It is within our technical and financial abilities to build and put into operation 30 billion gpd capacity by the year 2000. An overriding need for water suggests that the long-range forecast is perhaps conservative.

**B. Techniques of Desalination**

**1. Classification**

Figure 63 shows a listing of various major techniques of desalination. The processes can be divided into four broad categories: distillation, crystallization, membranes, and advanced processes in initial development.

**2. Distillation**

**a. Multiple-Stage Flash**  Almost all large desalination units now in operation or under construction use multiple-stage flash distillation. Incoming sea water and recirculated brine are preheated by the condensation of product water in a series of stages at consecutively higher temperatures. The heated sea water is elevated to the maximum operating temperature by condensing steam from an external source. The hot sea water is allowed to flash to

[38] *Water Desalination Report*, Vol. IV, No. 1, Jan. 4, 1968, p. 4.

## Figure 63
## CLASSIFICATION OF DESALTING TECHNIQUES

| Type | Examples |
|---|---|
| Distillation | |
| *Submerged Tube* | Ships, Offshore Platforms |
| *Film* | |
| Climbing Film | Submarines |
| Multiple Effect Falling Film Example: Long Tube Vertical Evaporation (LTV) | OSW Test Bed Freeport, Texas, 1961 1 mgd |
| *Flash* Single Effect Multiple Stage Flash (SEMS) | OSW Test Bed San Diego, California, 1962 1 mgd (36 stages) Later transferred to Guantanamo Bay |
| *Combination* of film and flash Example: Multiple Effect-Multi-Stage Flash (MEMS) | OSW Test Bed (Clair Engle), San Diego, California, 1967, 1 mgd |
| *Vapor Compression* | OSW Test Bed Roswell, New Mexico, 1963, 1 mgd |
| Crystallization | |
| *Direct or Vacuum Freezing* | Eilath, Israel, 1963 240,000 gpd; OSW Pilot Plant, North Carolina, 120,000 gpd |
| *Secondary Refrigerant Freezing* | OSW Pilot Plant, North Carolina, 15,000 gpd |
| *Hydrate* | OSW Pilot Plant North Carolina |
| Membranes | |
| *Reverse Osmosis* | OSW Pilot Plants: Colorado, New Mexico, 50,000 gpd |

(Continued on following page)

| Electrodialysis | OSW Test Bed Webster, South Dakota, 1962 250,000 gpd |
|---|---|
| Advanced Processes as Ion Exchange | OSW Mobile Pilot Plants |

vapor in a successive series of flash chambers, each at a lower temperature and pressure. The flashed vapor is condensed by the circulating sea water and is collected. A final condenser, using additional cooling sea water, maintains the final vacuum.[39]

The advantages of this flash method are as follows:[40]

—It has been demonstrated satisfactorily in several moderate-size plants throughout the world.

—The equipment configuration and process flow are relatively simple.

—Scale control by acid injection is within present technology.

An OSW demonstration plant was built in San Diego in 1962 rated at one million gallons per day. It subsequently was transferred to the Guantanamo Bay Naval Base in Cuba in 1964 and was expanded by the Navy to produce 2.1 mgd; it still is operating on a day-to-day basis to provide the total water requirements of the base.

**b. Multiple-Effect, Falling-Film** Multiple-effect, falling-film distillation, sometimes referred to as vertical tube evaporation, has been used successfully to produce fresh water from sea water in the Office of Saline Water Test Facility at Freeport, Texas. Sea water is evaporated from a thin film on the interior periphery of an evaporator in a series of effects. Heat released by the condensation of vapor from a previous effect is used to vaporize the water, and the condensed vapor is collected as the plant product. A large distillation plant now under construction in the Virgin Islands will use multiple-effect, falling-film distillation.

[39]McIlhenny, W. F., "Chemicals from Sea Water," *Proceedings of the Inter-American Conference on Materials Technology,* May 1968, p. 125.

[40]Porter, J. W., "Water Desalination by Distillation," *Ocean Industry,* Vol. 2, No. 8: 39-45, *39,* August 1967.

Although somewhat costlier, the process has the following important advantages over the multistage flash concept:

—Less pumping power required.

—Less inherent temperature losses.

—Fewer stages or effects required.

—The hottest brine is generally more dilute, an advantage in scale control.

—A smaller volume of sea water handled.

It is anticipated that this technique will be used with increasing frequency in the future.

**c. Multiple-Effect, Multiple-Stage** Both multiple-stage flash and multiple-effect processes have certain advantages; some designers now are considering various combinations of the two. One is the multiple-effect, multiple-stage concept. In this design, several stages of a conventional multistage plant are grouped into one effect to provide the heat input for another group of stages or effects. Principal advantages are: (1) It approaches the generally more efficient multiple-effect concept while retaining most of the structurally simple features of the multistage flash design, and (2) the brine concentration at the hot end of the plant normally approximates that of sea water rather than being the double concentrated sea water often used in multistage flash plants.

The Clair Engle OSW Demonstration Facility (Figure 64) completed in 1967 uses this technique.

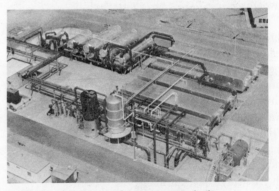

**Figure 64.** *San Diego saline water test facility, Clair Engle Plant. The one-million-gallon-per-day desalting plant tests advanced design multi-effect, multi-stage flash distillation sea water conversion process. (Office of Saline Water photo)*

While in operation only since August 1967, it already has achieved a performance ratio of 20 pounds of product water for every pound of steam input, double the performance ratio of the plant OSW operated in San Diego in 1962-1964.

**d. Vapor Compression** Vapor compression distillation is very competitive in small portable plants. In addition, it has primary application to plant systems where water, rather than a combination of power and water, is produced. It is also of interest for the following reasons: (1) It may be considered when only electrical energy is available, and (2) unlike the multiple-effect and multistage flash distillation processes, no large heat sink is required. This can be an advantage at inland sites.

The largest plant of this type is the OSW Test Bed at Roswell, New Mexico, operating on brackish well water, producing one million gallons per day.

Multiple-stage flash can be combined with vapor compression or vertical tube evaporation to better utilize thermal energy. Such combinations have been termed *hybrid* processes, and work now is under way on analytical investigations of such processes for a wide variety of water delivery rates. One such study considers an application whereby the shaft power from a gas turbine will drive the vapor compressor, and waste heat will be used to preheat the water in a multiple-stage flash system.[41]

### 3. Crystallization

The major crystallization process is freezing, involving separation of pure water solids (ice) from a salt solution. Crystallization also can occur through a process whereby a hydrate-forming material combines with water to form a solid. Of the two processes, vacuum freezing and secondary refrigerant freezing, the former is more advanced. The vacuum freezing test bed, which produces over 100,000 gallons per day of fresh water at the Wrightsville Beach, North Carolina, has been running life tests to determine long-term maintenance and operating problems and system economics. The first pilot plant utilizing the secondary refrig-

erant process also is in operation at Wrightsville Beach.[42]

Freezing has a unique role to play in brackish and polluted water conversion in the salinity range of 9,000 to 20,000 ppm, as well as in plant sizes from one to 10 million gallons per day. Electrodialysis, although suitable for lower salinities, is too expensive in the salinity range of 9,000 to 20,000 ppm. And, because of the typical higher concentration of scale-forming compounds in brackish waters, evaporation or distillation processes require expensive treatment to remove these compounds. Freezing, because of low operating temperatures, largely eliminates scale. In addition, it requires considerably less energy.[43]

In view of these potentials, a mobile vacuum freezing pilot plant now is under construction and will be tested on a number of brackish waters to determine basic system economics.

### 4. Membranes

Membrane processes involve diffusion through a semipermeable membrane. While still in the liquid state, salt solution and water are separated. The major types are electrodialysis and reverse osmosis. The electrodialysis process uses membranes with *electric current* as the driving force. This process has reached commercial acceptance in brackish water applicable up to 500,000 gpd and salinities up to 5,000 ppm. Modifications of this process are being studied to reduce capital costs which could result in substantial reductions in the cost of water.

In the reverse osmosis process, *pressure* is the driving force. Pressure in excess of the osmotic pressure of the saline feed is applied to a special membrane and water passes through.

Both processes appear to be economical for desalting brackish waters. However, efforts also are being directed toward development of membrane processes economical for desalting sea water. Presently, the reverse osmosis process is in the pilot plant stage and is considered advanced technology for ultimate application in converting

[41] Hearings before the Senate Subcommittee on Water and Power Resources of the Committee on Interior and Insular Affairs, 90th Congress, Second Session on S. 2912, February 1968, p. 24.

[42] Text of presentation to the Marine Engineering and Technology Panel by W. F. Savage, OSW, Nov. 16, 1967, p. 2.

[43] Senate Hearings, May 1965, testimony by J. W. Pike, President of Struthers Scientific & International Corporation, pp. 37-38.

polluted water. Three modular designs are being tested at plant sizes ranging from 1,000 to 5,000 gpd. It is believed that this process will have commercial application in sizes suitable for major municipal and industrial use in the next two to three years.

**a. Reverse Osmosis** The unique membranes utilized in the reverse osmosis process resist the passage of most dissolved contaminants. As a result, the process promises to be useful in a variety of applications. The rejection of ordinary salinity, the major sea water contaminant, and of hardness, scale and alkalinity factors predominant in many brackish waters make its use obvious for such purposes. Furthermore, the membranes hold back organic matter, including detergents, a major constituent of waste water. The membrane also rejects bacteria and virus so that the product is sterile. Mine drainage water also may be purified by this process as well as water contaminated by chemical, bacteriological, and radioactive agents.[44]

One major problem in this technique is the development of longer-life membranes.

Virtually all potential advantages of the reverse osmosis process derive from its room temperature operation. No intermediate formation of steam or ice is required which, for the distillation and freezing processes respectively, leads to the expenditure of large quantities of energy. Reverse osmosis, on the other hand, requires only pressurization energy, and the energy cost is relatively low. Furthermore, there is practically no scaling and little corrosion resulting in low maintenance costs; these advantages combine to promise an extremely low total operation cost.[45]

OSW has defined 10 types of brackish water typically found in the United States. It plans to develop data concerning the best process for the particular type of water.

**b. Electrodialysis** Figure 65 is a photograph of the OSW Test Bed at Webster, South Dakota. It is rated at 250,000 gpd and uses the electrodialysis principle. Electrodialysis is currently in use at 125 installations around the world, according to Senate testimony in 1965.[46] It was further stated that:

**Figure 65.** *Electrodialysis test bed at Webster, South Dakota. In operation since 1962, plant converts brackish well water to 250,000 gallons of fresh water daily. (Office of Saline Water photo)*

*Electrodialysis has the great virtue of being a simple process with high operating reliability. It is good for small towns in that the conscientious personnel available in small towns can do the job easily as shown in Buckeye and in Coalinga, Calif. In Buckeye, the operator spends a good bit of his day with other duties, such as repairing cars and trucks. Constant attention to the plant is not needed and no attention is provided during the two night shifts. Since it does not involve complicated, high-pressure equipment, but electricity, the local utility can be called on for help when needed.*

*Furthermore, the only sure, long-range source of water for most communities will be water that is reused. Water once used by a community has its mineral content increased by 300 to 400 parts per million. Normal water treatment plants remove suspended and organic matter, but not the minerals. Mild salinity of this order of magnitude is ideal for economic processing by electrodialysis.*

Although electrodialysis works well in Arizona and South Dakota, it requires a substantial chemical engineering effort to learn how to pretreat these brackish waters so that the process operates efficiently. Thus, if iron manganese is present in

---

[44] Senate Hearings, May 1965, testimony by Dr. B. Keilin, Aerojet-General Corporation, p. 81.

[45] *Ibid.*, p. 81.

[46] Senate Hearings, May 1965, testimony by R. L. Haden, Jr., President of Ionics, Inc., pp. 130-131.

brackish water it would foul up the membrane unless an adequate iron manganese removal filter were inserted.

OSW program for 1969 will test electrodialysis techniques on 10 types of brackish water typical of those found in the U.S. west central area.

## 5. Advanced Processes in Initial Development

The quest for new processes has led to promising findings in the area of electrode demineralizers, environmentally modulated ion absorption beds, new hydrate processes, electrogravitational separation techniques, and the transport depletion and electro-sorption processes. Recent developments indicate that ion exchange may be competitive as a means of desalting brackish water having less than 3,000 ppm.

## C. Projection of Water Costs

Mr. Frank Di Luzio, in testimony before the Senate, stated:[47]

*The factors that influence the cost of water to a customer fall into two main areas: First, factors that occur "within the skin" of the plant itself, engineering optimization of such effects as heat transfer rates, steam temperatures, chemistry of feed water, scaling, corrosion, fuel cost, construction costs, and many other factors. The second set of factors are those outside the characteristics of the desalination plant. These include the cost of money; the amount of water needed for a specific area—that is, size of the plant; availability of a properly sized storage and distribution system; the geographical need for large blocks of power in the case of a dual-purpose plant. Much too often we concentrate on the first set of factors and ignore the second.*

Testimony from Mr. Mark Dusbabek of the Fluor Corporation, Ltd., during the same hearings emphasized several points in estimating costs for the Metropolitan Water District of Southern California (MWD); i.e., the Bolsa Island 150 mgd distillation plant.[48] Cost for heat energy and capital amounted to about 70 per cent of the

total. Only about five per cent was for labor and general administrative expenses. The remainder comprised materials and electric power. Figure 66 shows the proposed Bolsa Island dual nuclear power and desalting plant that was to be located near Los Angeles.

Recently the Bolsa Island plans were terminated by mutual agreement of all participants, because escalating costs over the past three years made it uneconomical. However, the Office of Saline Water has indicated new plans are being prepared for an alternate dual purpose desalting-power plant having a comparable capacity at a more favorable location.

A reduction in water costs is enabled by use of dual purpose plants. During the 1965 hearings Mr. Dusbabek stated:[49]

*When a sea water distillation plant is coupled with a steam powerplant, both plants benefit from the more efficient use of heat. If all of the benefit is ascribed to the waterplant and, depending upon the economic situation, we would expect a reduction in water costs.*

Such reduction in water costs has been estimated more recently to be about 20 to 25 per cent.

Figure 67 is a recent projection of desalting costs made by OSW for a range of plant sizes. It is based on distillation technology. Note that the price per thousand gallons is expected to decrease to 50 cents for plants with capacities up to 10 mgd during the five years 1969 to 1973. Indications also are that during the same period, the larger dual-purpose plants, 50 to 150 mgd capacities, may produce water for 20 to 30 cents per thousand gallons. Such cost reductions would attract municipal and industrial users where water is in short supply or of poor quality.

Beyond 1975 the cost of desalting in large size plants may decrease sufficiently for such water to be used for agricultural irrigation. However, these decreases hinge on technological innovation in large scale desalting developments and on the attainment of such low-cost heat sources as nuclear breeder reactors.

During the 1967 Senate hearings it was pointed out that even at 22 cents per 1,000 gallons of water (slightly more than $80 per acre-foot), this

---

[47] Senate Hearings, May 1965, *op. cit.*, p. 137.

[48] *Ibid.*, p. 123.

[49] *Ibid.*, p. 123.

**Figure 66.** *Proposed Bolsa Island nuclear power and desalting plant near Los Angeles, once scheduled for completion in the 1960's, would have been rated at 150 million gallons per day. (Office of Saline Water photo)*

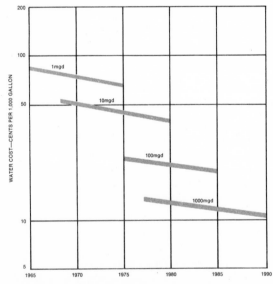

**Figure 67.** *Projection of sea water desalting costs for a range of plant sizes.*

is a long way from being applicable economically for irrigation. However, Mr. Di Luzio pointed out:[50]

*If you mean the cost of the present irrigation water, Senator, the answer of course is, "Yes." If you would expand that statement to include providing additional incremental water for irrigation, or perhaps better quality water for irrigation, then I think we are much closer to economic practicality than people think.*

In a subsequent dialogue at the same hearing between Senator Jordan of Idaho and Dr. Jack Hunter, Director of the Office of Saline Water, Senator Jordan pointed out that even at 16 cents per 1,000 gallons ($50 per acre-foot), possibly achievable with a billion gallon per day plant, this is still not cheap enough for agricultural water. However, conceivably at that cost it might be used once in several years as a supplemental supply of irrigation water to save a citrus crop or a citrus orchard.[51]

Mr. Hunter's reply indicated a subtle point:[52]

*I would also again like to remind you that the high quality water that we are speaking of has a value beyond much of the natural water available in, for example, the Southwest . . . For example, 10-cent desalted water might have equal value with 5-cent natural water.*

---

[50]Senate Hearings, March 1967, *op. cit., p. 11.*

[51]*Ibid.,* p. 23.
[52]*Ibid.,* p. 23.

In certain locations following a drought it might take as much as seven years to replace a seriously damaged crop. This being so, it is cheaper in the long run, even now, to employ desalting plants selectively for this purpose (as is being done with olive trees in Cyprus).

## D. Desalination Problems

### 1. General

In testimony before the Senate Committee on Interior and Insular Affairs, Thomas K. Sherwood, professor of chemical engineering at the Massachusetts Institute of Technology, discussed the research and engineering problems to be solved:[53]

*The desalination program would appear to have two objectives—first, to do better with the processes we have; and second, to discover and develop a new and much better process. The first will be accomplished by engineering—by simpler design concepts, inventions of process modifications, the use of cheaper materials of construction, and the development of more efficient system components. To accomplish these things the engineers will draw on the fruits of the basic research program devoted to materials, corrosion, scale, properties of brines, and on the supply of data basic to the design of the heat and mass transfer equipment which is involved.*

*It is most important to do better with the processes we now have, if only for the reason that we may never find better ones. Even modest cost reductions would justify the expenditure of a great deal of money for research and development. A cost reduction of only 10 cents per 1,000 gallons would mean a saving of $73 million in the 20-year lifetime of a single 100-million-gallon-per-day plant.*

*The second part of the desalination program encompasses the basic research which would lead to a really cheap process. Scientists, engineers, and inventors must be intrigued, stimulated, and supported. New ideas must be tested and promising leads pursued. It is a matter of faith that something enormously important will come of this, but research on similar problems in the petrochemical*

*and chemical industries has shown an excellent payoff record. Research of this kind is a form of gambling, but the odds are excellent.*

### 2. Scientific Problems

Desalination processes are limited by lack of fundamental knowledge. Typical questions to which we have incomplete answers are:[54]

*—Why is the aqueous component so sensitive to heat and to voltage while salt is not?*

*—Why does pressure affect water so much more than salt?*

*—Why is it that some natural membranes can desalinate?*

*—What takes place at and near the surfaces of growing ice crystals?*

Thus, research in desalination must remain as an important aspect of our national program.

### 3. Engineering Problems

Although large desalination facilities have been built (in the one to five mgd range) and much larger ones are being planned (in the 100 mgd range), almost all distillation plants built were based on empirical designs relying mostly on art as a prime factor. Several plants did not meet capacity or economy requirements and in some cases had to be scrapped. Occasionally, a different distillation technique was substituted, without much better results.

A major challenge to the Nation is the requirement to build giant desalination facilities (100 to 200 mgd size) to augment water supplies for large population centers and as a possible forerunner to large agro-industrial complexes which may require 1,000 mgd sizes. To supply such large water capacities may require full-scale model testing of critical parts to improve present reliability levels.

A typical engineering problem in distillation facilities is given to illustrate this point. The problem involves guaranteeing the proper rate of heat transfer for a fixed performance ratio at a

[53] Senate Hearings, May 1965, *op. cit.*, pp. 212-213.

[54] Hearings before the Committee on Interior and Insular Affairs, U.S. Senate, 90th Congress, First Session, on Scientific Programs in the Department of the Interior, May 18, 1967, pp. 80-82.

given top operating temperature. To increase plant capacity from 1 to 10 mgd, the heat transfer surface area must be increased tenfold to maintain the same heat transfer rate (assuming a linear extrapolation).

Going to 50 or 100 mgd would then require still further size increases. It is clear this would result in undue requirements for plant size and corresponding increases in material costs. In other words, how can a plant be scaled up so its new size need not be increased in direct proportion to its new capacity.

Many substantial technical factors other than heat transfer rates must be considered, such as scale control and construction materials. They are discussed in greater detail below.

**a. Materials of Construction** The single most important capital cost item in a multistage flash distillation system is the condenser tubing (as much as 20 to 30 per cent of cost). The condenser tubing's longevity is, of course, very important, and much more must be learned about the materials exposed to hot concentrated brine.

The diversity of opinion regarding tube material is demonstrated by a recent group of conceptual designs requested by the Office of Saline Water. Three contractors specified titanium, three chose aluminum-brass, four selected 90-10 copper-nickel, and two chose 70-30 copper-nickel, while three used some combination of these materials. The 70-30 copper-nickel has had somewhat longer exposure to hot brine in actual operations than the 90-10 combination. However, the latter indicates a higher life expectancy, which could result in lower overall costs. The 150 mgd Bolsa Island facility would have required about 15,000 miles of copper-nickel tubing.

**b. Heat Transfer Rates** Basic heat transfer in a multistage flash plant is from condensing steam through a tube wall to the circulating brine. An increase in the heat transfer coefficients would reduce the tubing area and result in reduced costs.

Resistances to heat flow from condensing steam to circulating brine are found in the brine's film resistance, tube wall resistance, outside or condensing steam film resistance, and in a fouling factor that includes the resistance due to scale or dirt on the tube or to non-condensable gases in the system.

The least understood of the various components in the overall heat transfer coefficient is the fouling factor, a strong function of the system's cleanliness and the degree of deaeration and decarbonation of the feed sea water. A research program is needed to isolate the fouling factor experimentally and to study its dependence on system variables.

**c. Scale Control** Formation of calcium carbonate, magnesium hydroxide, and calcium sulfate scales is a major problem in sea water distillation. Formation of the first two compounds can be prevented by injecting acid into the circulating brine stream and through subsequent deaeration. However, this does not prevent calcium sulfate deposition.

The accepted scale control technique in multistage flash distillation is to inject about 120 ppm of sulfuric acid into the sea water feed followed by deaeration. Calcium sulfate scaling is prevented simply by operating the plant at temperatures and concentrations at which the solubility product of calcium sulfate is not exceeded.

The addition of sulfuric acid normally adds about three to four cents per 1,000 gallons to water. Accordingly, it might be economical to manufacture sulfuric acid at the plant site, particularly in the case of very large plants.

**4. Brine Disposal**

Disposal costs of the brine from desalination processes must be considered; they may be as much as one-third of desalting expense for inland sites. It may be necessary to dispose of the brine in man-made evaporation ponds. Membranes have been developed to curb pond leakage and prevent contaminating aquifers or other underground water sources.

Concerning sea disposal, primary effort will be to determine the ecological and other effects of contaminants resulting from the plants themselves: copper from heat exchanger tubes; iron from water boxes, evaporator shells, and piping; and trace elements from several sources.[55]

**5. Inland Brackish Water Resources**

Although unlimited sea water exists, many areas where additional fresh water supplies are

[55] Senate Hearings, February 1968, *op. cit.,* p. 24.

needed are too far inland for sea water desalination to be feasible. One alternative is inland brackish water—but, at present, knowledge of these resources is very limited. Because the feasibility of inland desalination will depend greatly upon improved information as to availability and characteristics of inland brackish water resources, the need for regional and individual project studies and inventories is immediate.

A start has been made to determine these inventories (OSW with the U.S. Geological Survey), but this program should be accelerated and expanded.

## 6. Computers

The diversity of world-wide economic conditions necessitates consideration of many different costs for steam, power, interest, insurance, and tax rates (the last as they apply for Government or private customers). A tabulation of variables will yield about 80,000 different cases, requiring a computer to establish a suggested optimum design for each case. Such a program for multistage flash and vertical tube evaporator types of distillation is presently under way by OSW.

## E. Government-Industry Roles

The U.S. Government's future role will continue to be one of encouraging increased use of science and technology to lower water costs. Nearing completion in San Diego is a very important facility for the OSW engineering development program, a module of a 50 million gpd multistage flash distillation plant. Several of these modules would make up a full-size plant. This provides an economical method of confirming the essential process and structural designs required for the efficient and economical design, construction, and operation of very large desalting plants. The experimental module will produce about 2.5 million gpd, using pumps, evaporators, and other components sized to 50 million gpd production.[56]

Mr. Di Luzio has stated that OSW intends to increase its activity in brackish water areas and take a hard engineering look at the potential of desalting acid mine waters. This would complement the effort on large plants:[57]

---

[56]*Ibid.*, p. 7-8.

[57]Senate Hearings, May 1965, *op. cit.*, p. 146.

*We propose to maintain a balanced program. This is what we keep repeating over and over again. We are not going to sacrifice reasonable expenditure of funds in these other areas which are also the responsibility of the Office merely to put on a spectacular.*

The desired role of the private sector as seen by OSW was expressed by Mr. Di Luzio during the 1967 Senate hearings:[58]

*The private sector is involved in our cycle of development from the beginning. Most of our pilot plants and most of our programs are proposed by the private sector. In many cases, private firms have designed pilot plants. OSW can carry this technology up through the largest practical units to demonstrate, one, its technological capability to produce water; and two, the economics of the production of water. Industry will take over as soon as we have demonstrated this technology to our satisfaction, and to the satisfaction of the customer—which, if you will consider for a moment will be government bodies of various kinds. These plants are not being bought by private individuals, they are being purchased by villages, towns, states, and federal agencies. We think that putting money into carrying this technology to the absolute proof of the economic feasibility of the process and the design of the hardware is the better way of spending our money, and as soon as we prove that, industry takes it from that point on.*

## F. Conclusions

### 1. Background

The term desalting generally refers to obtaining usable water by removing salt from sea water. Perhaps equally as important, it also encompasses removal of such other impurities as those found in inland brackish water and pollutants from waste water.

The U.S. Government has been in a substantial expansion phase of its desalting program, with increasing emphasis on engineering development through module and prototype plant construction. The program recognizes the needs in the United States and the world community, which include supplementing an inadequate water supply and

---

[58]Senate Hearings, March 1967, *op. cit.*, pp. 9-10.

improving the quality of existing water. These needs stem from the rapid depletion of available natural sources of water, severity varying with specific locality. In addition, the quality of existing water is being degraded in many places. Desalination techniques applied to sewage treatment and brackish water represents a powerful tool for meeting these needs.

## 2. Technology Status and Problems

Desalination processes can be divided into four broad categories: distillation, crystallization, membranes, and advanced processes in initial development. Four operating plants in the continental United States have capacities of at least one million gallons per day; all use the distillation technique. Three are OSW demonstration plants. Indeed, the distillation technique, in a very advanced state of development, is being used widely and will be the basis for all very large plants (50 to 100 mgd) in the near future.

Nevertheless, no single technique is best for all kinds of water. While distillation will produce fresh water from any kind of water, it may not be economical. It should not be used to desalt water with 9,000 parts per million or less. At present, numerous small communities use electrodialysis on available inland brackish water supplies. Yet even electrodialysis cannot process all kinds of brackish water, nor can reverse osmosis, the newer membrane technique being developed. This is because there are certain kinds of contaminants in water as silicates, calcium, and iron which will foul the membranes very quickly.

The freezing process, operating at low temperatures, is not fouled by contaminants in certain kinds of brackish water. For all the processes mentioned for brackish water, pretreating may be an important key, rather than attempting to design a plant to treat all kinds of water.

While the reverse osmosis membrane process is in the pilot stage, the technique is being considered as an advanced technology to be used ultimately in converting of polluted water to fresh.

A major challenge to the Nation is the capability to build giant desalination facilities (100-200 mgd) to augment water supplies for large population centers and as a forerunner to large agro-industrial complexes producing 1,000 mgd. Supplying such large water capacities might require full-scale model testing of critical parts to improve reliability levels. Engineering problems include heat transfer rates, suitable materials (materials presently constitute up to 20-30 per cent of total capital cost), and scale control techniques. As an example, long period operating experience with several types of materials is needed urgently, under varying conditions of temperature, oxygen content, brine concentration, and flow velocity.

## 3. Outlook

Desalination is in an embryonic stage with a very optimistic future. Many ideas are being advanced to bring costs down, some either about to be or already in practice. These include dual plants for simultaneous electricity generation and desalting, the use of waste heat from incinerator plants, the ability to concentrate the brines sufficiently to extract useful chemicals economically, and the use of chemically pretreating brackish water. Finally, low-cost, small desalination plants for islands and hotels appear to be a promising source as soon as improved technology permits costs and reliability to improve.

**Recommendations:**

**The OSW research and development program should continue to be directed toward solution of two problems:**

**—Development of technology to supply large-scale regional water needs, including those of metropolitan areas near the coast, utilizing such tools as dual-purpose power plant-sea water conversion complexes. As a long-range consideration, efforts should be continued on technology requirements to meet agricultural water needs.**

**—Development of processes to make use of brackish water supplies adjacent to inland communities and to purify waste water from industries and municipalities for reuse.**

**Greater emphasis should be placed on solving engineering problems in those processes now technically feasible in order to maximize plant reliability, lengthen plant life, and minimize water costs. Development of hardware for prototype plants ranging up to 50 million gpd and more should be pursued.**

The OSW desalination program should continue to encompass basic research on the newer membrane processes for use with brackish and waste waters.

OSW's prime mission should continue to be advancing desalting technology, not supplying water. The final step in developing new or improved processes should be based on two major approaches, both in cooperation with private industry:

—OSW sponsorship in constructing and operating prototype or demonstration plants.

—OSW participation with water supply agencies in constructing and operating such plants.

Thus State, municipal, and private water supply agencies would have an opportunity to utilize new desalting technology in a first-of-a-kind plant wherein the risk is shared through Government financial support.

To permit reduced water costs, the OSW program should direct engineering efforts on heat transfer rates, steam temperatures, feed water chemistry, scaling, and corrosion. Emphasis also should be given such other factors as the cost of money, amount of water needed for the specific area, geographical need for large blocks of power in the case of a dual-purpose plant, and availability of properly sized storage and distribution systems.

## VII. POWER GENERATION

Major power generating concepts to exploit the ocean's potentials fall in two categories: (1) those which employ the advantages of the sea environment and (2) those which derive power from the various forms of abundant energy found in the sea. The first category includes power plants (conventional and nuclear) installed on the ocean floor, on artificial islands, or possibly on large stable surface or subsurface[59] platforms moored off the coast. This category also would include power plants built on shore with their cooling water intakes and

discharges located seaward to minimize thermal effects. The second category encompasses generation of electric power from the energy of ocean tides, waves, currents, thermal gradients, and geothermal sources.

Energy devices of lesser magnitude carried into the undersea environment to supply power for submersibles, habitats, etc., are discussed in Chapter 5, Subsection IB, Power Sources.

### A. Power Generation in the Ocean Environment

#### 1. Current Situation

a. **Nuclear Power Station Concept** The concept of huge nuclear electric generating stations built on the ocean floor or on artifical islands provides a possible alternative to the use of increasingly rare land sites. In addition, it represents the possibility of the system's effects being utilized to ecological advantage rather than creating a thermal pollution problem in rivers and estuaries.

The role of nuclear power systems in the sea's exploration and exploitation is as certain as man's ability to develop the technology, equipment, plans, and support operations to delve into the environment—and his determination to do so. In fact, nuclear energy already is playing a role of growing importance in oceanic activities in the form of electric power from nuclear land sources supplied to various locations by undersea transmission cables and of propulsion systems for submarines and surface ships.

Although conversion of nuclear energy to electricity is relatively new, the growth and acceptance of nuclear electric power over the past few years is spectacular. While total world electric power consumption is increasing steadily, installation of nuclear sources is growing much faster. In 1960, for example, about one-tenth of one per cent of total electric power was derived from nuclear sources. In 1967, nuclear capacity was one per cent of total electric power. But the real period of explosive growth, based on projections of current orders, will occur between now and 1980. Nuclear capacity will grow to an estimated 12.5 per cent by 1974 and about 30 per cent by 1980. Most recent estimates are 50 to 100 per cent higher than forecast three to four years ago. The effect of this demand for nuclear plant construction is a six to eight year backlog of orders.

---

[59]Where the water is deeper than 200 feet, a neutrally buoyant subsurface platform moored at a 150 to 200 foot depth would be advantageous, being easily accessible, clear of surface traffic, and beyond the effects of waves and winds.

Larger individual plant capacity, increased greatly from earlier years, makes nuclear electric power more economically competitive. Nuclear fuel costs are lower than fossil fuel costs in a growing number of locations. The equipment to generate electricity is very expensive, whether conventional or nuclear. Planners for undersea operations also will have to take such factors as size, distance from shore, and weather conditions into account when considering the costs of their projects.

**b. Studies** Several studies have been made by industry and government to determine the physical and economic feasibility of placing a nuclear reactor with its power generating plant on the U.S. Continental Shelf. One such study made by the University of California, Davis Campus, described, as an example, advantages and disadvantages of such a system in the New York area.

The first consideration was reactor safety. The radiation shield usually found on dry land reactors would be replaced by the water surrounding the pressure vessel. To be safe, a minimum of about 100 feet of water between the top of the vessel and the surface had been set; this put the bottom on which the reactor is placed at about 150 feet. The additional 50 feet of water overburden would act to reduce the spread of radioactive debris in the unlikely event of an accident involving the core.

The oceanographic characteristics of the sea south and southeast of Long Island were very important from a viewpoint of currents as well as climatic conditions.

More important for their potential to damage underwater structures are the large number of storms and hurricanes in this area. However, when a storm has reached as far north as New York, it has usually diminished substantially in intensity. Except for the largest storms, little disturbance is produced at depths greater than 200 feet.

Interference with the maritime and fishing industries was considered. The reactor must not impede existing shipping lanes, and the fishing industry must not be affected by contamination of fish near the reactor. Further, system design plans have provided for a possible nuclear accident or explosion.

**c. Plant Design** Two basic designs were examined, both dependent on the not-so-obvious fact that nuclear reactors do not need air to operate.

The first design places the reactor with the heat exchangers on the ocean floor. The power-producing turbines and generators are above the water surface, resting on a platform with foundations in the sea bottom. A vertical pipe carries the superheated steam from the reactor to the turbines.

The second design calls for both the reactor and electrical system on the sea floor. While the reactor can operate in a liquid environment, the turbines and generators require a gaseous envelope to function properly. Hence, a caisson must be built around the power-producing unit. If the gas pressure inside is the same as the hydrostatic pressure outside, the structure need support only the pressure difference between the top and the bottom of the caisson or pressure vessel, allowing a shell structure of considerable cost saving.

A platform with foundations on the sea floor must be built for the first design, in which the generating station is above the surface. At depths of 150 to 300 feet, it is possible to build this structure using modern offshore oil platform technology.

A compact system of turbines and generators will be arranged on the platform located immediately above the reactor so the platform legs can support the steam-carrying pipes. The turbines and generators are of conventional design, requiring a minimum of maintenance. The steam cycle is closed, the steam of lower temperature and pressure returning to a condenser located on the sea floor. Having concentric pipes, carrying the hot steam upward within the innermost pipe, reduces heat losses to the sea.

In the second design, the turbine-generator system is installed underwater beside the reactor, eliminating the platform. The gaseous environment in a caisson allows personnel to enter regularly to operate the system, to perform maintenance, and to respond to accidents. They can stay indefinitely, inconvenienced only by the prescribed decompression cycle when returning to the surface. Alternatively, the entire plant may be operated by remote control, personnel entering only occasionally for regular maintenance or in case of accident.

**d. Construction**  To build either plant, large sections must be preassembled on shore. Modules weighing up to 1,000 tons would be transplanted on barges, sunk in place, and assembled underwater by methods similar to those developed for vehicular tunnel construction.

**e. Storm Threat**  There are no technological or physical impossibilities in constructing a plant having its generating equipment on the surface. However, the frequency of storms on the Atlantic Coast cannot be ignored, and provision must be made to evacuate and secure the station before large storms. The surface structure and equipment is subject to the full force of the storm. The structure could be made sturdy to withstand a 500-year storm,[60] but this is not economically feasible.

The plant having generating equipment on the ocean floor is protected from storms, as the largest storms would produce only minor disturbances at 150 to 200 foot depths. However, transporting manpower to and from the sea floor station, performing maintenance on the large turbines and generators, and providing personnel quarters and subsistence would increase operating costs.

**f. Transmission**  Extra-high voltage cables in oil-filled pipes could be laid on the ocean floor to a distribution net ashore or to undersea sites. However, the maximum length of cable would be about 20 miles due to power losses; relay stations for longer distances add considerably to the cost and difficulties. Both designs require a site at 200 feet; the mean distance of such sites from the U.S. Atlantic Coast is 50 miles. A 50-mile line with two relays could be a very costly venture—an excessive amount for power transmission.

**g. Embedded and On-Bottom Plants**  On the Atlantic Coast or Gulf Coast distance between the power plant and the shore must be reduced. Five miles from the Atlantic Coast the depth averages about 60 feet. The reactor could be placed at the required depth by embedding in the ocean floor. A hole 100 feet deep in the sea floor would provide a total depth of 160 feet. The sea floor of the U.S. Atlantic Continental Shelf is basically alluvial

---

[60] A 500-year storm is the most severe storm statistically predicted to occur in such a period.

sediments, making excavation relatively inexpensive.

Embedded reactor design was studied recently by the Oak Ridge National Laboratory and the Bechtel Corporation. They proposed an artificial island one-half mile from shore in which a caisson-enclosed reactor is embedded to a depth of 130 feet. Total costs estimated by adding cost of building an artificial island and the enclosing caisson plus the cost of a conventional plant ashore appear unsatisfactory.

A plant built for the ocean bottom is similar except that the compact and efficient high temperature gaseous reactor is placed in an excavation at a depth of 150 to 200 feet. (The excavation could be made by nuclear explosion like those of Atomic Energy Commission Plowshare projects.) No caisson would be required, and water and sea floor sediments would serve as the radiation shield. The turbine-generator system on the sea bottom at 50 to 60 feet would be filled with air at ambient pressure. At this depth, decompression is minimal, simplifying maintenance problems.

**h. Costs**  A rough cost comparison with an onshore site can be formulated, although this is not possible if an onshore site is not available. The first major savings are in land cost and construction of the radiation shield.

Large units (500 to 1,000 tons) of the submerged nuclear power plant would be built on shore, floated to the site, and sunk in place, making the cost of the turbine-generator equipment the same as for an onshore plant. The cost of excavation on the U.S. Atlantic Shelf could be less than building a suitable island to support the plant. The other large item of expense is the structure containing the turbine-generator system.

## 2. Future Needs

With the continued need of nuclear power plants to supply economical power, offshore submerged plants must be given serious consideration. The foregoing example of a submerged nuclear power plant illustrates the feasibility of such a project. Added advantages which improve economic considerations are use of the ocean as a heat sink, improving ecological situations, and avoiding thermal pollution problems ashore. An artist's concept of a submerged nuclear power plant is shown in Figure 68.

**Figure 68.** *Artist's concept of submerged nuclear power plant. (Westinghouse photo)*

### B. Power from Ocean Energy

### 1. Tidal Power

**a. Current Status** The concept of harnessing tides as a commercial source of electrical power has been studied by several countries in close proximity to large tidal channels, specifically in France, Australia, Siberia, Canada, and the United States. One example dramatizing feasibility of such a project is the International Passamaquoddy Tidal Power Project (Figure 69) between Maine and New Brunswick.

*(1.) Passamaquoddy* An eminent American engineer, Dexter P. Cooper, proposed a plant in 1919 to harness the high tides in the Passamaquoddy area. Electric power was to be generated by building dams and sluiceways in the openings into the Bay of Fundy and a powerhouse between Passamaquoddy Bay and Cobscook Bay. The proposal lay dormant until 1956 when the International Passamaquoddy Engineering Board was appointed jointly by Canada and the United States. The board determined that a tidal power project could be built and operated in the Passamaquoddy area and that a two-pool arrangement was best suited for the site and water conditions of Passamaquoddy and Cobscook Bays. (Figure 69.)

In April 1961 the International Joint Commission (IJC) declared that the Passamaquoddy Tidal Power Project was not economically feasible under present conditions. However, the IJC said that the combination of the Passamaquoddy Tidal Power Project with incremental capacity at Rauben Rapids on the Upper St. John appeared feasible. In May 1961, the Secretary of the Interior was requested by the President to review and evaluate the report.

In December 1961, the Passamaquoddy Upper St. John Study Committee of the Department of Interior had a load-and-resources study made in the New Brunswick, Canada-New England areas (Figure 70). Its study clearly indicated that the Passamaquoddy Tidal Power Project would be feasible if developed as a peaking power plant sized for 1,000 megawatts instead of 300 megawatts as studied in the IJC report. This is consistent with current practices in the electric utility industry that tends increasingly to use large thermal conventional nuclear electric generating units to meet the base load and to use conventional and pumped-storage hydroelectric power to meet peak demands. The study concluded that the project was economically feasible (benefit-cost or B/C ratio of 1.27/1.0) and should be initiated.

In order to validate the recommendations, a review of power values used in the Department of the Interior report was made by the Federal Power Commission at the request of the Bureau of the Budget. Due to the then-lower power values published, the benefit-cost (B/C) ratio dropped from 1.27/1 to 0.89/1. As a result, further action on the project was stopped.

*(2.) Other Tidal Developments* The only actual development for tidal electric power under full-scale construction is the LaRance Tidal Project in France, the largest such project in the world. It has an initial power installation of 240 megawatts in 24 turbine sets and could have an ultimate installation of 320 megawatts. It represents the continued effort of French engineers over a 20-year period to harness the tides at San Malo where ideal conditions exist—a narrow estuary with a tidal range of 13½ meters (about 44 feet). The LaRance Tidal Project is operated for peaking capacity or energy. Since the units are reversible, the project is designed to take maximum advantage of the flood and ebb tides to supply power to the French electric system.

## Figure 70
### PEAK ELECTRIC POWER DEMAND ESTIMATES FOR 1960, 1970, and 1980[1]

| | 1960 Peak Demand (MW) | 1970 Peak Demand (MW) | 1980 Peak Demand (MW) | 1980 Re-serves (MW) | 1980 Require-ments (MW) |
|---|---|---|---|---|---|
| **UNITED STATES** | | | | | |
| Maine . . . . . . . . . . . . . | 575 | 920 | 1,390 | 167 | 1,557 |
| New Hampshire, Vermont, Massachusetts, | | | | | |
| Rhode Island, Connecticut . . . . | 5,820 | 9,740 | 15,170 | 1,820 | 16,990 |
| Upper New York State . . . . . . . | 4,900 | 8,800 | 12,900 | 1,548 | 14,448 |
| **CANADA** | | | | | |
| New Brunswick . . . . . . . . . | 227 | 520 | 1,190 | 178 | 1,368 |
| Nova Scotia . . . . . . . . . . | 258 | 610 | 1,460 | 219 | 1,679 |
| **TOTAL** . . . . . . . . . . . . . | 11,780 | 20,590 | 32,110 | 3,932 | 36,042 |

[1] Obtained from the Federal Power Commission and the New Brunswick Electric Power Commission. Peak loads are expected to occur in December.

Source: Department of the Interior, *The International Passamaquoddy Tidal Power Project and Saint John River, United States and Canada, Load and Resources Study,* Report to Passamaquoddy-Saint John River Study Committee (Washington: Department of the Interior, 1961), p. 2.

**b. Future Needs** The U.S. electric power industry needs economical peak capacity to satisfy future demands. In the New England area, the Passamaquoddy project, if economically feasible, could contribute to peak power needs. Re-evaluation of this project should be made, considering recreational values. Techniques developed by the Atomic Energy Commission in Project Plowshare to reduce dam construction costs also should be evaluated.

Recreational aspects of the Passamaquoddy Tidal development—Passamaquoddy Bay and Cobscook Bay, where the Passamaquoddy Tidal Power Project would be located—offer a panorama of water and scenic views complemented by the Fundy Isles of Campobello, Deer Island, and Grand Manan.

The power project itself would be the principal attraction to tourists. Operation of this engineering marvel would feature the rise and fall of the tides, the impounding of water in two natural pools, navigation locks for unrestricted movement of boats, emptying and filling gates, and power transmission.

## 2. Other Ocean Power

**a. Current Status** Several concepts have been suggested to harness natural ocean energy of waves, currents, thermal gradients, and geothermal sites. The best known devices to harness ocean energy on a small scale have been in use for years—bell buoys and whistle buoys, simple mechanisms that convert ocean wave energy to sound energy. A few other small test projects have been conducted, but no significant technical breakthroughs have been accomplished.

Ocean waves, generated mostly by winds, possess tremendous kinetic energy. A four-foot wave striking the coast every 10 seconds expends more than 35,000 horsepower per mile of coastline, but only an extremely small fraction is useable. In an attempt to harness such energy on the Algerian coast, waves are funneled through a V-shaped concrete structure into a reservoir. Water flowing from the reservoir operates a turbine to generate power.

Temperature differences between surface and deeper waters are a potential source of energy.

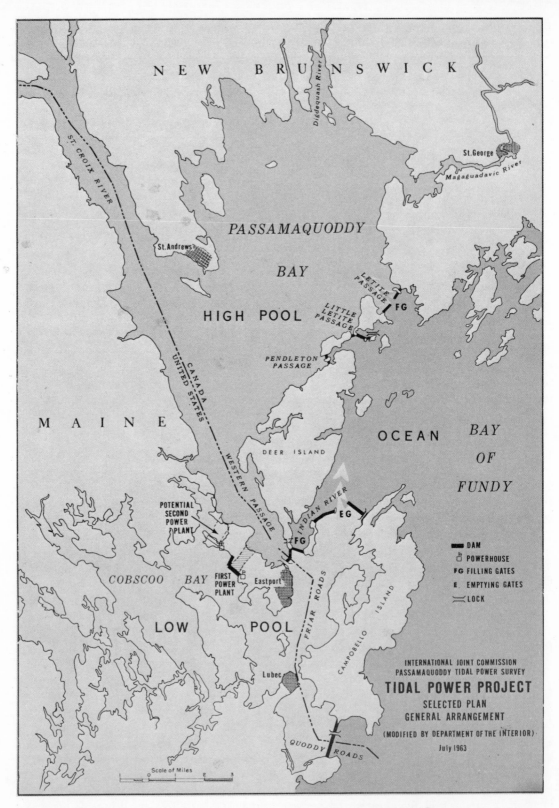

**Figure 69.** *Source: Department of the Interior,* The International Passamaquoddy Tidal Power Project and Upper Saint John River Hydroelectric Power Development, *Report to President, 1963.*

However, practical utilization is not likely to be competitive except where thermal gradients are large and near the consumer. One power plant applying this principle near Abidjan in West Africa has been under development for several years but is not yet in operation.

**b. Future Needs** Power generation from waves, currents, thermal gradients, geothermal sites, and other ocean sources offer potential. Continuing effort should be applied to improve our capability to exploit these potential power sources.

## C. Conclusions

A tidal power plant is technically feasible under special geographical conditions to meet peaking power requirements. The New England Passamaquoddy Bay area offers the most logical U.S. site for such a proposed project.

The role of nuclear power systems in the exploration and exploitation of the sea is as certain as man's ability to develop the technology to utilize the ocean environment—and his determination to do so. It is technically feasible to design and build an underwater nuclear reactor plant. The cost effectiveness of such a system depends on many factors—site, distance from land, depth of water, local use, and consideration of such advantages as thermal effect for ecological benefits and safety to the populace.

Recommendations:

**Proceed with a program to construct and operate as a National Project an Experimental Continental Shelf Submerged Nuclear Power Plant in the ocean.**

**Periodically evaluate the feasibility of a tidal power project, particularly in the New England area. The funding of this project, if proven economically acceptable, should be by private capital. The Federal Government should assist in such areas as navigation, safety, and recreation.**

**Implement a continuing study project to monitor progress and seek technical and economical means to generate large amounts of power from tides, waves, currents, thermal gradients, ocean floor geothermal wells, and other ocean sources.**

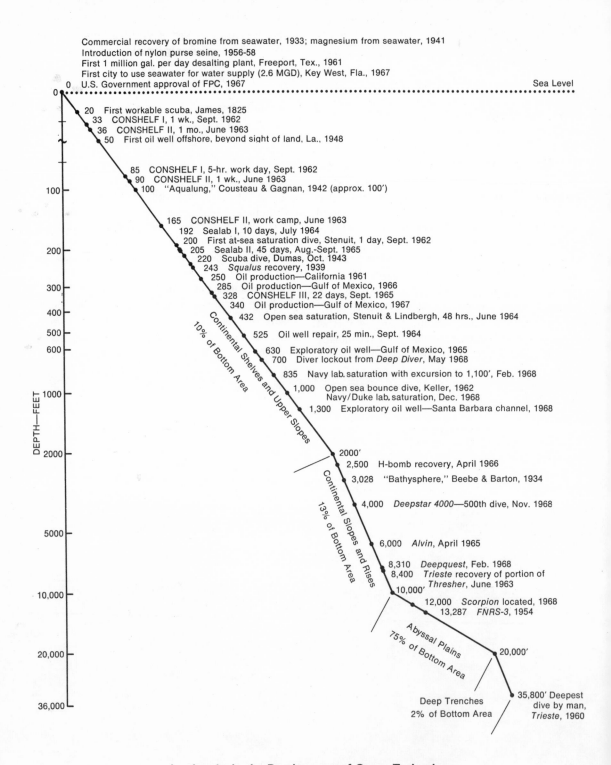

Commercial recovery of bromine from seawater, 1933; magnesium from seawater, 1941
Introduction of nylon purse seine, 1956-58
First 1 million gal. per day desalting plant, Freeport, Tex., 1961
First city to use seawater for water supply (2.6 MGD), Key West, Fla., 1967
U.S. Government approval of FPC, 1967 ........................................................ Sea Level

20   First workable scuba, James, 1825
33   CONSHELF I, 1 wk., Sept. 1962
36   CONSHELF II, 1 mo., June 1963
50   First oil well offshore, beyond sight of land, La., 1948

85   CONSHELF I, 5-hr. work day, Sept. 1962
90   CONSHELF II, 1 wk., June 1963
100   "Aqualung," Cousteau & Gagnan, 1942 (approx. 100')

165   CONSHELF II, work camp, June 1963
192   Sealab I, 10 days, July 1964
200   First at-sea saturation dive, Stenuit, 1 day, Sept. 1962
205   Sealab II, 45 days, Aug.-Sept. 1965
220   Scuba dive, Dumas, Oct. 1943
243   *Squalus* recovery, 1939
250   Oil production—California 1961
285   Oil production—Gulf of Mexico, 1966
328   CONSHELF III, 22 days, Sept. 1965
340   Oil production—Gulf of Mexico, 1967
432   Open sea saturation, Stenuit & Lindbergh, 48 hrs., June 1964

525   Oil well repair, 25 min., Sept. 1964

630   Exploratory oil well—Gulf of Mexico, 1965
700   Diver lockout from *Deep Diver*, May 1968

835   Navy lab. saturation with excursion to 1,100', Feb. 1968

1,000   Open sea bounce dive, Keller, 1962
Navy/Duke lab. saturation, Dec. 1968
1,300   Exploratory oil well—Santa Barbara channel, 1968

Continental Shelves and Upper Slopes
10% of Bottom Area

2000'
2,500   H-bomb recovery, April 1966
3,028   "Bathysphere," Beebe & Barton, 1934

Continental Slopes and Rises
13% of Bottom Area

4,000   *Deepstar 4000*—500th dive, Nov. 1968

6,000   *Alvin*, April 1965

8,310   *Deepquest*, Feb. 1968
8,400   *Trieste* recovery of portion of
          *Thresher*, June 1963
10,000'
12,000   *Scorpion* located, 1968
13,287   *FNRS-3*, 1954

Abyssal Plains
75% of Bottom Area

20,000'

Deep Trenches
2% of Bottom Area

35,800' Deepest
dive by man,
*Trieste*, 1960

DEPTH—FEET

0
100
200
300
500
600
1000
2000
5000
10,000
20,000
36,000

**Landmarks in the Development of Ocean Technology**

A series of National Projects in the 1970's is recommended to help assess and develop the most economical methods for this Nation to advance into the oceans and to provide a springboard for continuing developments in the period 1980 to 2000. The United States can and should be the unquestioned world leader in ocean technology well before the turn of the century.

Extensive new benefits from the oceans will require hard work, and not all will be immediately apparent. Unfortunately, today, most marine operations are restrained by tradition and outmoded technology. A bold, challenging, and carefully planned marine engineering and technology program is essential to the national goal of establishing the capability for exploring, occupying, utilizing and managing the oceans. The series of National Projects will assist materially in developing the capability to reap the ocean's potential benefits and to establish a foundation for future national growth.

## I. RELATIONSHIP OF NATIONAL PROJECTS TO THE DEVELOPMENT CYCLE

It is suggested that the Ten-Year Program of Undersea Development can achieve technological progress more rapidly by integrating fundamental technology development with a series of national facilities, programs, and projects generically called National Projects. National Projects will help advance fundamental technology, broadening the base for better future utilization of the ocean environment. Accomplishment of these projects will give incentive and support to numerous subsystem and component developments. The knowledge, experience, and confidence gained will enable the design, construction, and operation of many operational systems. These will produce manifold expected benefits—economic, social, political, scientific, and military.

The sequence of steps in Figure 1 suggests that numerous interchanges and feedbacks will

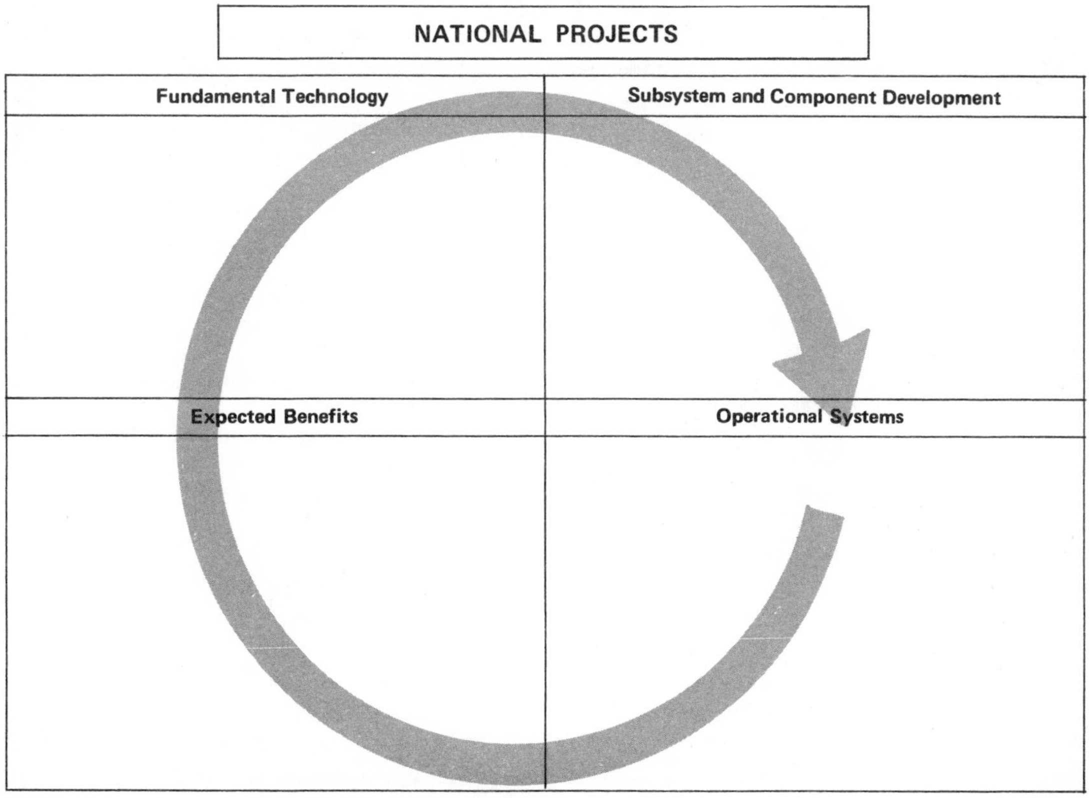

**Figure 1.** *Simplified marine technology development cycle.*

strengthen the entire cycle. Subsystem and component developments will make possible new operational systems. Expected benefits have been a primary concern in selecting these particular National Projects. It is difficult to foresee and define all the expected benefits; some endeavors will yield substantially greater benefits than originally anticipated. History proves that new and unexpected applications will evolve as technology expands.

## A. Fundamental Technology

The encouragement and advancement of fundamental technology is mandatory to provide the knowledge base for expanded and improved ocean operations. Upon this planners and engineers can make decisions on future programs and projects. In many cases this improved fundamental technology will be directly applied to or further developed through the mechanism of National Projects.

## B. National Projects

National Projects is the generic name used to identify projects, facilities, and programs large in scale and best accomplished by a unified and concentrated effort. Proper planning and execution of these projects often will facilitate application of fundamental technology initially to subsystems and components and later to operational systems. Several projects have been selected for consideration which span the field of technology. More details on these projects can be found in the latter part of this chapter.

## C. Subsystem and Component Development

New subsystems, component developments, and pilot developments will be undertaken by government, industry, and the academic community. These tasks may be performed at a facility provided by a National Project or by application of information and experience originating from a project. Results will supply information, experience, skills, and confidence applicable to operational systems. The responsibility and cost of a task will be borne by the interested group or mission agency.

## D. Operational Systems

Operational systems will be built by the interested group and operated to achieve expected benefits. For example, a commercial firm might establish a large scale shrimp raising operation for profit, based on advances in technology resulting from the national fisheries and aquaculture program.

## E. Expected Benefits

Expected benefits from each National Project are highlighted in each project description. These benefits will accrue in many areas, including economic, social, political, scientific, and military.

## II. DESCRIPTION OF NATIONAL PROJECTS

The essence of each suggested National Project is outlined on the following pages, together with a pictorial representation of the more significant elements. The projects are described in some detail but considerable additional studies and trade-offs must be conducted before a given project is considered firm. It is expected that the advisory committee recommended by the panel will review projects prior to initiation to recommend their goals and sponsoring agency. National Projects have the following characteristics:

—Scope sufficient to engender widespread usage and support by many sectors of the economy.

—Established in anticipation of future national needs.

—Challenging for a spectrum of technology and disciplines.

—Conservative enough to assure success.

—Capable of providing education and training.

—Generally in need of major U.S. Government participation.

These National Projects have been developed, reviewed, and evaluated with emphasis on the ultimate expected benefits, avoiding projects that would be mere spectacular performances. The primary orientation of some projects is industrial, while others are directed more toward military, scientific, and regional needs.

Several projects include the need for facilities which the Federal Government will establish and continue to operate in close coordination with industrial and academic communities. Where suitable facilities already exist, the project will utilize them to advance ocean technology and engineering. All National Project facilities will be available to interested parties on a cost-reimbursement basis, affording an economical means to conduct extensive investigations to understand the environment, develop less expensive equipment, or improve procedures for undersea operations.

It is anticipated that industrial groups would initiate projects that essentially are commercial operations, to be assisted by the Federal Government in ways appropriate to the particular project. Expected primary and secondary beneficiaries of various projects are shown in Figure 2.

**Figure 2**
**LIST OF NATIONAL PROJECTS**

| National Projects | Beneficiaries (P-Primary    S-Secondary) | | | |
| | Industry | Federal Government | Regions | Science |
| --- | --- | --- | --- | --- |
| **National Undersea Facilities** | | | | |
| 1. Fixed continental shelf laboratory | S | P | S | S |
| 2. Portable continental shelf laboratories | P | S | S | S |
| 3. Mobile undersea support laboratory | S | P | — | S |
| 4. Seamount station | S | P | — | S |
| 5. Deep ocean stations | — | P | — | S |
| **National Marine Programs** | | | | |
| 6. Pilot buoy network | S | P | S | S |
| 7. Great Lakes restoration program | S | S | P | S |
| 8. Resource assay equipment development program | P | S | — | — |
| 9. Coastal engineering and ecological studies program | S | — | P | S |
| 10. Fisheries and aquaculture program | P | — | S | S |
| **National Marine Projects** | | | | |
| 11. Experimental continental shelf submerged nuclear plant | P | — | S | — |
| 12. Large stable ocean platform | S | S | — | P |
| 13. Long-endurance exploration submersibles with 20,000-foot capability | S | S | — | P |
| 14. Prototype regional pollution collection, treatment, and processing system | P | S | P | — |
| 15. Prototype harbor development project | S | — | P | — |

# 1. FIXED CONTINENTAL SHELF LABORATORY

The U.S. capability to perform useful tasks in the sea is limited by sea keeping capabilities of surface support vehicles. In an area of such high work concentration as an offshore oil field an economic and effective support facility, in the 200- to 2,000-foot depth range would be fixed on the bottom.

The design of the Fixed Continental Shelf Laboratory suggested by the panel should include one atmosphere living and working quarters complemented by specially configured sections which can be pressurized to support divers performing long endurance saturation dives. An exit and entrance lock for easy access to the undersea work area and the pressure complex for comfortable decompression are needed. Logistic support for crews of 15 to 150 men will be supplied from shore, surface umbilicals, or submerged power sources. Additional support can be achieved via support submersibles with a mating capability.

A diver is uniquely suited to perform routine maintenance and repair functions necessary in offshore oil fields and to support mining, fisheries, and undersea test ranges. The laboratory will provide in an economical and timely manner the large amount of underwater operating time needed to evaluate undersea concepts. In addition, much beneficial technology will be gained for the future development of manned undersea military stations.

# 2. PORTABLE CONTINENTAL SHELF LABORATORIES

Exploration and resource development of the total continental shelf dictate the need for several Portable Continental Shelf Laboratories for manned habitation to 2,000-foot depths. Similar in many ways to the fixed station, a portable laboratory allows the utilization of a broad ocean area with a relatively small number of portable habitats. With the ability to deballast and be towed to another location, these laboratories, capable of supporting from 5 to 75 men, will provide comfortable one atmosphere living. Divers will be able to operate from and decompress in the pressurized section.

The three laboratories proposed will be funded initially by the U.S. Government. Government agencies, private industry, and scientific institutions will be able to utilize the facilities on a cost reimbursement basis for scientific tasks or resource development. The flexibility of the portable concept for resource exploration and development provides access to all continental shelves. Military use could include training, logistics, and technology development as well as quick reaction monitoring in areas requiring intense surveillance.

| NATIONAL PROJECTS |
|---|
| 1. Fixed Continental Shelf Laboratory |
| 2. Portable Continental Shelf Laboratories |

| Fundamental Technology | Subsystem and Component Development |
|---|---|
| Survey equipment | Fish survey methods |
| Decompression techniques | Fish attraction methods |
| Helium speech unscrambler | Artificial upwelling |
| Coastal ecology | Foundation techniques |
| Soil mechanics | Geophysical sampling methods |
| Group interactions | Submerged submersible support |
| Diver suits and tools | Pilot underwater fuel storage |
| Toxic materials | Submerged oil well completion methods |
| Navigation and positioning | In-bottom tunneling and lock construction |
| Power sources | Mating of transfer vehicle to habitat |
| Corrosion and fouling prevention | Mid-depth pipeline support |
| Underwater viewing | Local resource surveys |
| Anchoring and mooring devices | Experimental dredging techniques |
| Data handling | Underwater maintenance techniques |
| Environmental considerations | Underwater logistic support |

| Operational Systems | Expected Benefits |
|---|---|

*Economic*

Bottom based fishing system
 — Attraction devices
 — Pumping to surface
 — On-site processing
 — Artificial upwelling

Bottom based oil production system
 — Drilling
 — Completion
 — Crude treatment
 — Storage

Ocean pipeline
 — Fresh water
 — Petroleum
 — Chemicals
 — Slurry

Continental shelf mine
 — Completely in bottom
 — Preliminary processing

Deep water (100-500 feet) dredge


*Economic-Social*

Undersea petroleum tank farm

Off shore bulk terminal

Nuclear station on shelf
 — Electricity
 — Fresh water
 — Safety

*Scientific*

Ocean monitoring station
 — Currents
 — Pollution
 — Nutrients
 — Fish populations

*Military*

Undersea command and control system


---

*Economic*

Fishing
 — Reduced harvesting costs
 — Selective harvest
   — Conservation
   — Market demand
 — Improved quality of catch

Petroleum and Minerals
 — Lower off shore costs
 — Increased reserves

Coastal activities
 — Improved dredging
 — Undersea construction industry
 — Larger bulk carriers
 — Freedom of terminal location
 — Feasible ocean pipelines
 — Generally lower offshore costs for services and activities


*Social*

 — Dredging for channels minimized
 — Greater recreation potential
 — Reduced thermal pollution problem
 — Reduced urban congestion
 — Technology for coastal management

*Political-Economic*

 — Food from the sea programs
 — Protected access for U.S. industry to shelf resources
 — Increased raw material reserves
 — Better international bargaining position on shelf definition

*Scientific*

 — Scientists in the environment regardless of diving qualification
 — Data
    More reliable
    More easily collected

*Military*

 — Improved undersea capability
 — Stronger industrial and manpower base
 — Concealment and hardness

**Figure 3.** *Fixed continental shelf laboratory.*

**Figure 4.** *Diver adjusting tow line on sea plow used to bury undersea cables below ocean floor. Presence of man on the continental shelf is necessary for conduct of many operations. Divers will also be useful in resource recovery operations, which will become increasingly important as terrestrial sources are depleted. (American Telephone & Telegraph photo)*

**Figure 5.** *Portable continental shelf laboratory.*

**Figure 6.** *School of grunt with background of staghorn coral. These fish are edible but are not commercially fished; they may have potential as food supply. A portable laboratory would allow a detailed study of the species. (Photo by Bates W. Littlehales, © National Geographic Society)*

**Figure 7.** *Mobile undersea support laboratory.*

**Figure 8.** *School of migrating tuna. Following and studying fish during migrations are necessary to understand and improve fishery yields. (Bureau of Commercial Fisheries photo)*

# 3. MOBILE UNDERSEA SUPPORT LABORATORY

The hostile interaction of the ocean surface with the air is the major limiting factor to effective ocean support activities. A specially configured nuclear submersible vehicle capable of operating in the 1,000-foot depth range will be of great value in eliminating this difficulty for a wide variety of underseas tasks.

The Mobile Undersea Support Laboratory will possess long endurance and a high degree of mobility and maneuverability necessary for support and work missions. As a submerged support ship, it can carry submersibles to mate with Fixed and Portable Continental Shelf Laboratories, seamount stations, and other deeper ocean habitations for the purposes of effecting routine logistics, crew rotation, and emergency support. A broad suit of operational instrumentation, manipulators, lights, and observation ports, plus a diver lock-out capability will permit observing fish population densities, resource exploration and development, salvage tasks, and insurance investigations.

Much beneficial technology from the construction of this submersible will be applicable to possible future naval and commercial undersea capabilities. It will serve as an ideal test bed for instrumentation and equipment development.

| NATIONAL PROJECT |
| --- |
| 3. Mobile Undersea Support Laboratory |

| Fundamental Technology | Subsystem and Component Development |
| --- | --- |
| Survey equipments<br>Navigation<br>Anchoring and mooring<br>Environmental data acquisition<br><br>plus<br><br>Most of the advanced fundamental technology developments associated with the Fixed and Portable Continental Shelf Laboratories, but with the added data and experience gained from moving from one marine environment to another on a routine basis. | Fish population surveys in selected areas<br>Mineral surveys in selected areas<br>Study of deep scattering layer<br>Upwelling using waste heat from reactor<br>Circulation patterns in selected areas for<br>  — Fish migration<br>  — Pollution dispersal<br>Use of submersibles as part of an integrated fishing system<br>Submerged salvage preparation<br>Selected drilling for oil<br>Broad ocean data collection completely submerged and using submersibles |
| **Expected Benefits** | **Operational Systems** |
| *Scientific*<br>    Whenever the observer is remote from the area under examination, the question arises as to the meaning and validity of the samples and measurements taken. Thus, this mobile undersea laboratory will provide the following advantages:<br><br>*Physical Oceanography*<br>    Raise confidence factor in oceanographic measurements since by use of submersibles associated with the mobile laboratory one can actually view the instruments working.<br><br>*Geological Oceanography*<br>    Can take selective samples and thereby provide a more effective means to obtain needed data.<br><br>*Biological Oceanography*<br>    At present, conventionally acquired biological data is in doubt because of the difficulty of knowing what samples are actually being taken. | Bottom based fishing system<br>Continental shelf mine<br>Bottom based oil field<br>    In general, the possible system developments and benefits will be similar to those listed under the Fixed and Portable Continental Shelf Laboratories, the main difference being that this mobile laboratory will provide information in selected areas which pertain to the resource (oil, gas, ore, fish) of interest. |

## 4. SEAMOUNT STATION

A natural evolution and extension of the Fixed Continental Shelf Laboratory will be a Seamount Station permanently fixed on a submerged seamount at a depth less than 2,000 feet. The station, capable of supporting a crew of from 10 to 50 men for long periods, will receive power from a nearby nuclear reactor.

Because of its size and cost, it is anticipated that the Seamount Station will be funded by the U.S. Government and will be available to other Federal agencies, universities and private industry. Located on a seamount such as the Cobb off the State of Washington, it can serve as a traffic and weather monitoring station. It also will provide an ideal station for taking geophysical data and the operational testing of broad ocean surveillance and data collection systems.

Many tasks and experiments would be programmed for the Seamount Station. One task of considerable interest is the establishment of a secondary station tunneled into the bedrock below to provide additional living space and work area. The tunneled area could provide lock-out facilities for both divers and submerged vehicles. Experience gained in tunneling will provide technology of value to subsea petroleum and mineral production.

| NATIONAL PROJECT |
|:---:|
| 4. Seamount Station |

| Fundamental Technology | Subsystem and Component Development |
|---|---|
| Group interactions<br><br>Long range communications<br><br>Information handling<br><br>Environmental data acquisition<br><br>Soil mechanics<br><br>plus<br><br>Continuance of fundamental technology listed under Fixed and Portable Continental Shelf Laboratories | Open ocean<br><br>— Fish surveys<br>— Attraction techniques<br>— Upwelling<br><br>Diver installed transducers<br>Cable laying and protection<br>Ship and submarine tracking<br>Geophysical activity measurements<br>Data transmission<br>Nuclear plant at depth to support deeper stations<br>Tsunami measurements<br>Submerged tunneling |
| **Expected Benefits** | **Operational Systems** |
| *Legal and Political*<br><br>Improve knowledge and confidence for international negotiations on legal status of seamounts<br><br>*Scientific*<br><br>— Tsunami warning system<br>— Mid ocean tide measurements<br>— In situ laboratory<br><br>*Military*<br><br>— Generally improved undersea capability<br>— Extended sea power<br>— Improved broad ocean surveillance<br>— Broadened ocean support independent of surface | Ocean weather station<br>Ocean surveillance station<br>Command and control station<br>Undersea broad ocean support site |

**Figure 9.** *Seamount station.*

**Figure 10.** *Tsunamis generated by submarine earthquakes or slides may strike with disastrous effect over thousands of miles, severely damaging and tossing boats and even ships hundreds of feet inland. A seamount station could provide valuable input to a tsunami warning system. (ESSA photo)*

**Figure 11.** *Deep ocean station.*

**Figure 12.** *Manganese nodules on ocean floor. Recovery of metal-rich nodules will require deep ocean access for mining operations. Distance between reference marks on line is about one yard. (Bureau of Mines photo)*

## 5. DEEP OCEAN STATIONS

Utilizing the technology and techniques developed for shallower facilities, Deep Ocean Stations will be established on the continental slope, on the midocean ridge, and in the deep ocean up to 20,000 feet. Continental slope and midocean ridge stations will be in depths of about 8,000 feet and will be autonomous facilities supported by their own nuclear power plants. Accommodating crews of from 10 to 50 men at one atmosphere and supported by deep diving submersibles, these stations will be located in unique geographical areas. The deeper 20,000-foot depth station will serve to advance fundamental technology for understanding and utilizing the deep ocean.

These stations should be made available to the scientific community and private industry to pursue scientific or resource development programs. These stations will serve to increase the Nation's fund of basic knowledge while evaluating the economic and military significance of deep ocean systems. As an example, deep ocean stations will be required if we are to develop techniques for deep ocean petroleum production and the mining operations for copper and nickel nodules abundant in certain areas of the deep ocean.

---

### NATIONAL PROJECT

5. Deep Ocean Stations
 —Continental Slope
 —Midocean Ridge
 —Abyssal Depths

---

| Fundamental Technology | Subsystem and Component Development |
|---|---|
| Small group interactions | Open ocean surveys with submersible vehicles operated from station |
| Materials and structures | Work tasks with submersibles |
| Construction techniques | — Transducer placement |
| | — Cable laying and protection |
| Buoys and moorings | — Oceanographic sampling |
| High pressure sealing techniques | Ship and submarine tracking techniques |
| Buoyancy control | Geophysical activity measurements |
| | Logistic support techniques |
| | — Personnel exchange |
| | — Supplies |
| | — External maintenance |
| | Acoustic measurement equipments and effect of different depths |

| Expected Benefits | Operational Systems |
|---|---|
| *Legal and Political* | Ocean surveillance station |
| Improve knowledge and confidence for international negotiations on legal status of continental slope, ocean ridges, and abyssal depths | Deep undersea broad ocean support site |
| | Command and control station |
| *Scientific* | |
| In situ laboratory | |
| *Military* | |
| Deep broad ocean undersea support | |
| Improve understanding of tactical advantage of three-dimensional naval operations | |

## 6. PILOT BUOY NETWORK

An ever increasing demand for oceanographic data and global weather prediction information has accompanied the increased use of the ocean. A network of data-gathering buoys will provide information required to utilize more fully the sea and understand and predict the influences of the oceans on global climate and weather.

The Pilot Buoy Network program is the logical next step in the development of a world-wide system. Included in this program will be development of buoys to support sensors and withstand sea forces, a buoy service ship including a handling system to launch and implant buoys, and a sensor suit requiring minimum maintenance and repair. Techniques and developments in the areas of deep ocean anchoring, improved instrumentation, system reliability, and data transmission will be undertaken.

Meaningful engineering information for maritime, oceanographic, fishing, and resource development industries will be generated. In addition, the engineering developments generated in the pilot program will provide technology which can be applied to other national ocean programs.

The Pilot Buoy Network will be tied into existing data centers maintained by military, space, airline, and maritime groups. This effort will complement other national programs for rapid taking, sorting, evaluating, disseminating, and storing data to assure safer and more economical operations on land as well as at sea.

| NATIONAL PROJECT |
| :---: |
| 6. Pilot Buoy Network |

| Fundamental Technology | Subsystem and Component Development |
| --- | --- |
| Long life power systems<br><br>Corrosion resistant materials<br><br>Anchoring and mooring devices<br><br>Environmental data acquisition<br><br>Information handling | Buoy handling and maintenance<br><br>Various anchoring concepts<br><br>Evaluate candidate<br>— Instruments<br>— Data storage techniques<br>— Data transmission techniques<br>— Materials<br><br>Buoy spacing |
| **Expected Benefits** | **Operational Systems** |
| *Scientific*<br>Acquisition of data that will improve weather prediction<br><br>Acquisition of scientific data to increase greatly knowledge of the oceans and the atmosphere<br><br>*Economic-Military*<br>Provides a valuable world navigation aid<br><br>*Social-Political*<br>Provides a program satisfying the needs of many Federal agencies<br><br>The world buoy system will establish a focal point for international cooperation | — Complete system of coastal buoys<br><br>— World buoy system<br><br>— Special purpose buoy systems for selected areas of interest |

**Figure 13.** *Pilot buoy network.*

**Figure 14.** *Above, hurricane winds battering the Florida shore. Below, storm damage to a shore residence. Improved weather forecasting and storm warning on land or sea require data gathered simultaneously from hundreds of locations on the world's oceans. (Upper photo by Otis Imboden, © National Geographic Society; lower photo by B. Anthony Stewart, © National Geographic Society)*

**Figure 15.** *Great Lakes restoration.*

**Figure 16.** *Down Ohio's Cuyahoga River glide iceberg-like masses of detergent suds carrying large quantities of nutrients to overly enriched, severely polluted Lake Erie. (Photo by Alfred Eisenstaedt, Life Magazine © Time Inc.)*

## 7. GREAT LAKES RESTORATION PROGRAM

Increasing populations, industrialization, and pollution have created within the 20th century a decline in fresh water resources. The fresh water resources of the Great Lakes and major rivers must be protected and controlled. The establishment of the Great Lakes Restoration Program will provide the knowledge and technology necessary to reverse the disastrous trends of declining natural fresh water resources. Pollution can be controlled through new abatement technology coupled with effective legislation. These steps are necessary before a fresh water restoration program can be implemented.

Emphasis will be placed on basic ecological understanding of the Great Lakes. Possible restorative actions might include algae removal, restocking, the introduction of various forms of beneficial plant and animal life, and artificial destratification.

Considerations must be made of the beneficial and detrimental effects of increased population centers and their basic social needs. A complete cost-benefit analysis will be a logical first step. Techniques successful in the Great Lakes will be applicable to other fresh water resources.

| NATIONAL PROJECT |
|---|
| 7. Great Lakes Restoration Program |

| Fundamental Technology | Subsystem and Component Development |
|---|---|
| Pollution measurement<br><br>Light transmission<br><br>Air and oxygen solubility<br><br>Fresh water ecology | Aeration techniques<br><br>Outfall design<br><br>Use of additives<br><br>Large scale mixing techniques<br><br>Introduction of various forms of plant and animal life<br><br>Effect of blocking-off sunlight<br><br>Use of artificial bottom coatings<br><br>Use of thermal heat for upwelling<br><br>Filtering of inlet<br><br>Harvesting algae |

| Expected Benefits | Operational Systems |
|---|---|
| *Economic*<br>Develop a whole new industry of fresh water renovation<br><br>Protect and enhance coastal property values<br><br>*Social*<br>Provide additional fresh water areas clean enough for recreation<br><br>Provide satisfaction that pollution is not a necessary result of civilization and that the trend can be reversed | All out program to clean up the Great Lakes<br><br>Reservoirs and artificial lakes for urban areas<br><br>Control stations to combat unfavorable effects on fresh water lakes<br><br>New industries to accomplish clean-up tasks, e.g.<br>— Aeration of water<br>— Artificial bottoms<br>— Circulation<br>— Surface covers<br>— Algae removal<br>— Destratification |

# 8. RESOURCE ASSAY EQUIPMENT DEVELOPMENT PROGRAM

Before any meaningful national program to utilize the world's oceans can be effectively implemented, precise surveys of the ocean must be conducted. Utilizing every resource which can be brought to bear upon the problem, the United States must begin immediately to survey accurately the continental shelves and deep ocean and measure and sample anomalies of interest.

The Resource Assay Equipment Development Program is a cornerstone for exploration, utilization, management, and development of ocean resources for commercial, scientific, and military programs. It is considered that this program will provide the basic broad scale resource information necessary for industry to plan and evaluate commercial operations realistically.

**NATIONAL PROJECT**

8. Resource Assay Equipment Development Program

| Fundamental Technology | Subsystem and Component Development |
|---|---|
| Survey techniques<br>  — Magnetic<br>  — Acoustic<br>  — Gravimetric<br>  — Towed and untethered<br><br>Testing techniques<br><br>Environmental considerations<br><br>Navigation and positioning<br><br>Underwater viewing<br><br>Data handling<br><br>Soil mechanics | Evaluate a variety of platforms<br>  — Surface ships<br>  — Submarines<br>  — Airplanes<br>  — Towed devices<br>  — Untethered vehicles<br><br>Evaluate sensors for particular applications<br>  — Oil<br>  — Gas<br>  — Metals<br>  — Fish<br>  — Aquifers<br><br>Evaluate sample extraction equipments |
| **Expected Benefits** | **Operational Systems** |
| *Economic*<br><br>Provide data for industry to make decisions concerning exploitation of ocean resources<br><br><br>*Military*<br><br>Provide data to assess status and availability of critical raw materials | U.S. continental shelf resource assay followed by surveys of slope, rise, and deep ocean |

**Figure 17.** *Resource assay equipment development.*

**Figure 18.** *ECHO soundings allow accurate depth measurements from a transitory ship. Great areas of little known ocean bottom and the need to evaluate resource potentials require yet more sophisticated and advanced rapid survey equipment and systems. (Coast and Geodetic Survey photo)*

**Figure 19.** *Coastal engineering and ecological studies.*

**Figure 20.** *Storm waves' damage to valuable beach front. Assateague Island, Maryland, erosion of barrier beach, left, May 25, 1961, right, March 24, 1962. (Coast and Geodetic Survey photos)*

## 9. COASTAL ENGINEERING AND ECOLOGICAL STUDIES PROGRAM

The persistent natural and man-induced coastal process, considered in light of requirements of a growing population for living and recreational areas along the coasts, dictates that coastal zones be well understood and carefully managed. Requirements for increased use of coastal lanes for transportation, mining, fishing, and waste disposal complicate this multiple-use situation.

Systems solutions must be sought. Particularly, the national program to develop valuable waterfront must concern itself with the possible disastrous effects of coastal development on the ecology of marshes, rivers, estuaries, and the near ocean. This area includes the spawning grounds of the majority of the ocean's living resource. Its natural balances are fragile and can be disastrously disarranged by seemingly minute adjustments of marine ecology. Changes in water quality can make waters aesthetically undesirable and unsafe for recreation.

The Coastal Engineering and Ecological Studies Program stands as a major requirement for maximizing the benefits and utilization of coastal areas.

| NATIONAL PROJECT |
| :---: |
| 9. Coastal Engineering and Ecological Studies Program |

| Fundamental Technology | Subsystem and Component Development |
| --- | --- |
| Power sources and machinery | Outfall design |
| Materials | Large scale mixing techniques |
| Tools | Introduction of various forms of plant and animal life |
| Coastal engineering | Effects and use of waste heat |
| Biomedicine | Chemical additives |
| Underwater viewing | Applied coastal engineering |
| Environmental considerations |    — Beach creation<br>   — Beach replacement |
| Data handling | Aeration techniques |
| Coastal ecology | |
| Soil mechanics and sediment transport | |
| Modeling techniques<br>   — Mathematical<br>   — Hydraulic<br>   — Ecological | |

| Expected Benefits | Operational Systems |
| --- | --- |
| *Economic* | |
| Develop an entirely new industry of coastal and estuarine water renovation | All-out program to clean up U.S. estuaries and coastlines |
| Protect and enhance coastal property values | Stations for coastal water quality control |
| *Social* | New industries for water quality renovation |
| Provide additional coastal areas clean enough for recreation | Coastline alteration |
| Provide satisfaction that pollution is not a necessary result of civilization and that the trend can be reversed | |

# 10. FISHERIES AND AQUACULTURE PROGRAM

The phenomenal expansion of world population has challenged the ability to produce and distribute protein vitally needed for nutrition and health. A national program utilizing the combined resources of science and engineering to increase the quantity and quality of marine life is a necessity.

Some knowledge has been gained in increasing marine population growth and shortening the life cycle of marine organisms in controlled experiments. The continuation of this effort requires the compilation of information on species' behavior and the development of scientifically based resource management schemes. In addition, harvesting and processing technology in combination with distribution systems must be developed, with regard to both natural marine populations and controlled aquacultural projects.

Available resources such as waste heat, chemical additives, and natural nutrients can be coupled with predator control, species control and selection, and improved processing and distribution techniques to derive from the ocean increased amounts of protein rich foods.

| NATIONAL PROJECT |
| :---: |
| 10. Fisheries and Aquaculture Program |

| Fundamental Technology | Subsystem and Component Development |
| --- | --- |
| Fence effectiveness<br>— Air screen<br>— Chemical<br>— Nets<br>— Acoustic<br><br>Ecological engineering<br>— Environmental control<br>— Predator control<br>— Metabolic control | Feeding rates<br><br>Harvesting methods<br><br>Food additives<br><br>Use of waste heat<br><br>Small fish protection methods<br><br>Special feeding prior to harvest<br><br>Selective breeding<br><br>Larva control |
| **Expected Benefits** | **Operational Systems** |
| *Economic*<br>The development of an entirely new marine food industry<br><br>More stable and reliable source of selected marine products<br><br>Better quality control | Fish farms for high-value species<br>— Lobster<br>— Clams<br>— Oysters<br>— Salmon<br>— Scallops<br>— Shrimp<br>— Crabs<br>— Selected finfish<br>Fish farms for low-cost protein<br>— Mullet<br>— Milk fish<br>— Mussels<br>Farms for commercially useful algae |

**Figure 21.** *Fisheries and aquaculture.*

**Figure 22.** *The world's growing food problems call for active fisheries and aquaculture programs to help meet nutritional demands of an expanding world population. (Photo by Terence Spencer, Life Magazine © Time Inc.)*

**Figure 23.** *Experimental continental shelf submerged nuclear plant.*

**Figure 24.** *A thickly populated coastal area. The increasing scarcity of large, unpopulated areas suitable for nuclear power stations will require construction of plants in the sea. (Port of New York Authority photo)*

# 11. EXPERIMENTAL CONTINENTAL SHELF SUBMERGED NUCLEAR PLANT

Generation of large quantities of power will be required for the development of the resources of the continental shelves. In addition, expanding population and industry require increasingly large amounts of economical electrical power. The intensive development of coastal regions for living, recreational, and commercial purposes greatly limit the availability of large tracts of land needed for nuclear power generation facilities.

Shallow submerged areas where adequate cooling capacity is available provide ideal near shore locations for the establishment of submerged nuclear facilities. The development of an Experimental Continental Shelf Submerged Nuclear Plant will prove the feasibility and cost effectiveness of placing future large power generating stations in close proximity to major urban areas.

Other benefits expected to be derived from this experimental facility are support for subsea oil and minerals production, aquaculture and continental shelf laboratories. Power generation for deeper ocean tasks will evolve logically from the technology developed in this program.

## NATIONAL PROJECT
### 11. Experimental Continental Shelf Submerged Nuclear Plant

| Fundamental Technology | Subsystem and Component Development |
|---|---|
| Soil mechanics<br><br>Underwater construction methods<br><br>Handling heavy loads at sea<br><br>Materials | Comparison of operation at one atmosphere versus ambient pressure<br><br>Use of waste heat for useful applications:<br>— Upwelling<br>— Warming swimming area<br>— Melting harbor ice<br>— Aquaculture<br><br>Combination of desalting plant with nuclear plant |

| Expected Benefits | Operational Systems |
|---|---|
| *Economic-Social*<br><br>Technical solution to the thermal pollution problem that presently threatens many rivers and estuaries and will with time threaten coastal waters<br><br>Source of power and fresh water close to source of demand<br><br>Availability of waste heat to improve other activities<br>— Aquaculture<br>— Recreation<br>— Harbor ice removal<br><br>Release valuable coastline for more people-oriented uses<br><br>*Economic-Military*<br><br>Less vulnerable system for power generation and fresh water<br><br>Power for future commercial and military undersea operations | Large municipal station (up to 500 megawatts) located at sea providing:<br>— Power<br>— Fresh water<br>— Warm water to assist<br>   Aquaculture<br>   Ice removal<br>   Recreation<br><br>Modest size (2,000 to 10,000 kilowatts) underwater power source to support exploitation of shelf resources<br>— Oil and Gas<br>— Mining<br>— Fishing<br>— Surveillance station |

## 12. LARGE STABLE OCEAN PLATFORM

Scientific investigations and resource exploration in remote ocean areas will benefit greatly from a multipurpose Large Stable Ocean Platform. The utilization of semi-submersible drilling platforms by the petroleum industry has proved that this all-weather concept is technically sound and economically acceptable.

Self-propelled, relatively insensitive to adverse sea conditions, and large enough to support the heavy equipment necessary for deep ocean work, the Large Stable Ocean Platform will provide a highly flexible multipurpose island which can remain on station in the open ocean for long periods of time.

Similar platforms located for resource recovery or military considerations, could also provide at-sea bases for weather monitoring, aircraft traffic monitoring and control, and surface and subsurface vessel replenishment. By virtue of its great size, stability, storage capacity, and long endurance station keeping capability, the Large Stable Ocean Platform will be a mid-ocean facility of great military, commercial, and scientific significance.

| NATIONAL PROJECT |
| --- |
| 12. Large Stable Ocean Platform |

| Fundamental Technology | Subsystem and Component Development |
| --- | --- |
| Fabrication techniques<br><br>Wave motion dynamics<br><br>Mobile breakwaters theory<br><br>Damage stability criteria<br><br>Concrete construction | Deep ocean drilling<br><br>Support a wide range of oceanographic investigations in broad ocean areas<br><br>Resource surveys<br>  — Oil and gas<br>  — Minerals<br>  — Fish<br><br>Large deep water heavy lifts |
| **Expected Benefits** | **Operational Systems** |
| *Social*<br>Move activities away from the coastline<br><br>*Scientific*<br>Provides valuable home base platform for scientific investigations in broad ocean areas<br><br>*Military*<br>Provides knowledge as to the usefulness of a mobile ocean basing system. It would allow support of operations in the far corners of the world without making the commitment necessary when most logistic support is provided from the land<br><br>*Economic*<br>Provides inexpensive topside support for as-yet undefined ocean resource harvesting systems | Off shore airport<br><br>Off shore city<br><br>Mid ocean basing system for the military<br><br>  — Observation<br>  — Surveillance<br>  — Logistic support<br>  — Air field<br><br>Fishing system with top side facility to:<br><br>  — Process catch<br>  — Provide power<br>  — Store product until pick-up by ship<br><br>Mining system with top side facility to:<br><br>  — Process ore<br>  — Provide power<br>  — Store product until picked up by ship |

**Figure 25.** *Large stable ocean platform.*

**Figure 26.** *Turbulent sea surface. Hazardous conditions of working on the ocean surface will necessitate development of large stable ocean platforms. (Photo by Ellsworth Boyd)*

## 13. LONG-ENDURANCE EXPLORATION SUBMERSIBLES WITH 20,000-FOOT CAPABILITY

Effective utilization and management of the deep ocean must be based on thorough knowledge of the environment. The 20,000-foot depth capability provides access to 98 per cent of the total ocean bottom area. Many military, scientific, and industrial programs could benefit from an ability to do useful work for long periods in the deep ocean.

There is no substitute for human involvement in a remote environment. A long endurance capability must be developed to operate effectively at great ocean depths.

Since the commercial value of the deep ocean areas is as yet undefined, the U.S. Government should assume responsibility for the initial development of these submersibles. Technology created in this program will have far reaching benefits not only in submersible technology but also in almost all other areas of undersea exploration and usage.

Based on experience and expertise developed to date, the Long-Endurance Exploration Submersible can be started immediately. The utilization of this submersible will benefit many ocean programs and will be especially important to support subsea laboratories and stations.

| NATIONAL PROJECT | |
|---|---|
| 13. Long-Endurance Exploration Submersibles with 20,000-Foot Capability | |
| **Fundamental Technology** | **Subsystem and Component Development** |
| Power sources and machinery | Deep ocean resource surveys |
| Materials | Acoustic propagation |
| Test facilities | Marine life surveys |
| Navigation and positioning | Equipment and instrument evaluation |
| Vehicle tools | Navigational references |
| Communications | |
| Underwater viewing | |
| Environmental considerations | |
| Buoyancy materials | |
| **Expected Benefits** | **Operational Systems** |
| *Political* Improved knowledge and confidence for international negotiations on legal status of deep ocean basins | Deep ocean station (depth to 20,000 feet) |
| *Scientific* Short term (few days) *in situ* measurements | — Military missions — Long term scientific investigations |
| *Military* Improved understanding of tactical advantages of truly three-dimensional naval operations | — Submarine traffic control |
| *Economic* Improved technology available for a variety of yet-to-be-determined tasks | |

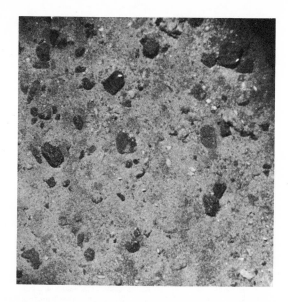

**Figure 27.** *Bottom of Romanche Trench at a depth of approximately 24,000 feet. Note tiny fish or shrimp; four or five can be spotted by their shadows on the bottom. A long-endurance exploration submersible with 20,000-foot capability will help uncover the many mysteries of deep ocean areas. (Photo by Harold E. Edgerton)*

**Figure 28.** *Long-endurance exploration submersible with 20,000-foot capability.*

## 14. PROTOTYPE REGIONAL POLLUTION COLLECTION, TREATMENT, AND PROCESSING SYSTEM

To date, one of the penalties of increased population and industrial centers has been intensified pollution of rivers, estuaries, and bays. At the same time, requirements for fresh water and recreational areas have been increasing. The construction of a Prototype Regional Pollution Collection, Treatment, and Processing System will serve as an important step in a long range program to stem the disastrous effects of pollution while providing additional fresh water and other usable products.

It is well within existing technical capability to design and construct this type of system. Conversion of former waste products into usable products may well serve to offset the costs of the system for municipalities or public utilities.

The disposal of untreated or partially treated pollutants into fresh and salt water areas greatly reduces their utility. As populations increase and available land areas diminish, space requirements for urban pollution treatment systems will become more critical. Immediate implementation of this program is of real importance to the national interest.

| NATIONAL PROJECT | |
|---|---|
| 14. Prototype Regional Pollution Collection, Treatment, and Processing System | |
| **Fundamental Technology** | **Subsystem and Component Development** |
| Basic treatment technology<br><br>Contaminant measurement devices<br><br>Coastal ecology<br><br>Environmental considerations<br><br>Coastal engineering | Development of useful and marketable products<br><br>Rational division between primary industry treatment and that performed by regional system |
| **Expected Benefits** | **Operational Systems** |
| *Social-Economic*<br><br>Opening of many coastal areas closed because of excessive pollution<br><br>A technology that will save presently unpolluted areas from future pollution<br><br>Reuse of materials that are presently discarded. This is of increasing economic importance as raw material reserves become more expensive to extract<br><br>Creation of a new pollution equipment industry<br><br>Improved health and enjoyment for present and future generations | Regional pollution collection, treatment and processing systems |

**Figure 29.** *Prototype regional pollution collection, treatment, and processing system.*

**Figure 30.** *Typical urban water pollution. Growing industry and increasing population burden local waste treatment plants, making it necessary as well as economical to construct regional pollution collection, treatment, and processing systems. (FWPCA photo)*

**Figure 31.** *Prototype harbor development project.*

**Figure 32.** *A crowded, degenerated waterfront area. New supertankers with deep drafts and container ships with requirements for new cargo handling systems will compel construction of new offshore harbor facilities, releasing former waterfront lands for urban development. (Port of New York Authority photo)*

## 15. PROTOTYPE HARBOR DEVELOPMENT PROJECT

Growing international trade requires larger ships and more efficient handling systems. Antiquated port facilities severely limit the application of improved ship designs. New harbors and handling systems must be developed and existing facilities improved. Private industry, stimulated by funds from various levels of government, should take the lead in harbor development programs.

A Prototype Harbor Development Project will serve as a model program upon which to create new and improved techniques for cargo handling and storage, all-weather navigational aids, ship handling concepts, fast and accurate record keeping, and data processing facilities. Additional benefits which will derive from the prototype harbor project will include new underwater construction techniques, increased knowledge of soil mechanics (of particular importance in the areas of anchoring and mooring), and sediment stabilization technology. In addition, consideration will be given to the very important problems relating to labor, urban population, pollution, and the economic impact on business.

| NATIONAL PROJECT |
|---|
| 15. Prototype Harbor Development Project |

| Fundamental Technology | Subsystem and Component Development |
|---|---|
| Soil mechanics<br><br>Underwater construction<br><br>Coastal engineering<br><br>Environmental data acquisition<br><br>Anchoring and mooring devices | Methods of moving various dry cargoes by:<br><br>— Pipeline<br>— Conveyor<br>— Barge<br><br>Underwater attachment methods<br><br>Off shore bulk storage<br><br>Various mobile breakwaters<br><br>Underwater navigation aids |
| **Expected Benefits** | **Operational Systems** |
| *Social-Economic*<br><br>Minimize dredging and associated harmful effects<br><br>Increased freedom of port location<br><br>A technology that allows design of future systems to minimize coastal use conflicts<br><br>Construction and operation of considerably more cost effective ships<br><br>More coastal areas available for other than commercial and industrial uses | Large, deep-draft dry bulk carriers<br><br>Entire new port complexes remote from present cities which have minimum effect on coastline<br><br>Offshore bulk terminals |

Many persons and organizations were contacted by panel members and staff during the preparation of this report. Following are the names of those individuals who contributed through interviews, conferences, submission of written materials, and review of report drafts.[1] Every effort has been made to make this list inclusive and the panel apologizes for any inadvertent omissions. Although the report reflects these contributions, the recommendations are those of this panel, arrived at after study of all materials and comments.

| Name | Organization |
|---|---|
| Abel, Robert B. | NSF—Sea Grant Program |
| Allen, Robert C. | U.S. Navy Mine Defense Laboratory |
| Anderson, Richard | Battelle Memorial Institute |
| Andrews, Dan | Naval Undersea Warfare Center |
| Arata, Winfield | AIAA—Northrop |
| Arnold, H.A. (R) | National Council on Marine Resources and Engineering Development |
| Aron, William (R) | Smithsonian Institution |
| Austin, Carl | Naval Weapons Center |
| Bagnell, Fred (R) | Westinghouse Electric Corp. |
| Bankston, G.C. | Shell Oil Co. |
| Barker, Samuel B. | University of Alabama |
| Bascom, Willard (R) | Ocean Science and Engineering Inc. |
| Bates, Charles | Coast Guard Headquarters |
| Bavier, Robert N. | Yachting Publishing Corp. |
| Beck, Earl | Naval Civil Engineering Laboratory |
| Bennett, J. E. | Lockheed Missiles and Space Co. |
| Beranek, Leo (R) | Bolt, Beranek and Newman |
| Bermas, S. | Columbia Gas Systems Service Corp. |
| Bernstein, Harold (R) | DSSP—Navy Department |
| Beving, Lcdr. D.U. | Naval Material Command |
| Blake, F. Gilman | Chevron Research Company |
| Blanford, Russel . Staff, House Armed Services Committee |
| Boatwright, V.T. | General Dynamics—Electric Boat |
| Boller, Capt. Jack W. USN (R) | Navy Department |
| Bolton, G.H. | Columbia Gas Systems Service Corp. |
| Booda, Larry | Undersea Technology |
| Borop, Capt. J.D.W., USN | U.S. Navy Mine Defense Laboratory |
| Boyd, Walter K. | Battelle Memorial Institute |
| Brauer, Ralph | Wrightsville Marine Bio-Medical Laboratory |
| Breckenridge, R.A. | Naval Civil Engineering Laboratory |
| Breslin, John | AIAA—Davidson Laboratory |
| Britain, K.E. | Tennessee Gas Pipeline Co. |
| Brown, G. Edwin (R) | Atomic Industrial Forum, Inc. |
| Bugg, Sterling | Naval Civil Engineering Laboratory |
| Burk, Creighton (R) | Mobil Oil Co. |
| Burkhardt, William | Naval Civil Engineering Laboratory |
| Bussmann, Charles | Undersea Technology |
| Cain, Stanley | Department of the Interior |
| Caldwell, Joseph | Coastal Engineering Research Center—Corps of Engineers |
| Carpenter, Cdr. M. Scott, USN | DSSP—Navy Department |
| Carsey, J. Benjamin | American Association of Petroleum Geologists |
| Carsola, Alfred | Lockheed California Co. |
| Cestone, Joseph | DSSP—Navy Department |
| Chapman, Wilbert M. (R) | Van Camp Sea Food Co. |
| Clark, Allen F. | Philadelphia Port Corp. |
| Clark, John | Lorain County Regional Planning Commission |
| Clark, Robert | Hayden, Stone |
| Clay, E.J. | Hahn and Clay |
| Clotworthy, John H. | Oceans General, Inc. |
| Cloyd, Marshall P. | Brown and Root, Inc. |
| Coates, L.D. (R) | Lockheed California Co. |

| Name | Organization |
|---|---|
| Coene, G.T. (R) | Westinghouse Electric Corp. |
| Compton, Frank | North American Rockwell Corp. |
| Corell, Roger | The Oceanic Foundation |
| Corley, C.B., Jr. | Humble Oil and Refining Co. |
| Cotter, Edward | Delaware River Port Authority |
| Coyle, Arthur J. | Battelle Memorial Institute |
| Craven, John P. (C) | Navy Department |
| Cristen, Robert E. | U.S. Navy Mine Defense Laboratory |
| Culpepper, William B. | U.S. Navy Mine Defense Laboratory |
| Dalton, George F. | MTS—General Electric Company |
| Damskey, L.R. | Bechtel Corp. |
| Davidson, W.H. | Transcontinental Gas Pipeline Corp. |
| Davis, Berkley (R) | General Electric Company |
| Davis, James | Wilmington (North Carolina) Port Authority |
| Dean, Gordon (R) | Bureau of Mines |
| Dishman, M.K. | Shell Oil Co. |
| Doig, Keith (R) | Shell Oil Co. |
| Donaldson, Lauren | University of Washington |
| Donner, Hugh | Marcona Corp. |
| Duffy, Ben King | National Council on Marine Resources and Engineering Development |
| Dunsmore, Herbert J. | U.S. Steel, Lorain |
| Eckles, Howard (R) | Department of the Interior |
| Ela, D.K. | Westinghouse Electric Corp. |
| Eliason, J. (R) | Battelle Northwest |
| Elliot, Francis E. (R) | General Electric Company |
| Ephraim, Frank G. | Maritime Administration |
| Evans, W. | Naval Undersea Warfare Center |
| Feil, George | Corps of Engineers |
| Feldman, Samuel | DSSP—Navy Department |
| Flack, Newton D. | Cleveland Electric Illumination Company |
| Fortenberry, J.P. | Tennessee Gas Transmission Co. |
| Foster, William C. (R) | Ralston Purina Co. |
| Fries, Robert | Battelle Memorial Institute |
| Frosch, Robert (R) | Navy Department |
| Full, Ray | Kishman Fish Company |
| Fulling, Roger (R) | E.I. du Pont de Nemours and Co. |
| Garrison, M.E. | Office of the Oceanographer |
| Gascoigne, Earl | Cedar Point, Inc. |
| Gaul, Roy D. | Westinghouse Electric Corp. |
| Germeraad, Donald | AIAA—Lockheed Missiles and Space Company |
| Geyer, Leo | AIAA—Grumman Aircraft Engineering Co. |
| Gillenwaters, T.R. | State of California |
| Gilman, Roger H. | Port of New York Authority |
| Glasgow, James S. | Battelle Memorial Institute |
| Glass, Cdr. C.J., USCG | Coast Guard Headquarters |
| Gluntz, Marvin | Society of Naval Architects |

---

[1](C), Consultant, denotes persons who provided broad policy guidance and review; (R), Reviewer, denotes persons who reviewed portions of panel report preliminary drafts.

| Name | Organization |
|---|---|
| Nelson, J. | Naval Undersea Warfare Center |
| Nelson, Thomas W. | Gulf Publishing Co. |
| Niblock, Robert W. | Oceanology Week |
| Nicholson, Capt. William H. USN | DSSP–Navy Department |
| Odom, William T. (R) | U.S. Navy Mine Defense Laboratory |
| Olson, V.A. | Society of Naval Architects |
| Orlofsky, S. (R) | Columbia Gas System Service Corp. |
| Osborne, J. | Department of Transportation |
| Osri, Stanley M. | American Institute of Chemical Engineers |
| Owen, Lynn W., Jr. | U.S. Navy Mine Defense Laboratory |
| Paden, John | Department of the Interior |
| Page, Rye B. | Greater Wilmington Chamber of Commerce |
| Palmstrom, William | National Geographic Society |
| Parker, John M. | American Association of Petroleum Geologists |
| Parkinson, John B. | AIAA–National Aeronautics and Space Administration |
| Paszyc, Alex | Naval Civil Engineering Laboratory |
| Penberthy, Larry | Penberthy Electromelt |
| Peterson, Stanley S. | U.S. Navy Underwater Sound Laboratory |
| Petrie, Benjamin R. | Naval Material Command |
| Podolhy, William | United Aircraft Corporation |
| Pomponio, Albert | Port of New York Authority |
| Porier, Ruber H. | Battelle Memorial Institute |
| Porkolab, Alfred | Lorain County, Ohio |
| Prior, W.W. | Trunkline Gas Co. |
| Pruitt, M.E. | Dow Chemical Co. |
| Pruter, Al (R) | Bureau of Commercial Fisheries |
| Quick, Stanley S. (R) | Westinghouse Electric Corp. |
| Rawls, John | University of South Alabama |
| Ray, C.T. | Boeing Company |
| Raynor, Albert C. | Coastal Engineering Research Center–Corps of Engineers |
| Rechnitzer, Andrew (R) | North American Rockwell |
| Rice, RAdm. J.E., USN | ASNE–Naval Electronics Systems Command |
| Rich, G.E. | Lockheed Missiles and Space Co. |
| Richards, Ralph A. | Alabama Fisheries Association |
| Richter, Cdr. T. USN | Bureau of Medicine and Surgery |
| Rickover, VAdm. H.G. USN | Atomic Energy Commission |
| Robb, J.E. (R) | Bechtel Corporation |
| Robinson, Charles W. | Marcona Corp. |
| Rockwell, Julius | Department of the Interior |
| Rogers, Hon. Paul G. | House of Representatives |
| Romano, Frank | Naval Ship Systems Command |
| Rorholm, Niels | University of Rhode Island |
| Rowley, Louis N. | American Society of Mechanical Engineers |
| Russell, J.S. | Boeing Company |
| Rylands, R. N. | B.F. Goodrich, Avon Lake |
| Saunders, Capt. E.M., USN | Naval Facilities Engineering Command |
| Saunders, Capt. L.N., Jr. USN | Naval Civil Engineering Laboratory |
| Savage, G.H. | University of New Hampshire |
| Savage, William | Office of Saline Water |
| Saville, Thornkike | Coastal Engineering Research Center–Corps of·Engineers |
| Sawyer, George | Battelle Northwest |
| Shaefer, George V. | MTS–Naval Oceanographic Office |
| Schafersman, Dale | Natural Gas Pipeline Co. of America |
| Scheel, Alvin J. | U.S. Steel, Lorain |
| Schmidt, Howard R. | Lockheed Missiles and Space Co. |
| Schuerger, Richard G. | Cleveland Electric Illuminating Co. |
| Schuh, Niles | U.S. Navy Mine Defense Laboratory |
| Sezack, Stanley | Naval Applied Science Laboratory |
| Shaw, Frederick G. | Port of New York Authority |
| Shaw, John | International Nickel Co. |
| Shaw, Milton | Atomic Energy Commission |
| Sheets, Herman | SNAME–Electric Boat Company |
| Shigley, C. Monroe (R) | Dow Chemical Co. |
| Shumaker, Larry | Lockheed Missiles and Space Co. |
| Shykind, Edwin B. (R) | National Council on Marine Resources and Engineering Development |
| Siebenhausen, C.H. (R) | Shell Oil Co. |
| Sieder, E. (R) | Office of Saline Water |
| Simons, Manley | Marine Technology Society |
| Simons, Merton (R) | Phillips Petroleum Co. |
| Singer, S. Fred | Department of the Interior |
| Singleton, Leon | Gulf Publishing Co. |
| Small, Fred | Office of the Oceanographer |
| Smeder, RAdm. O.R. USCG | Coast Guard Headquarters |
| Smith, Blakely | Houston, Texas |
| Smith, Cdr. Frank USN | Atlantic Undersea Test and Evaluation Center |
| Smith, H.J. (R) | Lockheed Missiles and Space Co. |
| Smith, Ray J. | Naval Civil Engineering Laboratory |
| Snyder, Capt. J. Edward, USN | Navy Department |
| Sorenson, James E. | Battelle Memorial Institute |
| Sorkin, George | Naval Ship Systems Command |
| Sorrell, Samuel | Gulf Publishing Co. |
| Spadone, Daniel (R) | DSSP–Navy Department |
| Sparks, William L. | Westinghouse Electric Corp. |
| Speakman, Edwin A. | Department of Transportation |
| Spiess, Fred | Scripps Institution of Oceanography |
| Spodak, William | DSSP–Navy Department |
| Steele, Harry | Water Resources Council |
| Stephan, Edward (C) | Ocean Systems, Inc. |
| Stephen, Charles R. | Florida Atlantic University |
| Stout, Ernest | AIAA–Lockheed California Co. |
| Stover, Lloyd A. | University of Miami |
| Stowers, H.L. | Texas Gas Transmission Corp. |
| Strobel, Joseph J. (R) | Office of Saline Water |
| Styles, Fred | Bureau of Outdoor Recreation |
| Sullivan, E. Kemper | Maritime Administration |
| Sutton, Sheldon S. | Westinghouse Electric Corp. |
| Swain, James C. | Battelle Memorial Institute |
| Swift, Ward (R) | Battelle Northwest |
| Swigum, George | Naval Material Command |
| Taggert, Robert | SNAME–Robert Taggert Inc. |
| Talkington, Howard R. | Naval Undersea Warfare Center |
| Tate, Robert H. | Greater Wilmington Chamber of Commerce |
| Teague, Dorwin | Dorwin Teague, Inc. |
| Thomas, Bertram D. | Battelle Memorial Institute |
| Thompson, Floyd L. | American Institute of Aeronautics and Astronautics |
| Tibby, Richard B. | University of Southern California |
| Touhill, C. Joseph (R) | Battelle Northwest |
| Treadwell, Capt. T.K., USN | Naval Oceanographic Office |
| Tuthill, Arthur (R) | International Nickel Co. |
| Vaeth, Gordon (R) | Environmental Science Services Administration |
| Valerio, Gerald A. | Annapolis, Maryland |
| Van Antwerpen, F.H. | American Institute of Chemical Engineers |
| Vetter, Richard C. | National Academy of Sciences |
| Vidal, Numa | Ohio Edison Company |
| Vine, Allyn | Woods Hole Oceanographic Institute |
| Vyhnalek, Henry J. | Cleveland Electric Illumination Co. |
| Wakelin, James H., Jr. (C) | Ryan Aeronautical Co. |
| Waters, RAdm. O.D., USN | Navy Department |
| Wedin, John (R) | Staff, Senate Commerce Committee |

| Name | Organization | Name | Organization |
|------|-------------|------|-------------|
| Weinberger, Leon | Department of the Interior | Williams, William H. | U.S. Navy Mine Defense Laboratory |
| Weir, Carl L. | Maritime Administration | Williamson, William R. (R) | American Machine and Foundry Co. |
| Weisnet, Donald | Naval Oceanographic Office | | |
| Weiss, A.M. | Natural Gas Pipeline Co. | Wolff, Capt. Paul USN | Fleet Numerical Weather Facility |
| Welling, C.G. | Lockheed Missiles and Space Co. | | |
| Wenzel, James G. | Lockheed Missiles and Space Co. | Wolff, Richard | Garcia Corporation |
| Wheaton, Elmer P. (C) | Lockheed Missiles and Space Co. | Wood, L.A. | Boeing Company |
| Whiddon, Frederick | University of South Alabama | Woodbury, Brig. Gen. H.G. USA | Corps of Engineers |
| Wieskopf, Al | Mobile Chamber of Commerce | Wooldridge, Dan E. | Ohio Edison Company |
| Wilcox, R. Howard | Naval Undersea Warfare Center | | |

☆ U.S. GOVERNMENT PRINTING OFFICE : 1969 O—333-091